HERTFORDSHIRE LIBRARY SERVICE

This book is due for return on or before the date shown. You may extend its loan by bringing the book to the library or, once only, by post or telephone, quoting the date of return, the letter and number on the date card, if applicable, and the information at the top of this label.

RENEWAL
INFORM-
ATION

The loan of books in demand cannot be extended.

I   Please renew/return this item by the last da[r]

So that your telephone call is charged at l⌣ please call the numbers as set out below:

From Area codes 01923 or 0208:	From the rest
⌐ als: C⌐ ⌐⌐⌐	01438 737373
	01438 737⌐

NAPOLEON'S SURGEON

Frontispiece—Portrait of Larrey attributed to Mme. Benoit.

NAPOLEON'S SURGEON

by
J. HENRY DIBLE

William Heinemann Medical Books Ltd
London

First Published 1970

Printed in Great Britain by The Whitefriars Press Ltd., London and Tonbridge

To
My Mother
Who gave to me all that any mother can give to any son.

My Godfather

J. K. Stothert

Who helped my education, was a good friend and counseller to me,
and who left me with the injunction:

"Be a Man. Be a White Man. Be a Gentleman."

and to

Mr. Charles Holmes

Lower VI Form master at King Edward VI Grammar School,
Southampton, who roused my interest in the
French Revolution and the men of its period.

"What do I care, do you suppose, for the lives of two hundred thousand men?"

Napoleon to Metternich, June 1813.

"L'expérience du passé diminuera, sinon la somme, du moins la gravité des maux de la guerre."

D. J. Larrey.

Preface

How this book came to be written

When I was released from the army in 1918 I was appointed to a lecture-ship in Pathology at Manchester University. At that time the sort of sudden impulse which sometimes overtakes the best regulated institutions caused the Royal Infirmary to decide to sell its library. The books were sent over to the University where they were piled, higgledy-piggledy, in one of the vacant rooms in the Physiology Department, with the under-standing that members of the Manchester Medical Society might buy such works as interested them. Some of these were valuable, such as those by Bright and Addison, Cruveilhier's *Anatomie Pathologique du Corps Humain*, Culpepper's *The English Physician*, Harvey's *Opera Omnia*, J. Hunter's *A Treatise on the Venereal Disease*, W. Hunter's *Atlas of the Anatomy of the Gravid Uterus* and four volumes of Larrey's *Mémoires de Chirurgie Militaire*. I bought such of these as a shallow purse permitted, and afterwards sold most of them at a considerable profit. Larrey's four volumes I kept, and at a later date had the good fortune to pick up his *Campaigns et Voyages* (1815–1840) in Cambridge. These I dipped into from time to time, in the midst of much teaching, and came to realize that the old man had a lot worth saying that had never been said before, and that he was a much greater man than he had been credited with being. Finally I sat down and translated the whole set but found difficulty in publication. My early efforts having been abortive, I decided to write an entirely new book, for which purpose my wife and I travelled over a large part of France, Italy and the Netherlands and incidentally slept a night in the little inn on the field of Waterloo, where there was no hot water but we had the best bottle of Vin Rosé we have ever drunk. We also visited the French military hospital at Val-de-Grâce, and in Ireland the general hospitals and Swift's Asylum:

> "He gave the little wealth he had
> To found a house for fools and mad;
> And shewed by one satyric touch
> No nation wanted it so much."

Larrey was a great man: little enough known in this country and worthy of being better so.

It is in the hope of doing him justice that I have produced this book.

J. Henry Dible
November 3rd, 1969

viii

In the production of the book I have been helped by a number of people, more especially my good friend Dr. John Mills who has criticized most of my writings, frankly and sometimes devastatingly, for my good. To Dr. Elspeth Stanford who introduced me to Dr. Raymond Greene I owe a great debt, this applies also in full measure to Mr. Richard Emery, who has guided my uneasy footsteps through the mazy paths of the production of a book on history. Mr. Jonathan Goodman has helped me in many ways, more especially in the typing of earlier and rather confusing scripts, whilst my faithful secretaries at the British Postgraduate Medical School, Mrs. Ryde-Butcher and Miss Rooker, have endured my insatiable demands upon their patience.

Lastly, but by no means least, I owe a great debt of gratitude to my wife, for putting up with my moments of abstraction and the trial of seeing her dining room table cluttered up with the confused array of discarded manuscripts, maps, files *et hoc genus omne* which go to the making of a considerable historical study.

J. H. D.

September, 1970

Vale

C'est l'homme le plus vertueux que j'aie connu. . . . The pen scratched on and was silent. The candle flickered and the rats scampered behind the wainscot.

He had known many men—most of those who mattered in the world—and in the long solitudes of the black island where he was dying he could reflect upon them without passion. Kings and Emperors! Franz of Austria, who had become his father-in-law; Alexander, once his ally; Frederick-William of Prussia, forever wriggling to be free; Frederick Augustus of Saxony, more loyal than most. The politicians: Talleyrand, the slippery snake; Fouché—he should have hanged Fouché. That rigid prig Lafayette with his doctrinaire principles. Sieyès, the weaver of systems. Carnot, the organizer of victory, upright, reluctant and needy. All serving him whilst it served themselves. . . . *Pourvu que ça dure,* Mme. Mère had said. . . .

The soldiers: Desaix—there was a man for you! Brave, loyal and avid of glory; but Desaix had died in his hour of victory at Marengo. Murat, an incomparable cavalry leader for all his braggadocio, but he had married into the family and kingship had turned his weak head and he was shot in cold blood like a dog. Ney, the bravest of the brave . . . he had behaved like a madman at Waterloo . . . and he, too, had died in the same way in a filthy yard in the Luxembourg gardens. And old Berthier: he should have been beside him in 1815, the old scribbler, but Berthier had skulked in Brussels and taken his own life.

The family: Jerome . . . too slow in that affair with Bagratian . . . one could not be everywhere oneself. Joseph, with his futilities in Spain and his conceit . . . he had lost his head in Paris. Lucien: Lucien had always gone his own way, but he had been loyal when loyalty counted most. That was something . . . besides . . . he had sons. And the women: Caroline, feathering her nest with her precious Joachim. And Pauline with her men—the strumpet! Kittle cattle the lot of them. Well, perhaps the men were as bad.

Désirée. Walewska. Josephine . . . roses at Malmaison . . . he should have stuck to Josephine. He had leaned too much on the family. Mme. Mère should found a colony at Rome . . . judicious marriages. . . .

The candles flickered and guttered and the heavy head nodded. There they were: tall Kléber, Bessières, Desaix, Lannes, Bernadotte[1]—that Gascon traitor—Macdonald, Duroc, Marmont . . . one should never be sentimental . . . France would deal fairly with Marmont's memory. . . . They marched by, trailing sabres and jingling spurs, or with tossing

[1] "Since writing this I have read the delightful book DÉSIRÉE by Annemarie Selinco, which has caused me to revise very much my opinion of BERNADOTTE."

plumes and a clink of curb chains. And there in the shadows were the darker pictures one could not forget . . . Lannes . . . Duroc's blood on his kerseymere waistcoat. Fugières, his arm shot away, proffering his useless sword. Duroc had died horribly, but Fugières had lived thanks to Larrey. What a man was that one! Not a courtier like Corvisart, but the right fellow on a battlefield. Egypt, Ulm, Austerlitz, Eylau, the Moskova, Dresden, Leipsic, Waterloo . . . he had been at all of them and he had never failed.

"The ink, Montholon."

The pen scratched and the writing trailed on. There was so much to do and time was growing short: so many to be remembered, both the great and the little. A legacy for Marbot: *I bid Colonel Marbot to continue to write in defence of the glory of the French Armies and to the confusion of calumniators and apostates.*

And Larrey: *Je lègue au chirurgien-en-chef, Larrey, cent mille francs. C'est l'homme le plus vertueux que j'aie connu.*

He had known plenty. The glitter had gone and the darkness approached.

*   *   *   *   *

Baudéan

If you drive south-west across France towards the Spanish border and the Pic du Midi, Route Nationale No. 135 brings you to the pleasant but rather decayed watering-place of Bagnères de Bigorre in the foothills of the Pyrenees. About two miles farther on you will see on your right an ancient church, rising above a small village round which the main road sweeps leaving its single narrow street as the string across a bow. This is Baudéan and I doubt if it has changed much in the last hundred years. Half-way up the village, on the left hand side, is a solid unpretentious house, its stuccoed wall abutting the gutter and its woodwork painted a faded grey, like so many small houses of provincial France (Fig. 2). Opposite there is a modest wine shop with a flagged floor. On the wall of the house are three plaques. The one on the right reads:

> Here was born in 1766 Baron Larrey,
> Surgeon-in-Chief of the Imperial Armies.
>
> "C'est l'homme le plus vertueux que j'aie connu"
> Testament de Napoléon.

That on the left:

> *Infants' School*
> Founded in memory of his father by Baron Hippolyte Larrey,
> Inspector of the Health Council of the Armies,
> Surgeon-in-Ordinary to H.M. Napoleon III, etc., etc.
> In gratitude from the Commune of Baudéan, August, 1857.

The third, and this is a small mean tablet, bleakly states:

> *Communal Girls' School*
> Secularised by the Prefectural Law of August, 1902

What sort of a man was this Larrey? We are told that he was a Surgeon-in-Chief to the Imperial Armies. He was much more than this, for he was a notable practitioner of the Surgical Art in the era before anaesthetics or antiseptics were known, and as such he was described in the 19th century by Dupuytren as: "a connecting link between the surgery of the last age and that of the present day." His name is worthily inscribed on the Arc de Triomphe. He was an innovator of surgical practice, a reformer of the medical service of armies, a historian, a man of sensibility and a philanthropist. Larrey has claims upon posterity on all these counts. Not a man of the *salons* or of nice manners, and of much the same age as Napoleon whose devoted follower he was to become. A rugged, forthright, common-sense fellow, as one may judge from his autobiography; combining with these qualities great humanity, an immovable rectitude, and an unending and unsatisfied desire to know, to understand, to record and to teach. He has much in common with our John Hunter.

I have used the word autobiography, but it is inexact for Larrey left no autobiography other than his *Mémoires de Chirurgie Militaire* (Fig. 3) based upon notes made throughout his life, his twenty-six campaigns, and his *Rélation Médicale de Campaigns et Voyages* which is a sequel to the other. Together these constitute a great surgical classic and a contemporary account of the French armies in a momentous historical period. Indeed, so much of his writing is history that one is torn between the drama of the period, in which he was sometimes an actor, sometimes a spectator, but always a participant, and what is more strictly of surgical interest. The temptation is there to neglect the latter for the former, but to do so would be unfair to a man whose impact on the surgery of his time is not easy to assess, but of whose prescience and practical knowledge in surgical matters there can be no doubt, nor can there be two opinions about his stature. The campaigns in which Larrey found himself immersed were the backcloth before which the surgical drama is revealed, and it is against this he would wish to be judged by his contributions to his Art.

This book is about him.

Contents

Chapter		Page
1	Baudéan. Newfoundland. Paris 1789. The Army of the Rhine. Idea of mobile ambulances.	1
2	Toulon. The treatment of burns. Sieges of Figueras and Rosas. Peace of Bâle.	9
3	Early days of the Revolution. Rise of Napoleon. Preparation for French expedition to Corfu. Anthrax. Campo Formio.	15
4	Expedition to Egypt. Landing at Alexandria. The Battle of the Pyramids. Capture of Cairo. Ophthalmia. First signs of plague.	23
5	Syria. el-A'rych. Jaffa. St. Jean d'Acre. Retreat from Syria. Poisoning of wounded at Acre. Return to Cairo. . .	30
6	The plague in Egypt. Death of Masclet. Leeches in the throat.	36
7	Turkish landing at Aboukir. Fugière's sword. Turkish invasion from Syria. Battle of Heliopolis. Recapture of Cairo. Assassination of Kléber. Torture and death of the assassin. Command assumed by Menou. Prostitution and syphilis. .	41
8	English landing at Aboukir. Siege and capture of Alexandria. Scurvy. Return to France. Larrey's report to French government.	48
9	The Empire. Consecration by the Pope and Napoleon's self-coronation. Trafalgar. Battle of Ulm. Vienna. Austerlitz. Embalming. Epidemic at Brün. . . .	58
10	Jena. Berlin. Asphyxia. First Polish campaign. Marie Walewska. Battle of Eylau. Commandant of Legion of Honour. The Polish Plica.	67
11	Courland to Tilsit. Meeting of Napoleon and Alexander. Larrey made Chevalier de la Couronne de Fer. . .	80
12	Napoleon's first Spanish Campaign. Intrigues in the Spanish Court between Godoy and the Royal Family. Bull fighting. Madrid hospitals.	86
13	Gangrene. Case of Antoine Barre. The Madrid colic. .	91
14	Joseph Bonaparte in Spain. Accident to Lannes. . .	100

15 Second Spanish Campaign. Summa-Sierra. Moore's retreat to Corunna. The English wounded. Cure of a case of amaurosis. Typhus in English prisoners. Larrey's typhus. . . 103

16 Second Austrian Campaign. Eckmühl and Ratisbon. Essling. Lannes' death. Wagram. Casualties. Return to Paris. . 109

17 The Surgery of amputations. Importance of early operation. The shoulder joint. The tibial condyles. The hip. Aseptic healing. Importance of immobilization. Larrey's *appareil inamovible*. 119

18 The Surgery of arteries. Pathology of aneurysms. Arrest of haemorrhage. Collateral circulation and arterial canalization 137

19 The Russian Campaign (1). Preamble. The Vistula. The Moscow Campaign. Wilna. Witebsk. Casualties. Smolensk. Valutina. Dorogobouje. 144

20 The Russian Campaign (2). The Moskova battle. Wounds near the knee. Casualties. Entry to Moscow. The Moscow hospitals and other buildings. The Kremlin. Burning of Moscow. Murat surprised by Kutusoff. 161

21 The Russian Campaign (3). The retreat from Moscow. Engagement at Malajaroslaw. Mozaisk. The Dneiper. Ney's rearguard. Smolensk. Krasnoë. Cognats. Mme. Bursay. The Beresina tragedy. Napoleon's departure. Increase in cold. Wilna. Kowno. Königsberg. 175

22 The Russian Campaign (4). Increase in cold. York's defection. Macdonald's defeat. Murat's desertion. Deaths from cold. Larrey's typhus. Königsberg. Leipsic. Frostbite and the effects of cold. Trench foot. 193

23 The campaign of Saxony. Napoleon at Mersbourg. Lutzen. Casualties and operations. Bautzen. Death of Duroc. Armistice of Pläswitz. Accusations of self-mutilation by recruits. Medical commission of investigation. Comparison of casualties. 201

24 Defeats of Oudinot, Ney and Macdonald. Battle of Dresden. Casualties. Vandamme's defeat at Külm. Battle of Leipsic and French retreat. Wrede's defection and defeat. Case of young Robsomen. Arrival at Mayence. 212

25 The last campaign. Napoleon's strategy. Brienne. Champaubert. Montmirail. Château-Thierry. Vauchamps. Nangis. Montereau. Treaty of Chaumont. Soissons. Craönne. Laon. Advance of Allies. Fall of Paris. Napoleon's abdication. Larrey's account. Defence of wounded at Craönne and Soissons. End of Vol. IV of Memoirs. 220

26 Preamble. Napoleon's escape from Elba. Larrey at Waterloo. Jealousy of Percy. Departure for Belgium. Ligny. Waterloo. Grouchy's absence. Louvain. Guthrie's hip amputation. . 233

27 A Surgical Miscellany. Breadth of Larrey's experience. Wounds of the skull and trephining. Head pierced by a ramrod. Treatment of wounds of the head and face. Of the throat, thorax, empyema, bladder. Surgery of the abdomen. Hernia of the omentum. Suture of the intestines. . . 244

28 Departure for Ireland. Dublin hospitals. Excision of the lower jaw. The Foundling Hospital. Political situation in Ireland and suggestions for its amelioration. . . . 274

29 British hospitals. Chester. Liverpool. Carlisle. Glasgow and its Asylum. Edinburgh. 286

30 London. Greenwich Hospital. The Rosetta Stone. A comparison of English and French Surgery. 299

31 Abolition of branding of prisoners. The July Revolution. Inspection of the Belgian Medical Service. Ophthalmia. Larrey's recommendations. Return to Paris. Reforms at *Les Invalides*. Italy. *Mme. Mère*. Cardinal Fesch. Criticism of Roman administration. 309

32 Cholera in the Midi. Fear of burial alive. Views on nature of cholera and its treatment. 319

33 Something of the man, and the last phase. . . . 329

Appendixes 336

Index 339

Baudéan. Newfoundland. Paris 1789. The Army of the Rhine. Idea of mobile ambulances.

The opening act of the French Revolution was the summoning of the States General in 1789, at which time Dr. Larrey had just returned from a voyage to Newfoundland as surgeon to King Louis' frigate *Vigilante*, which had sailed from Brest to protect the French interests in the cod fisheries on the Grand Banks and Newfoundland.[1] He had left his home at Baudéan at the age of thirteen to study medicine in Toulouse, where his uncle, Alexis Larrey, was professor of surgery. At twenty-one he had completed his initial medical studies and then decided to travel to other universities to perfect his professional knowledge. He arrived in Paris in August 1787 and hearing that there were vacancies for assistant surgeons in the navy he made application and was accepted. He travelled the three hundred and fifty miles to Brest on foot, lodging *en route* at the famous Trappist monastery of Savigny la Trappe, near Mortagne—a monastery founded by the Comte de Perche in memory of his wife Matilda, who perished in the ill-starred White Ship with her brother William, heir to Henry I of England. The monastery was destroyed in the flames of the Revolution, but was rebuilt on the same site by the Order between 1815 and 1895, and may be seen by the visitor today.

At Brest he was posted to *Vigilante* and spent six or seven months in port, during which his natural curiosity for information on all matters concerning ships and the sea, and his special responsibility for the vessel's medical equipment and stores, still left him time to give lessons in anatomy and surgery to students. The ship sailed on May 3rd, and Larrey suffered so badly from seasickness that he was moved to analyse this unpleasant complaint in great detail and to write a considerable account of it and its treatment. In spite of perils from icebergs they safely made their landfall at Belle Isle, a small island to the north of Newfoundland which still remains French territory. As they neared land they saw men waving from the shore, and the ship's long boat being launched it brought off more than twenty castaways from a vessel which had been crushed between an iceberg and the ice barrier. Most of the ship's company had jumped onto the barrier and been lost; only the captain and twenty-two men who had put off in the gig reached land. When sighted three days later they were perishing from cold, thirst and hunger, and two of their company had died. A number were suffering from frostbite for which partial amputations were required.

[1] Newfoundland was ceded to England by the Treaty of Utrecht, but the French retained the right of fishing along two-fifths of the coast.

Vigilante moored in Croc Bay on July 31st, 1788. The voyage had produced a large crop of cases of scurvy[2] and catarrhal affections but, "a change in the temperature, the use of vegetables which we either grew ourselves from seed or obtained locally, fresh bread and the exercise of hunting and fishing helped me to effect a rapid cure of both these illnesses. Cod's heads, cooked with vegetables and plants, provided a splendid broth which was delicious and an excellent anti-scorbutic". On shore they were not without their discomforts, for the temperature towards the end of July often reached 93–95°F in the more sheltered valleys and harbours, and they were tormented by "a peculiar kind of gnat called a mosquito, the bite of which caused local inflammation and fever". Camphorated oil and the use of gauze veils served to abate this inconvenience.

On July 31st, the ship left Croc Harbour for the Bay of Canaries where there was a waterfall, and here were caught a great many salmon, the smallest weighing fifteen pounds! They sailed on to White Bay and then into the Arctic Sea as far as the Bay of Orange, in longt. 55°—56°W., but owing to ice were unable to pass the strait of Belle Isle and enter the Gulf of St. Lawrence, so had to put back to Croc Bay whence they sailed to St. Johns, the main English colony on the south-east of Newfoundland. H.M.S. *Salisbury*,[3] Captain Riou, was in the harbour and entertained the officers of *Vigilante* very hospitably; so much so that the company which sat down to table at mid-day was still there at mid-night. At this juncture Captain de Sacques de Tourès of *Vigilante*, who seems to have returned to his ship rather earlier than his junior officers, signalled that the ship was about to sail. The party broke up hurriedly. The anchor was weighed at once, but the wind which had been gradually rising reached hurricane force and the frigate was in danger of being blown onto a lee shore. However, she succeeded in anchoring again and at daylight was able to sail for the French port of Saint-Pierre de Miquelon. But bad weather put them over two hundred leagues off their course and they only made their destination on September 23rd. Once again a sudden gale sprang up and the ship was in danger of being driven ashore, but the great bower anchor held. At the height of the gale the cutter's warp parted and she began to drift. The boatswain and eighteen men volunteered to go after her in the long boat, but in the wind and heavy seas both boats were lost sight of from the ship. The next morning the storm moderated and a third boat was sent ashore, but returned with the melancholy news that they had found only the battered remnants of the long boat together with two of the crew's caps. The unfortunate men were given up for lost, but

[2] It was universally accepted that scurvy was due to a lack of fresh food in the sailors' diet. But many years were to pass before Hopkiens discovered vitamins and L. J. Harris could write:

"The scurvy flew through the schooner's crew as they sailed on an Arctic sea,
They were far from land and their food was canned so they got no vitamin 'C'."

[3] H.M.S. *Salisbury*, 50 guns, built in 1769, was wrecked on the Isle of Avache, near San Domingo, on May 13th, 1796.

a few hours later some fishermen hailed the ship and brought back the boatswain and another sailor whom they had rescued from an isolated rock. The former was beyond recovery, but Larrey succeeded in reviving the sailor who told them that the two had reached and scrambled aboard the cutter but that she had then become separated from the long boat and dashed onto a rock to which they had managed to cling. Ultimately all the other missing men were recovered. Their boat had gone ashore and been smashed, but the crew had been rescued and tended by Esquimaux who guided them back to the harbour the next day.

The trials and perils of this voyage were not yet over, for on their return passage foul winds and adverse currents drove them up the English Channel and for many days they were beating back before they were once more off Ushant. Food and water were by this time short and the ship's company increased by the castaways from Belle Isle. Rations were reduced to four ounces of biscuit per man and a single measure of putrid water, which had to be strained through linen to rid it of worms. They had sighted no other ships, and were still sixty leagues from the coast and at the end of their tether when they fell in with a Danish ship sailing on an opposite course. They closed her and hoisted a signal of distress and hailed her, but she, no doubt fearing piracy, went about and crowding on all sail made away. They fired some futile cannon shot after her in anger and disappointment.

At last, when on the verge of starvation and with a crew seriously enfeebled, the wind changed and twenty-four hours later, on October 31st, 1788, they fetched up in Brest roads. They had suffered from scurvy, which had affected about a half of the ship's company, various fevers, and had had a case of confluent smallpox on board, but nevertheless had only lost one man, and him from drowning. The failure of the smallpox to spread would indicate a high rate of inoculation or immunity amongst the crew. Larrey wrote that he attributed his success in general to: "the good medicaments I had on board, the light and cooling foods, the excellent broth, generous wine and fresh bread. . . . The excellent state of the ship, the fumigation by nitre and sulphur which I enforced regularly, the change of air by ventilators and sails, the daily hammock drill which was carried out at my request, the frequent ablutions with water and vinegar I prescribed for the sailors, the regular exercise except during the hours of repose, the dancing, the good food with drink tinctured with brandy or vinegar—these were the means I used to maintain the health of the ship's company and to hasten the convalescence of those who had been sick."

We may ask ourselves with what degree of equanimity would a young ship's surgeon today on his first voyage, lacking all but the simplest drugs and most of these inert by modern criteria, without antiseptics, anaesthetics or antibiotics, regard the task of dealing with a ship's company mostly on the edge of scurvy and some of them dangerously ill, including a case of confluent smallpox?

*   *   *   *   *

Paris 1789

Back in Paris, at the beginning of the winter of 1789, the early storms of the Revolution had begun to break. On April 27th a crowd demonstrated against Réveillon's paper factory, alleging that the proprietor had said that "A journeyman could live handsomely on fifteen sous a day." The disorders which followed were only crushed after three days, when Benseval called up the Swiss guard with artillery. There were "four or five hundred" dead. Most of the wounded were civilians from the Faubourg Saint-Antoine and many of them were taken to the Hôtel Dieu where Larrey was following a course of clinical surgery under the celebrated Desault. Three points of the latter's teaching especially impressed the young man: (1) That the then customary use of spirits for the dressing of gunshot wounds was harmful and that soothing applications were to be preferred. (2) That excessive *débridement* might produce muscle hernia. (3) That the mere incising of wounds of this type did not convert them from complex to simple ones, and that for satisfactory *débridement* it was necessary to cut away the contused margins with the knife. Only wounds of the face were suitable for immediate suture after this treatment.

The riots which led to bloodshed in the Tuilleries garden on July 13th, followed by the fall of the Bastille on the next day, and the yet more serious clash in the Champ de Mars of July 17th, 1791, brought many more wounded to the Hôtel Dieu and enlarged Larrey's experience of the effects of musket fire and cold steel. His active brain had been at work on this problem and he presented to the Royal Academy of Surgery an improved form of semi-circular surgical needle, having a lancet-shaped cutting point and an eye grooved to accommodate the suture. This won for him a gold medal worth a hundred livres. He also presented an improved aneurysm needle, but the revolutionary disturbances and the death of the secretary to the Society prevented the publication of these inventions (Fig. 4).

Beyond France's frontiers a slow grouping of the Prussians and Austrians for armed intervention had been taking form, complicated by mutual suspicion and the equivocal attitude of Russia, at that moment more interested in Warsaw than in Paris. But the Legislative Assembly was in aggressive mood and on a wave of popular enthusiasm, on the night of April 20th, 1792, declared: "war against kings, and peace with all peoples," and this in spite of a disorganized army rent by internal dissension. ". . . two great parties in Paris were reckoning on a French defeat: the anti-revolutionists, to stifle the Revolution; the revolutionists, to let it loose once more. Never was a war prepared and desired with so many scarcely concealed ulterior motives" (Madelin).

The opening of hostilities was catastrophic for the French. On April 28th Dillon and Biron attacked on the Belgium frontier and on each occasion the soldiers threw down their arms and fled, the unfortunate Dillon being murdered by his panic-stricken men.[4] These easy successes contributed not

---

[4] Biron was guillotined during The Terror.

a little to the vastly different later results, since the allies believed that there was no real resistance to be met and that an easy march to Paris lay in front of them. They delayed further action, and in so doing gave time for the tremendous upsurge of patriotic feeling which provided the men who stood their ground at Valmy. On August 19th, 1792, the Prussian and émigré army crossed the frontier, capturing Longwy and Verdun without difficulty. Dumoriez, who commanded in the north, was thrown back across the Aisne, but Brunswick was slow to follow up this success and gave time for Dumoriez to oppose the passage of the Argonne and for Kellermann to come up and occupy the plateau of Valmy, so closing the road to Paris. Here, on September 20th, the Prussians received a sharp check and discouraged by this, as well as by disease in his army and discontent with his émigré allies, Brunswick retired across the frontier. It was the turn of the tide.

*   *   *   *   *

At the outbreak of hostilities Larrey was ordered to join the army of the Rhine under Marshal Luckner, who was soon to be replaced by Custine, as an assistant surgeon or surgeon to the hospitals, and reached headquarters at Strasbourg on April 1st, 1792. For some weeks he and his companions were kept busy making dressings and other preparations for the campaign, but characteristically enough he formed a medical society for the discussion of every sort of matter concerning military surgery. The allied retreat in the north had hardly been effected when Custine debouched from his encampment, crossed the Rhine, and attacked the enemy's rear. Spire was surprised and the garrison promptly surrendered, but as the commander and his staff entered the town firing broke out from cellars and windows. One of Custine's aides was killed at his side and another severely wounded. The French replied with musketry and cannon, and drove the unwounded remnant of the garrison into a small enclave of the river where they were made prisoner. The town was given over to pillage.

This was Larrey's first experience of a serious military engagement and it brought home to him the difficulties under which the army ambulances did their work. The regulations required them to be stationed a league[5] in the rear of the army, so that the wounded were left to lie on the battle-field until the fight was over, when they were collected together at some convenient spot to which the ambulances were brought. But this was often anything but easy as circumstances might change, and other army transport of greater importance block the way, so that twenty-four to thirty-six hours or more could well elapse before these unfortunate men received any treatment, with the result that most of them died from lack of attention. At Spire some three hundred and sixty wounded were taken to a large convent but to Larrey's great mortification many lives which might have been saved were lost. From this there grew up in his mind the idea of devising a type of ambulance fulfilling a very different function.

[5] About 2·42 English miles.

One which could be put to use on the battlefield itself, both to bring aid to the wounded and to carry them out of danger. But the time was not propitious and the idea had to wait for some years to reach fruition.

After the capture of Spire Custine advanced on Mayence which though strongly fortified was full of sympathizers with the Jacobins, and after three days' demonstration a capitulation was proposed by the defenders and accepted. The populace streamed out to welcome the liberating apostles of equality and fraternity; the French entered and the National Convention promptly annexed the town.

Whilst temporarily at Mayence Larrey carried out some early experiments on the electrical stimulation of nerves, such as those demonstrated by Galvani. "After having made numerous experiments on living animals I was very anxious to try them on man. An unfortunate accident to one of our soldiers gave me an opportunity. An artillery wagon had passed over his leg, causing so much damage that it was necessary to amputate through the thigh. As soon as the limb had been severed I left the ligation of the vessels and the dressings to a competent assistant and without delay dissected out the popliteal nerve which I wrapped in a piece of sheet lead. I then laid bare the bellies of the gastrocnemius muscle and took a silver coin in each of my hands. With one I touched the piece of lead and with the other the muscles: the result was to produce a strong convulsive movement of the leg and foot. Dr. Strak repeated the experiment, but we found that pieces of iron or steel did not produce such marked effects. A silver probe as a conductor gave even stronger results, although the heat of the limb had by now fallen considerably. The encouraging outcome of these experiments led me to hope that galvanic or electrical stimulation, carried by wires directly to the exposed subcutaneous nerves, might restore the function and vitality of paralysed limbs. . . . The meagre results which have been obtained by the use of galvanism and electricity in a number of maladies have caused me to give up my project, so that the question is still undecided."

Custine's facile and spectacular successes were received with immense joy in Paris and by the National Convention. Unfortunately they encouraged the commander to more hazardous adventures. In November he pushed on to Frankfort which opened its gates, and Hanau, Friedburg, Usingen, Weilbourg and Königstein, a strong fortress on the right bank of the Rhine, all yielded in turn. But a check awaited him at Limbourg, where his advance guard met the Prussians under King Frederick-William and was defeated, causing the main body to fall back to a position between Hochst and Frankfort.

Once again Larrey was shocked by finding that the wounded received no treatment on the battlefield and were abandoned in the retreat. He delayed no longer, but approached the civilian Commissary-General Villemansy with the idea of mobile ambulances.[6] The commissary, a

[6] Ambulance wagons would be more correct. The word "ambulance", as will be evident, is used both in this sense and to denote a military unit comprising these, as well as the surgeons, orderlies and so on, destined to render first aid in battle and to collect the wounded for transport to front-line hospitals: the equivalent of our Field Ambulance.

humane man, gave him authority to develop it. Larrey's first thought had been to transport the wounded on pack-horses with modified panniers—an idea to which he was later to revert in Egypt—but he now abandoned this in favour of light sprung-carriages which would be at the same time strong and mobile. A number of these vehicles were built and the sight of them made a great impression on the soldiers, who now for the first time saw a real effort being made to succour them should they be wounded. The commanding officer was also impressed, and ordered the experimental ambulance unit to a forward position with Houchard's advance guard, which was in bivouac on the Oberuchel mountains near Königstein. Here the story might well have ended, for the position was betrayed by a deserter and surrounded and overrun during the night by a superior enemy force. Houchard, however, managed to cut his way out, and after a difficult and trying retreat in terrible weather rejoined the main body. The new mobile ambulances were given a sharp test in this action and proved their worth, since it had been possible to dress the wounded on the battlefield and afterwards to carry them to safety.

It was Larrey's first real experience of battle. This engagement, he wrote, "which I saw at such close quarters affected me very much, but pleasure at the thought of how important a service my new ambulance had rendered to the wounded overcame all my emotions, and since that time I have always remained calm during the various battles at which I have been present."

The recapture of Frankfort, where the garrison was slaughtered by the Prussians, forced Custine to retreat on Mayence and Landau, both of which he garrisoned before abandoning them, and ultimately to withdraw behind the fortified lines of Weissembourg, which closed the northern end of the gap between the Vosges and the Rhine and protected Alsace.

On May 17th, 1793, having been severely censured by the politicians in Paris for his inactivity, Custine made an ill-concerted attack and was routed. He was relieved of his command and sent to the Army of the North which had been left by Dumouriez in a very demoralized state, and was succeeded by Alexandre de Beauharnais, the husband of Josephine, whilst Houchard was sent to command the Army of the Moselle. All three of these generals ultimately perished on the scaffold. Custine was accused of lack of courage and ineptitude. At his trial his accusers said: "You pitied Louis XIV; you were sad on the 31st of May; you wanted to hang Dr. Hoffmann, president of the Jacobins at Mayence; you prevented the circulation of the Journal of Père Duchêne and the Journal of the Mountain in your army; you said that Marat and Robespierre were disturbers; you surrounded yourself with aristocratic officers; you never had at your table good republicans." These were his real crimes. Houchard, who was charged with cowardice, tore open his clothes and shewed the scars of his fifty-five wounds. Beauharnais was no more fortunate than his predecessors. He made a vain attempt on July 20th to relieve Landau and Mayence, but failed. He nevertheless paid a generous tribute to his surgeons, for he wrote in his dispatch to the Convention: "Amongst the many brave men whose intelligence and activity served the

Republic so brilliantly, I cannot fail to mention Adjutant-General Bailly, Abbatouci of the light artillery, and military surgeon Larrey with his comrades of the light ambulance, whose indefatigable care in the treatment of the wounded lessened the inevitable human suffering of such a day, and who served humanity itself by helping to preserve the lives of the brave defenders of the country."

Of this action Larrey recorded in a diary that with the help of five dragoons he drove off a party of Prussians who were about to strip and kill (as was their custom) four wounded Frenchmen lying in front of a Prussian battery. They succeeded at the cost of the dismounting of a single dragoon, and carried off the wounded by ambulance to a sheltered spot where he operated on them and thus preserved the lives of all four.

Mayence fell and Beauharnais was recalled to France to face accusation and the guillotine. The Weissembourg lines were forced, and the army dissolved in rout only to halt under the ramparts of Strasbourg. Larrey himself was in great danger and was slightly wounded in the leg. But the allies failed to make the most of their victory and after passing for a time under the command of Pichegru, the Army of the Rhine was united to that of the Moselle under the generous Hoche, who threw the enemy back across the river and raised the siege of Landau. Winter came down, fighting ceased, and in April 1794 Prussia signed a separate peace at Bâle, leaving the left bank of the Rhine to the French and the Austrians alone in the field.

*   *   *   *   *

Chapter 2

Toulon. The treatment of burns. Sieges of
Figueras and Rosas. Peace of Bâle.

In April, 1794, Larrey was sent to Paris by the army commanders and the representatives of the Convention, to complete the organization of his mobile ambulances which had been so successful in the fighting on the Rhine. This he was prevented from doing as the exigencies of military service caused him to be moved almost at once to Toulon, as Surgeon-in-Chief to the Army of Corsica, but a brief stay in Paris *en route* permitted him to be married to Elizabeth Laville-Leroux, a daughter of Louis XVI's last finance minister.

The avowed object of this expedition was the re-capture of Corsica, which Paoli in 1793 had offered to the British monarchy, a move which caused the Buonoparte family to break with him and flee the island. The British fleet entered St. Florent in February 1794 and Bastia was captured by Nelson in May of that year. The possession of Corsica more than confirmed the British domination of the Mediterranean and for its re-capture security of the sea route was essential. The Toulon squadron was fitted out urgently, but on putting to sea it was decisively defeated and the whole scheme collapsed. Although the expedition was abortive it was momentous for Larrey, for here he met a young republican general of Corsican origin who had been chosen to command the artillery and with whom his future was to become bound.

The British blockade confined the French fleet in the Gulf of Juan, and the assembled troops were for the meantime encamped along the coast, with their headquarters at Nice. Being for the moment unemployed, Larrey was invited by the civilian commission with the Army of Eastern Spain to go to that front as director of its surgical service, and he reached La Junquière on the 25th Brumaire of the Year III (Nov. 15th, 1794).

In March of the previous year France had declared war against Spain, who had refused to recognize the Republic and later joined the first coalition. The early hostilities went very much in Spain's favour; Rousillon being overrun and Hendaye captured, whilst at sea the Spanish fleet co-operated with the English in the occupation of Toulon. The next year, however, things went otherwise. In May the French under Dugommier and Dagobert, won an important victory in the Eastern Pyrenees, forcing the Spanish to retreat, so that Larrey arrived on the 30th Brumaire, in time for a later struggle.

"A number of important engagements had already taken place, and the constant success of the Army had brought it to the front line of the enemy's entrenchments. The resistance which the Spaniards appeared likely to oppose to us in front of the plain of Figueras, was such that General Dugommier ordered immediate preparations for a general assault on the largest scale. By his orders I was put in charge of the arrangements for the wounded in the battle which was fixed for the next day, the 27th. Under the stimulus of this proof of the illustrious general's confidence I used the time at my disposal to make ready everything that pertained to my service.

"By dawn our advance guard had already engaged the Spaniards, and soon afterwards the battle became general. The enemy's first lines were captured with the bayonet and several strong points protecting them taken by assault. But our success was arrested by an early disaster, as the enemy blew up two of these redoubts at the moment our troops occupied them. One can imagine the terrible picture resulting from these explosions. More than a hundred of our volunteers were in the fortification when the mines were sprung; all were blown up, together with the stone parapets and the guns used to defend them. Guns, stones and human bodies, or parts of them, were hurled pell-mell by the explosion and scattered around from a considerable height. We rendered aid to such as were not entirely crushed or hopelessly burnt, of whom there were no less than seventy-six. Some had one or more limbs torn off, others were burnt over the whole body or large parts of it. A certain number who had suffered very severely from the force of the explosion, or whose burns extended to the abdominal viscera, died within a few hours of reaching the ambulance. I was obliged to amputate both thighs of one soldier who survived the explosion and the gangrene which invaded them as a result of the widespread destruction of the tissues; in addition to this his face, chest and hands were burnt. In spite of losing his legs and of the enormous burns which covered him, this brave Béarnais' life was saved and he recovered completely.

"A second soldier, whose left thigh and right arm I amputated, and who was equally severely burnt, also recovered. Both these men showed a most intriguing phenomenon: they recovered their full appetite and soon became fat, but since their nutritional circuit was diminished as a result the operation of their alvine evacuations became more frequent. A third man, in whom I amputated the leg and forearm and whose face had been burnt, recovered as completely as the other two. A fourth had both arms amputated and was cured. I also performed two amputations of the arm through the shoulder joint with the same success as I had with the Army of the Rhine and one of the foot between the two sets of tarsal bones.

The treatment of burns

"I have long been struck by the ill effects which are produced in deep burns by such repellent remedies[1] as ammoniacal water, oxycrat, *eau végétominerale*[2] and the solution of opium in ice water—although these are recommended in a number of modern works and widely used—and I believe that wounds of this

[1] *Répercussifs*: remedies designed to repel the humours into the interior (e.g. astringents).
[2] Goulard water: *Liq. plumbi subacetatis dil.* An astringent solution of lead subacetate.

sort are often fatal because of the lack of a more rational treatment. I therefore feel that in these pages it is my duty to break with the habitual lines of treatment and to lay down new ones. I should like to see all such burns dressed with old fine linen steeped in safron pomade, which has the effect of relieving pain to some extent and of preventing irritation, as well as protecting the nerve endings from contact with the air and the pressure of dressings or clothes. The use of the pomade, which may be replaced by honey in the absence of a satisfactory oil for its confection, is continued until suppuration occurs. Once this is established I employ styrax ointment to maintain the tone of the underlying vessels and to facilitate the separation of the sloughs and arrest putrefaction. After the sloughs have come away I go back to safron pomade, for which I gradually substitute dry lint smeared with cerat[3] and fastened by many-tailed bandages. When the granulations become exuberant I cauterize them with nitrate of silver. I also employ at times lotions of weak oxychloride of mercury and sulphate of copper.

"I am in the habit of prescribing soothing and antispasmodic drinks to be taken warm, such as sweetened and nitrated milk of almonds, mead, rice water, etc. The wounded were allowed an abundant light diet, such as broths, meat jellies, fresh eggs, soups, etc.; experience having shewn me that soldiers withstand a starvation diet much less well than persons leading a sedentary life, moreover since healing is slow in cases of burns where there is loss substance, it would be contrary to the teachings of Hippocrates to restrict the diet. The above simple treatment, which is mildly tonic and sedative, has generally succeeded in my hands.

"To illustrate the advantages of our method over that employed by the majority of practitioners, it is only necessary to consider the phenomena of deep burns due to boiling liquids, and the application of a burning substance to a large part of the body's surface. In the first case the skin is soft, insensible and livid, with detachment of the epidermis; in the second, which is the more common, the fire has killed the epidermis and dried the dermis and cellular tissue in immediate contact with it so as to form an eschar. The fluids of the part are brought to boiling point at the site of the burn and diffuse rapidly carrying great heat to the adjacent tissues, which diminishes as the distance increases. The sufferer cries out and suffers from acute pain, which is the cause of his fever, thirst, and inability to sleep. In either case the damage is worse than it actually appears and it is only some days later that we are able to judge of the extent of the dead tissues.

"It is a matter of indifference whether superficial burns are dressed with repellents or emolients—nature is well able to effect a cure—but with deep burns the wrong treatment is extremely dangerous. We have seen that in these some of the affected parts are completely destroyed whilst others are more or less on the verge of destruction, according to their distance from the centre of the burned area. The repellents, such as iced water, acids, preparations of lead or chalk, can only from the very outset weaken what is left of the vital forces of the affected parts and thus encourage the development of gangrene. Opium is no good, either internally or externally; externally it stupefies the parts instead of encouraging a healthy inflammation; taken internally in sufficient quantity, after a transitory excitement, it enfeebles all the organs. If the use of repellents is continued until the time of the separation of the sloughs they irritate and increase the sensitivity of the bare nerve filaments of the exposed dermis. Pain, which increases with each dressing, brings on increased erethism[4] and

[3] An ointment with a base of wax and oil.
[4] The effect of an irritating cause.

interferes with suppuration, and from this convulsions, metastases, gangrene and death result. A considerable number of people who were burnt in the unfortunate fire at the Austrian Embassy in Paris in 1810 succumbed to this treatment; whereas we have usually succeeded in saving those treated by our own method.

"The explosions which did us so much harm did not however prevent us from pursuing the enemy as far as his second line of entrenchments, and doubtless our victory would have been complete had not the Commander-in-Chief, Dugommier, been struck by a shell in the midst of his success, which caused him to share the lot of the many brave men who terminated their career so gloriously on this day. By the time I reached the field to aid him he had expired: the shell having passed through a part of his chest and torn the principal organs of that cavity.

"An armistice of twenty-four hours was ordered, so that we could celebrate the obsequies of the general. His body was taken for burial to the fort of Bellegarde. A sense of profound consternation and a heavy silence, interrupted only by the strains of plaintive music, gave this funeral a most lugubrious character.

"The engagement I have been speaking of provided us with some seven hundred wounded, about a third of them dangerously. Together with the small number of surgeons in my ambulance I operated on and dressed almost the whole of these within twelve hours. I have reported my most important observations on this occasion in my dissertation upon amputation of the limbs. Most of our operations were completely successful.

"Two days after we had buried our general the attack was resumed under General Pérignon.[5] These later engagements were more successful, for we captured the forts and redoubts which defended the plain of Figueras (the Spanish Commander-in-Chief, Launion, being killed) and reduced the fortress of the town where we took almost ten thousand prisoners, compelling the withdrawal of the rest of the Spanish army a part of which sought refuge in the mountains around Barcelona whilst the remainder retreated to the port of Rosas. We found an immense amount of war material and provisions in this fortress as well as a great number of animals of all kinds. I have never seen such splendid stores of surgical materials; the stuff for dressing wounds being like *batiste* and the lint as fine as *byssus*—a kind of silk produced by the *Pinne marine*, in former times much sought after for the fabrication of the mantles of the Roman Emperors. This lint had been made up into small packets tied with different coloured favours, by the Queen of Spain and the ladies of her court. The fortress of Figueras, be it said, is one of the masterpieces of Vauban.

"After rendering first aid to the wounded and setting up a hospital for their reception in the town, I undertook the direction of the ambulances to serve at the siege of Rosas, my place at general headquarters in

[5] One of the considerable number of battalion commanders elected by the volunteers of 1791, who subsequently became a Marshal under the Empire.

Figueras being taken by M. de Lagrésie, Surgeon-in-Chief of the army, a man distinguished by his merit and administrative ability. For my ambulance headquarters I chose the village of Palau, as being nearest to the line of circumvalation, and placed two sections at the most important points of the trench.

"The siege lasted through the whole winter of 1795–96, which was almost as hard as that of 1789. The thermometer fell to 3°F, and on several days we suffered so much from the extreme cold that a number of the sentinels on both sides were found dead by their reliefs and many of our soldiers had frozen feet. (I shall deal with the phenomena of frostbite in my Polish Campaign and endeavour to explain how it is caused.)

"On account of the natural strength of the town the siege was extremely arduous, since it was defended on the east by the sea, on the west by swamps and deep ditches, and on the north-east by a snow-covered mountain range. Moreover, the Spanish fleet was moored in the roadstead which made our approach still more difficult. However we overcame all these obstacles, and by using the hours of darkness to advance our investing works we cut a winding track through the mountains across which we man-handled our cannon; an important operation which was directed by General Victor.[6] In this way we managed to establish a number of batteries on the heights, which greatly contributed to the success of the siege operations.

"The ditches and marshes which protected the west side of the town eventually became frozen over, so that the third parallel was constructed from which a breach was made. At the moment when the assault was about to begin the Spanish garrison, except for about a hundred men, succeeded under cover of an exceptionally dark night in embarking in some ships and set sail. The next day flags of truce were flying on the ramparts and we entered Rosas by way of the breach. The town had been reduced to ashes, the fortifications were almost entirely demolished, and we found the shore and ditches strewn with dead bodies. No fortified town ever shewed greater resolution or a more obstinate defence.

"The numerous sorties by the garrison and the work of sapping the trenches cost the lives of many of our soldiers and gave us a corresponding number of wounded, for the most part severely so. It was during this siege that I was once more able to verify the immediate effects of cannon balls or other round objects projected at high speeds by gunpowder; and these I pointed out to M. Antoine Dubois, then Director of Health Services of the Armies, who visited our ambulance in that capacity. He was also able to see the advantages of immediate amputation after wounding. I shall deal with some of these matters in my Memoir on Amputations. M. Dubois participated for some days in our dangers and the difficulties and privations which burdened our work, especially at the end of the siege when a sudden thaw and the mountain torrents it brought in its train interrupted our communications with General Headquarters and with other parts of Catalonia.

[6] Today Marshal of the Empire, Duke of Bellune.

"After the capture of Rosas the enemy sent emissaries to treat for peace. Whilst the discussions were going on the army went into cantonments and encamped around Figueras. I had hardly returned there when I was ordered back to my original post at Toulon by the Committee of Public Safety, and to rejoin the Mediterranean expedition which was once more being organized. I left the Army of the Pyrenees at the time peace was concluded and proceeded to my new destination. As the departure of the expedition seemed still a long time ahead I was permitted to return to Paris to recover my health and to see my family."

Peace with Spain was signed at Bâle on July 12th, 1795. France gave up all her conquests, and in return Spain recognized the French Republic and ceded it the port of St. Domingo.

*   *   *   *   *

Chapter 3

Early days of the Revolution. Rise of Napoleon.
Preparation for French expedition to Corfu. Anthrax.
Campo Formio.

Life in Paris in the Year IV of the Republic was not very pleasant. Paper
money was fast becoming valueless, the Directory was uneasily assuming
authority and there was great scarcity of bread. To his disgust the young
surgeon was given the unpleasant responsibility of directing an ambulance
serving the troops sent to restore order in the Faubourg St. Antoine. He
was probably glad enough when orders came to report at Toulon, where
he was placed in charge of the military hospitals of the town and able to
employ his talents, in a way more suited to his temperament, in the conduct of classes on clinical and systematic surgery which were enthusiastic-
ally attended by surgeons of the army and navy who were stationed there.
  Here he wrote a graphic and penetrating account of anthrax, based on
a number of cases he saw at this time. He recognized and described with
admirable clarity the local and general forms of the disease as well as its
infective nature. In the midst of gratifying success in teaching and private
practice, Larrey was ordered to return to Paris and take up the appointment of professor of anatomy and operative surgery at the new Army
School of Medicine at Val-de-Grâce. This famous convent in the Rue
Saint-Jacques—which remains a military hospital today—was built by
Anne of Austria between 1645 and 1665 to the designs of Mansard and
Lemercier and transformed into a hospital by the Convention. The post
gave Larrey full scope for the teaching and investigation so dear to him.
The four professors, two of medicine and two of surgery, who formed the
staff held public conferences on important cases, where diagnosis and
treatment were discussed and if an operation were deemed necessary it was
performed forthwith before the assembled professors and students. Anatomical demonstrations and physiological experiments on animals were
carried out and the future of the college seemed bright indeed. But fate
had not destined Dominic-Jean Larrey for an academic career. Across the
Alps young Napoleon Bonaparte (he had dropped the italianate spelling
now), in a short and amazing campaign had swept Austria out of northern
Italy—endowing France with the imperishable legacy of such names as
Lodi, Arcola and Rivoli—and crowned this achievement by the Treaty of
Leoben, later to be superseded by the peace of Campo Formio.
  In the lull which followed the conclusion of these hostilities and in the
full consciousness of his now formidable authority, General Bonaparte
turned some of his restless energy to the better equipping of his armies

and called for the services of the surgeon of whose advanced ideas on the treatment of casualties in the field he had heard. Larrey received orders to join the army of Italy and to organize and direct a mobile ambulance service, such as he had devised when with the army of the Rhine in 1793.

He set out from Paris on May 1st, 1797, passing through Lyons and Pont-de-Beauvoisin and the picturesque mountainous road to Les Echelles and the Maurienne Valley, whose deep and gloomy gorges were largely populated by goitrous peasants and cretinous children; the district from which Balzac created his picture of the cretinous village. "This unhappy state of affairs," wrote Larrey, "appears to be the consequence of the habitual use of snow-water, the privations the people endure, faulty diet, and the unhealthy air breathed in their dwellings."

Snow and high wind stayed the party in Lanslebourg for forty-eight hours, before guides would consent to conduct them over the Mount Cenis pass, where on the previous evening fifteen prisoners of war and their escort had been swallowed up in an avalanche; but the weather improving they reached Suze on the Piedmont side after eight or nine hours' perilous and difficult march.

At Milan they found that the Leoben peace preliminaries had been agreed, and Larrey was at last free to devote himself to one of the major achievements of his life, the organization of his mobile ambulances. To appreciate the revolution he accomplished in the treatment of the wounded on the battlefield we have to recall that the army regulations required the ambulance wagons to be stationed a league in rear of the armies. These in any case were heavy cumbersome vehicles, having as their main function the transport of the surgeons and their materials. The picture of an ambulance wagon designed about this time by Baron Percy, Larrey's famous senior colleague who shared with him most of the responsibility for the direction of the surgery of the armies, and which may therefore be looked upon as of advanced contemporary form, shews a four-wheeled vehicle with a pole down its centre, serving as a kind of saddle on which the surgeons sat astride (Fig. 7) whilst being taken to the battle area after the engagement had been decided. Should the army retreat the fate of the luckless wounded was to be left on the field with every chance of being slaughtered by the victors; a common practice amongst many of the combatants at this period.[1] Even after victory the wounded lay where they had fallen until they could be carried to some nearby town or village at which treatment might reach them. And since in all the movements of an advancing army precedence had to be given to guns, ammunition wagons, moving troops and commissariat vehicles, two or three days might elapse before assistance reached these unfortunates. Little wonder that the mortality was high and their lot dreadful.

Larrey made two outstanding innovations. Firstly, he designed light mobile ambulance wagons which could keep up with the troops and allow the surgeons to work in the actual area of fighting. Secondly, he used these vehicles to pick up wounded on the battlefield and transport them out of

[1] Guthrie (1815), writing of the Peninsular war, remarked that the French always left their wounded upon the battlefield.

FIG. 1. Baudéan Church. (By permission of Les Editions D'Art, Arcueil, and La Societe Artistique des Dessins et Modeles, Paris.)

[*To face p.* 16

Fig. 2. Larrey's birthplace at Baudéan.

MÉMOIRES

DE

CHIRURGIE MILITAIRE,

ET

CAMPAGNES

DE D. J. LARREY,

Premier Chirurgien de la Garde et de l'Hôpital de la Garde de S. M. I.
et R., Baron de l'Empire, Commandant de la Légion-d'Honneur,
Chevalier de l'Ordre de la Couronne de Fer; Inspecteur général du
service de santé des Armées; ex-Professeur au ci-devant Hôpital
militaire d'instruction du Val-de-Grâce; Docteur en Chirurgie et en
Médecine; Membre de l'Institut d'Égypte, des Sociétés de la Faculté de
Médecine de Paris, d'Émulation, Philomatique; Associé correspondant
de celles de Montpellier, de Toulouse, de Bruxelles, etc.; de l'Académie
Joséphine impériale de Vienne; de celles de Turin, de Madrid, de
Naples, de Munich et d'Jéna.

Eò adductus sum ut multis meorum æqualium hinc
indè errantibus viam monstrarem et aliquantulùm
munirem.   BAGL. PRAX. MED., *lib. I*, *cap. I.*

TOME I.

Chez J. SMITH, Imprimeur-Libraire, rue de Montmorency.

1812.

FIG. 3. Title page to Vols. 1–3 of Mémoires.

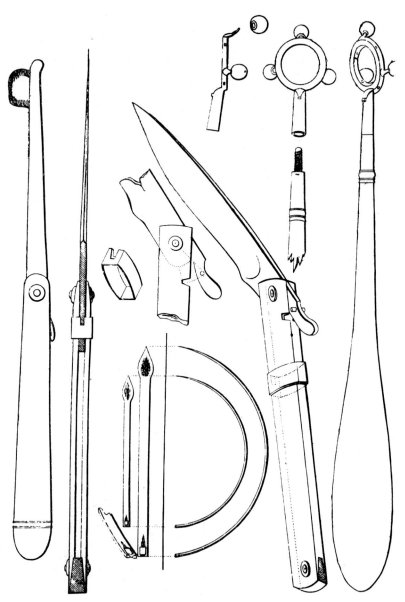

FIG. 4. Larrey's instruments.

On the left the *lenticule;* on the right the *porte-moxa;* in the middle a collapsible knife, and below this his surgical needles.

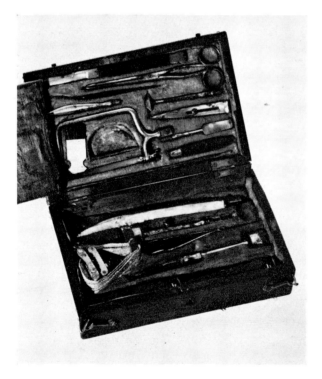

FIG. 5. Instrument case of Surgeon William Beatty R.N.
(By kind permission of the Royal College of Physicians
and Surgeons, Glasgow.)

Fig. 6. The military hospital at Val-de-Grâce. (By permission of Editions Chantal, Paris.)

AMBULANCE DU BARON PERCY.

Fig. 7. Percy's ambulance.

FIG. 8. Larrey's light ambulance.

FIG. 9. Photograph of a model of Larrey's light ambulance (M.J.D.).

Fig. 10. Ambulance men and surgeons.

the firing line, thereby saving them from the enemy and bringing them early surgical aid.

He had realized the importance of the early treatment of war wounds at the outset of his army career, and by teaching this and insisting on it on every possible occasion he saved many lives. He operated in the field under the enemy's fire as we shall see in the details of his different campaigns, and when an operation was unnecessary or impossible he made it his business to see that the wounded were conveyed to a suitable spot where he could supervise their treatment with the least delay.

Each ambulance unit had a strength of some 340 men under the direction of a Chief Surgeon. It was constituted into three divisions, each of these in charge of a surgeon of the first class, aided by two assistant surgeons of the second class and twelve assistant surgeons of the third class,[2] the latter only partially trained men, and it included two pharmacists. Each division had eight two-wheeled ambulance wagons and four four-wheelers, with the necessary drivers, orderlies, clerks, etc. There were also four ordinary transport wagons assigned to each division. The light two-wheeled ambulances were especially designed for flat country and were well-sprung box-like vehicles (Fig. 8), into which two stretchers could be slid side by side on rollers. They were drawn by two horses each mounting a postilion. The stretchers were provided with iron handles to take leather straps or the soldiers' belts. The larger four-wheeled wagons, designed to take four men, were for use in mountainous country and opened by sliding panels on each side, so that the wounded could be lifted in or out whilst lying flat: they were drawn by four horses with two postilions. When in action an ambulance division could if necessary be split up into single units under a mounted medical officer, who would thus have at his service a mounted orderly and a mobile vehicle equipped with all the requisites for first-aid (Fig. 9). In steep mountain country mules or pack-horses were made use of to carry panniers containing the dressing materials, instruments, and other medical necessaries. A secondary, and rather macabre duty of the ambulance units, was to collect and bury the dead. This was the work of unmounted orderlies and was directed by a military police officer, who was empowered to requisition the necessary labour from the local inhabitants.

Whilst the work of constructing the new ambulances was in progress and their personnel being selected and equipped, Larrey was asked to accompany Villemanzy on a tour of inspection of the medical service of the army in Italy. They left Milan on May 25th, 1797, journeying through Lodi, Cremona and Pizzighettone, in all of which they established military hospitals, and so on to Mantua which he considered unhealthy, especially for visitors, on account of its heat and summer humidity. Although knowing nothing of the malarial mosquito, Larrey ascribed the great prevalence of fevers to the expanse of stagnant water near the town. A hospital was for a time set up in the convent of S. Benedetto, but this was later to prove unsatisfactory from overcrowding and the marshy

---

[2] The considerable number of surgeons to each unit explains how Larrey could leave behind him so many surgeons at various places.

nature of the ground. At Verona they found a large hospital full of French wounded, and organized two more before going on to Vicenza and Padua. The Padua hospital Larrey considered the finest in Europe, and he brought as many of the sick and wounded as possible to it and established a School of Surgery for army medical officers. From Padua he went to Mestre and thence by gondola to Venice: "Through the watery mists of the Adriatic the town at first glance looks like a great fleet, its towers and spires resembling so many ships of the line. But as you approach the houses come into view, and slowly the whole extent of this noble city arises in the midst of the waters." Although the fate of Venice was still in the balance, the activities of the French liberators were well in evidence, and Larrey saw the famous winged lion, "which today adorns the fountain of the terrace of the Invalides at Paris, removed from the top of one of two columns which stand in the Piazza Saint-Marco, where it had been since the twelfth century." He added: "The cathedral is remarkable for its construction, architecture, and ancient mosaics, and more especially for the four Corinthian horses which formerly surmounted the doorway, and which I also saw taken down to be sent to Paris, where they now form the superb quadriga above the triumphal arch of the Tuilleries." Restitution for these atrocious acts of vandalism was made in 1816, when both sculptures were restored to Venice—the Lion of St. Mark, alas, in pieces! He also visited the glass works, like many a modern tourist, and admired with curiosity the richly decorated galley *Beaucentaure*, moored in the port and used for the ceremony of the marriage of the Doge with the Adriatic, which we may admire today in Canaletto's picture in our National Gallery. He thought the Venetians avaricious, but hospitable, courteous and obliging, and he remarked that they had "deteriorated from the valorous republicans whose very name was once feared by the Turks." He deemed them incapable of maintaining the independence with which Bonaparte for a short time endowed them. At a later date he thought them fortunate in that their state was absorbed into the Kingdom of Italy under Napoleon's sceptre, and his enthusiasm led him to say: "Marching henceforth under the banners of the illustrious Chief of our Empire, this people will regain, in common with so many other nations, both the valour and the virtues which formerly distinguished their ancestors."

* * * * *

Early in the year 1797 an expedition was in process of being fitted out in Venice for the capture of Corfu, and Larrey was given the task of organizing its medical service. His account of the condition of the transports destined for this task is candid and remarkably vivid: "They were *Victoire*, *Gloire* and *Eole*. The first was old, badly built, deficient in rigging and unseaworthy; in the ordinary way she did not leave harbour. It was thought, however, that she would serve for the expedition and preparations were going on to fit her out. The other two ships, each capable of carrying four hundred troops and crew, were of better construction and in better condition, but they had recently returned from an expedition to the Ionian Islands, where they had lost two hundred and fifty men from an epidemic which had prevailed there about twelve months earlier. The return to Venice had diminished the severity and effects of the disease in these ships, but nevertheless some thirty men had died during the month they had been lying in the roadstead.

"Details, which I was able to obtain from the army surgeons and from a number of sick who were still aboard, shewed that the disease was a contagious eruptive fever (typhus) which would have had the gravest consequences had the surgeons not taken the step of bringing the patients up on deck. Many of them were also suffering from worms and these, according to the reports of the medical officers, died between the fifth and ninth day. If the fourteenth day were passed and the eruption had reached its maximum the worst was over and convalescence followed; but even so a considerable number relapsed into their earlier state, which became complicated by a dysenteric flux and ended fatally. Those who escaped death had as a rule a long and tedious convalescence.

"My inspection of these two vessels and the information I was able to gather made it easy to discover the source of this epidemic. During the time they were anchored in the bays of the island of Corfu, etc., where marine phosphorescence is very marked in summer—as it is in the Venetian canals and signifies their unhealthiness—the ships were continuously exposed to the southerly wind, or sirocco, the summer having been extremely hot and the winter mild and rainy. Moreover the habit had been formed of keeping the ports closed during this season. The troops and ship's company had long been on a faulty regimen; the sailors subsisting entirely on biscuit, farinaceous vegetables and bad brandy, and furthermore the sanitation in both vessels was extremely bad. In *Gloire* this was general; there was a foetid and nauseating stink everywhere: in the batteries, in the lower deck and in the forecastle. The sailors' belongings were strewed in disorder all about the ship. Tarry *débris* of cordage encumbered the decks; the men's underclothes were full of vermin, and almost the whole of the ship's company and the soldiers grubbed along in heedless idleness. On *Eole* dejecta were lying in every corner and the same disorder was apparent. In the part of the lower deck where sick soldiers or sailors are usually berthed, we found three unfortunates dying of the disease. They were stretched on filthy pallets and completely abandoned.

"According to the report of the surgeon these three men had been convalescent two days earlier but had suffered a relapse; no doubt because the corpse of one of their comrades who had died rather suddenly had been left lying with them.

"All these factors had contributed to the development of the disease, from which the soldiers and sailors had suffered the worst. The officers, being better fed, less crowded and in better ventilated quarters, furnished only a few victims, none of whom perished.

"I pronounced the following measures to be necessary to arrest the epidemic in these ships and in the hospitals, and to prevent further and more serious developments.

"I required that all the sick from the ships should at once be sent to the nearby hospitals, and that the troops should be disembarked and put under canvas in a healthy locality near the shore. This measure was necessary for the health of the men and made it possible to cleanse the interior of the vessels. Within forty-eight hours this was done and I then arranged for the following: the interior and outside of the vessels to be scraped; the inside to be tarred and whitewashed and the outside painted. The decks to be sanded and holystoned. The whole of the interior to be fumigated, especially the lower deck and the bilge, by the Guyton-Morveau process,[3] which consists of burning a number of small broken masses of sulphur and saltpetre on stones or bricks placed a certain distance apart in the lower deck and the bilges; a method I had found useful in the North American campaign. The bedding of the sick and the hammocks and linen of the sailors to be scoured and washed in lye, and a fresh issue made of new cotton clothes for the summer and of woollen ones for the winter, both to these men and to the troops who had been landed.

"Finally, I superintended the provisioning myself. I took great care to have on board a large quantity of light foodstuffs and suitable liquors. These things being done the troops and the ship's company came on board again and were ready to sail as soon as the signal was given. I also gave instructions to the army surgeons for the maintenance of the health of the soldiers and sailors. The first of these, which had for its object the prevention of diseases and contagion, embodied some of my views on hygiene which I shall not repeat here as they have been given in my account of the campaign in America. They emphasized the supreme importance of seeing to the cleanliness and sanitation of the vessels and detailed the means of preventing the ill effects of idleness by constant exercise. The second set of instructions laid down rules for the placing of medical officers in ships, their duties during a voyage and at the time of landing, and for the dispersal between the ships of surgical instruments, materials for dressings, medicaments and light foods. It is especially important to impress upon surgeons destined for far off expeditions that they should not assemble all their materials in one and the same place, on account of the dangers inherent in a voyage and the possibility of everything being lost should the vessel unhappily founder. Such things ought to be as widely distributed as possible, which makes for easier transport and is infinitely more convenient, as we found by experience in Egypt.

"The expedition sailed in the early days of Messidor of the year V (June 1797) and quickly reached its destination."

*　　*　　*　　*　　*

With his departure from Venice Larrey completed his extensive tour of northern Italy and then returned to Milan where a conference of the chief medical officers of the army had been convened. As a result of his reports

---

[3] Guyton de Morveau, L. B., *Digressions Académiques*. Dijon 1772.

a number of measures were decided upon, such as the establishment of mobile ambulances, and the formation of schools of anatomy and military surgery in every important town in Italy in which troops or hospitals were stationed. The direction of those east of the Piave, as far as and including Udine, devolved upon him. The first completed ambulance unit was based on the latter town, where he exercised it daily in training and manoeuvres.

It was here that Larrey was called upon to investigate an epizöotic which was the cause of serious loss of domestic animals in Venetian Friouli. In many villages and hamlets it emptied the stables and byres, and the inhabitants themselves, who were found to be liable to infection, were filled with alarm. In his usual thorough fashion he visited the affected farms and had autopsies performed on some of the dead animals. Then, the better to observe all the stages of the disease, he improvised a veterinary hospital in the stables of a convent. The malady proved to be anthrax, on which he carried out studies and post-mortem examinations and experimented on methods of treatment. Rules of hygiene and recommendations for treatment were drawn up and translated into Italian for communication to the local people. "In a short preamble I defined the characters and different stages of the disease. I then went on to say that when it was very advanced or intense, treatment was uncertain or useless and ought not to be undertaken: that it was better to kill the animal than to use remedies which cost more than was worth while, even supposing that such remedies might save its life, and that it was equally wrong from motives of avarice to skin the hides from beasts which had died of the disease, or had been killed during its course. I recommended that care should be taken to bury the animals promptly and deeply without skinning them, and that they should be covered with a number of layers of quicklime; that the meat should on no account be eaten, as in the opinion of doctors it is unwholesome, and that the raw flesh should not be given as food to other animals as it promptly communicates the contagion, as has been shewn a great many times."

Either from the natural exhaustion of the epidemic or as a result of his vigorous promulgation of hygienic measures the disease ceased to progress and in the end disappeared. The local populace gave Larrey the credit, and made known their sentiments in the following rather pathetic letter:

"*To M. le Chirurgien-en-Chef Larrey.*

Your work in the curing of cattle attacked by the epizöotic has merited our recognition. We have waited to see the effect of the treatment in order to speak about it, and we are very happy to be able to assure you that the remedies have been used with advantage wherever they have been able to be employed. Our lot has been hard, as circumstances have not allowed us to use these everywhere, seeing that it has been necessary to take even affected oxen to provide transport for the Army; this has caused the loss of many of them, some whilst actually in use. All this only makes your work the more valuable, even allowing that we have only been able to save a few of those attacked. Our unfortunate circumstances prevent us from shewing you our appreciation by any other way than by the most lively and sincere feelings. You have put us in your debt, and will always have the satisfaction of having relieved the sufferings of the unhappy people of this country, who will be able through your efforts to save the lives of their cattle which are so necessary for their own subsistance."

Signed by the President BATOLDI.

*   *   *   *   *

After the signing of the peace of Campo Formio, Bonaparte reviewed the whole army, and having seen the manoeuvres of the first division of Larrey's mobile ambulance, which was attached to the advance guard under Bernadotte, he expressed his satisfaction with both the wagons and the organization of its personnel. Turning to Larrey he said: "Your work in this matter is one of the finest conceptions of our time: it will of itself establish your reputation." A flattering general report on his work was also forthcoming from Villemanzy.

The campaign in Italy having come to an end Larrey returned to his professional post in the Val-de-Grâce hospital, at the beginning of the winter session of 1797.

Almost at once he was promoted a Surgeon-in-Chief and ordered to report to the Army of England, in which he was attached to the right column under his friend Desaix, whose headquarters were at Lille. But the orders were hardly issued when they were countermanded by others instructing him to return to Toulon where an expedition was being prepared for an undisclosed destination. "Little did I know," he wrote later, "that I was destined to follow the French Army under General Bonaparte into the richest and most interesting country in the world."

*   *   *   *   *

Chapter 4

Expedition to Egypt. Landing at Alexandria.
The Battle of the Pyramids. Capture of Cairo.
Ophthalmia. First signs of plague.

Amongst the varied duties of a Chief Medical Officer was the engaging
of assistants. For this purpose Larrey wrote to the medical schools of
Montpellier and Toulouse, asking for a supply of well qualified surgeons:
"men of courage, able to endure prolonged and arduous campaigns"—
qualities which were indeed to be required of them. He soon assembled a
hundred and eight surgeons under his orders, exclusive of those attached
to the different regiments. It was his further province to make up chests
of the materials necessary for a campaign, together with the surgical
instruments, appliances and stretchers. His medical colleague, Desgenettes,
the Physician-in-Chief, was likewise responsible for the army's purely
medical needs. Unfortunately the mistake was made of putting the whole
of his supplies into a single vessel. This was captured by the English, and
the loss caused serious deficiencies at the outset of the Egyptian campaign.
The lesson was a costly one and he never ceased to preach its moral.

The squadron set sail on the 30th Floréal (May 19th), defiling before
the flag-ship *Orient* on which were Bonaparte, Admiral Brueys, and the
headquarter's staff, including Larrey and Desgenettes. *Orient* was destined
to be blown up at the Battle of the Nile, with the loss of her admiral and
the commodore, Casa Bianca, with his young son, well known to English
school boys through Mrs. Hemans' poem. Malta was reached in twenty-
one days and although formidably fortified the Knights of St. John
surrendered the island after a mere pretence of resistance. In the meantime Nelson, who had been driven by bad weather from the blockade of
Toulon to the lee of Sardinia, returned to find that the French fleet had
sailed, and hastening east again to Alexandria, where he hoped to catch
it, he passed to the south of Brueys' fleet to find that harbour vacant. The
French sailed from Malta on June 18th and disembarked at Marabout,
about fifteen miles to the west of Alexandria, on July 1st, 1798.

Alexandria fell after a few hours' fighting, in which the French had
about two hundred and fifty casualties, including the divisional commanders Kléber and Menou. An ambulance division had been attached
to each wing of the army, whilst Larrey himself was at the centre with a
third division, in close contact with the Commander-in-Chief, so that all
the wounded were promptly attended to. Kléber received a superficial
wound in the right temple, which Larrey dressed at the foot of Pompey's
column. Alexandria having been occupied, permanent hospitals were

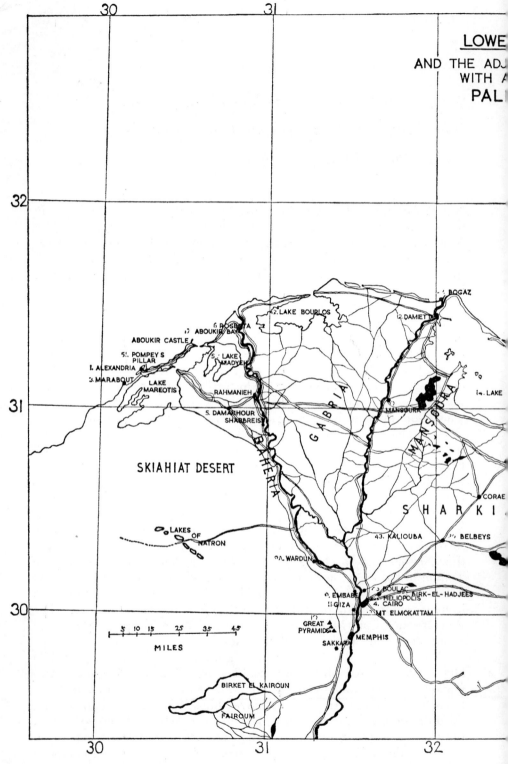

30 31

32

2. LAKE BOURLOS 12. DAMIETTA BOGAZ

6. ROSETTA
17 ABOUKIR BAY
ABOUKIR CASTLE

5'. POMPEY'S
PILLAR 5. LAKE
MADYEH

1. ALEXANDRIA
3. MARABOUT
LAKE
MAREOTIS RAHMANIEH

31 GABRIA MANSOURA 14. LAKE

5. DAMANHOUR
SHABBREIS

BAHERIA

SKIAHIAT DESERT

SHARKI CORAE

LAKES
OF
NATRON 43. KALIOUBA BELBEYS

30. WARDUN

BOULAC BIRK-EL-HADJEES
9. EMBABE HELIOPOLIS
11 GIZA 4. CAIRO
MT ELMOKATTAM

GREAT
PYRAMIDS
SAKKARA MEMPHIS

30

5 10 15 25 35 45
MILES

BIRKET EL KAIROUN

FAIROUM

30 31 32

Fig. 11 and 12. Ma

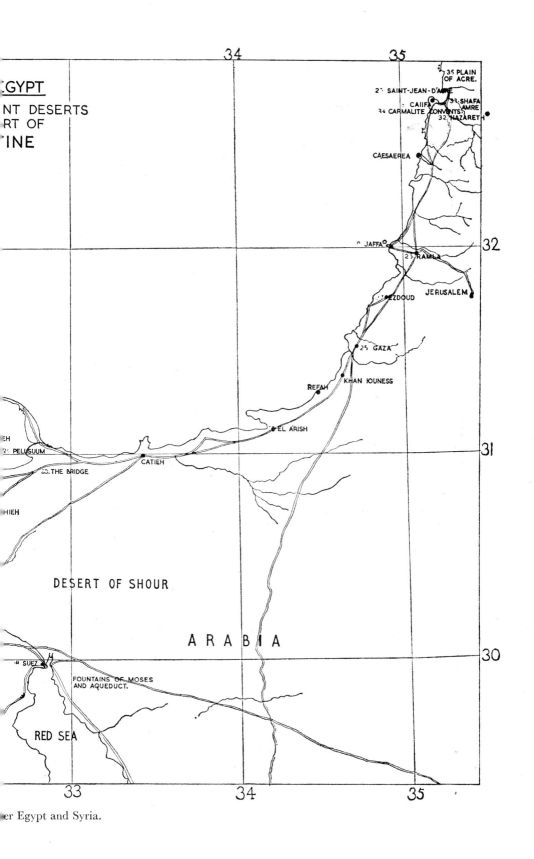

EGYPT

NT DESERTS

RT OF

INE

35 PLAIN OF ACRE.

27 SAINT-JEAN-D'ACRE

CAIIFA   33 SHAFA AMRE

34 CARMALITE CONVENTS

32 NAZARETH

CAESAEREA

32

JAFFA

23 RAMLA

JERUSALEM

EZDOUD

25 GAZA

KHAN IOUNESS

REFAH

EL ARISH

31

EH

21 PELUSUUM

CATIEH

23 THE BRIDGE

HIEH

DESERT OF SHOUR

A R A B I A

30

SUEZ

FOUNTAINS OF MOSES AND AQUEDUCT.

RED SEA

33   34   35

er Egypt and Syria.

organized and, in preparation for the advance on Cairo, Larrey attached an ambulance to each of the five divisions of the army, and retained a reserve of surgeons under himself with a sixth ambulance at headquarters. The surgical service at Alexandria was left to the care of a young surgeon of brilliant promise, Masclet; the command of the garrison to Kléber.

The march on Cairo began on July 6th (Fig. 11), with Dessaix's division as the advance guard. Simultaneously another division under General Duga, advanced along the coast, captured Rosetta without resistance, and having overrun the delta made contact with the main army. The latter took the route across the edge of the Libian desert, marching without supplies and living on the country as the French army was wont. After five days: "marching on foot, under the rays of a burning sun, over sand which was even hotter, across immense plains of a frightful barrenness, where it was only occasionally possible to find a few stagnant pits of foul water—so muddy as to be almost solid—even the strongest of soldiers, devoured by thirst and overcome by heat, succumbed under the weight of their arms. The vista of distant lakes, an effect of the mirage seemed to promise an end to our woes, but only served to aggravate our distress and to produce the extreme form of collapse and physical prostration that I saw in many of our brave fellows. Summoned to them, too late to be of any use, I saw many perish from exhaustion. Such a mode of death seemed peaceful and even pleasant, for during the last moments of his life one of them told me that he was 'comfortable beyond words.' Nevertheless I was able to revive a certain number by means of a little fresh water, fortified with a small quantity of brandy and sugar, which I always carried with me in a small leather bottle. I also used with success alcoholized aether or Hoffman's mineral liquor[1] and syrup."

The French soldiers were probably rather soft after their confinement on shipboard and not in the best state for this abrupt transition to Africa. Climatic perils were not the only ones, for they were harassed on their march by Arabs, who killed one of the surgeons of Larrey's ambulance.

The capture of Damanhour brought welcome relief to the exhausted men, for there they found water and provisions which quickly restored their strength and spirits. It was here that Bonaparte was kicked in the right leg by an Arab horse. The blow was a severe one and gave Larrey some anxiety, but no complications developed in spite of the hardships of the advance and the commander's "natural activity which was not conducive to rest". The Nile was reached at Rahhmanieh where the troops drank their fill and bathed in it at their nightly halts as the advance continued along the left bank. How many contracted bilharziasis we cannot estimate, since Larrey does not specifically refer to this condition, but there can be no doubt that it was one of the many diseases that reduced the strength of the French forces in Egypt. The men's chief food was the water melon known as pastèque; they had no bread, since they had neither mills to grind corn nor ovens to roast it in. At Rahhmanieh they made contact with a flotilla under Rear-Admiral Perrée, which had

[1] Liquor mineralis anodynus Hoffmani: a mild stimulant containing alcohol and nitrous aether.

ascended the Nile and thereafter kept on the army's flank. Bonaparte put a number of non-combatants aboard the ships, his secretary Bourienne being amongst these, and took their horses for the troops. At Chébreisse the vessels were attacked from both the river and the land, and were in a critical situation but were saved by the arrival of the army which drove off the enemy, chiefly Mameluke cavalry, with small loss to themselves. Three days later the main army of the Mamelukes was encountered, drawn up between the pyramids and the Nile and protected by an entrenched battery at Embabeh. The celebrated Battle of the Pyramids followed, in which the Mameluke forces were decisively defeated and split into two; one group under Mourad Bey retreating towards upper Egypt, and the other towards the Syrian border. Bonaparte had discovered before the battle that Mourad's guns were so placed that they could fire in only one direction, and so manoeuvred his forces that they would not be exposed to these. His men formed squares to meet the cavalry attack and he forbade them to fire until the enemy were at the muzzles of their muskets. The wild Mameluke horsemen were unused to disciplined warfare of this sort and after many desperate charges they broke and fled. A part of the defeated force threw themselves into Embabeh, where after a short resistance panic took charge, a number of the defenders being janizaries and fellahin of poor fighting quality with little heart for the battle of the Mamelukes. Many were driven into the Nile and were either drowned or escaped by swimming. From the military point of view the battle was no more serious for the French than a skirmish, for Larrey only had two hundred and sixty men seriously wounded, but tactically its results were decisive. Cairo lay open to the victors and the power and reputation of the Mamelukes were irretrievably damaged. The wounded were taken to the château at Giza, which was converted into a large hospital, and here they were dressed and operated upon.

On July 25th, Bonaparte entered Cairo and his troops occupied the citadel. The town yielded supplies of every kind, and hospitals were quickly established to which the wounded were transferred from Giza. Desaix's division was despatched to upper Egypt in pursuit of Mourad Bey, and Vial's to Damietta. Napoleon left on August 5th in pursuit of Ibrahim Bey who was retreating through the province of Sharkia and with him went Larrey. After three days' forced marching they overtook Ibrahim at Sâléhyeh. The French cavalry charged vigorously and dispersed the fugitives, losing a few men killed and having about fifty wounded. These were dressed on the sand and carried to the mosque, which Larrey converted into a stationary ambulance. Most of the wounds were sabre cuts from the Mameluke swordsmen, some of them so severe that they severed entire limbs. An example was Brigadier-General Destrès, who received seven deep sabre wounds, two of which cut through his epaulettes and the muscles and a part of the bone of his shoulders and a third a portion of the muscles of the back, the spine of the seventh dorsal vertebra, and the other four wounded the muscles of the arms. He was also shot in the chest, the ball fracturing two ribs on the right side and causing haemothorax which led to empyema, for which Larrey operated later. The General recovered and subsequently commanded the Royal Guard of King Joachim I of Naples (Murat).

During the return of this expedition to Cairo news was received of the French naval defeat by Nelson at Aboukir Bay. Bourienne tells us that this threw Napoleon into the depths of despair. Cut off from all communication with France, in a hostile country with a murmuring, disillusioned and discontented army, there seemed no future but a degrading ultimate capitulation. However this mood of depression passed, and he was soon engaged in optimistic schemes of a vast turning movement through Syria, and of leading his army back to France by way of Damascus, Constantinople and Vienna.

The first step to this end was to make effective the occupation and pacification of Egypt, and to organize her finances and administration, and this he put in hand with his customary vigour and ability. He also opened negotiations with Djezzar Pasha, the "Butcher of Acre", offering him friendship and protection, but Djezzar, confident of his own strength and of English assistance, refused to receive the first envoy and true to his name beheaded a second. It became clear that any advance into Syria would be opposed so measures were taken to prepare for this campaign in the spring of 1799. But in the meantime much was happening in Cairo. On October 21st, the inhabitants rose in revolt, but the Commander had been warned and the insurrection was swiftly repressed. In the affray General Dupuy, who commanded the garrison, was struck in the left axilla by a lance which pierced his axillary artery. As he lay stretched in the street Larrey made his way through his assailants and endeavoured to staunch the bleeding. He had the general carried into the house of his friend General Junot, where he expired shortly afterwards. Larrey then went at once to the main hospital to attend other wounded, and to his horror found in its gateway the bleeding corpses of two of his surgeons, Roussel and Mongin, who had been slaughtered whilst defending their patients.

Whilst these events were taking place in Cairo, Desaix's pursuit of Mourad Bey into upper Egypt had prospered. A decisive victory was gained at Sedment, in an engagement fought on the lines of the Battle of the Pyramids, with the French forming squares and the Mamelukes attacking on horse. The French losses amounted to about three hundred men. The wounded were attended to on the battlefield and later sent down to Cairo by water. Desaix pursued the enemy as far as the cataracts and so gave the Commission of Arts an opportunity of examining the monuments of Thebes, and the temples of Tentyra, Carnak and Luxor.

*　　*　　*　　*　　*

Ophthalmia

Of the many plagues of Egypt this disease of the eyes is one which over the centuries has caused untold suffering, especially amongst invading armies. Whilst it is generally accepted that the Egyptian Ophthalmia, which so severely affected both the French and British at this time, was trachoma, and Larrey is credited with the first full description of the disease, it seems clear that certain of his cases were gonorrhoeal, and we shall see that he remarks upon a connection between ophthalmia and venereal disease in the Memoir he wrote for the guidance of his junior surgeons.

The extent of the infection may be judged from his statement that only a few persons escaped the disease during the last few months of 1797 and the early ones of 1798. He attributed this special seasonal incidence to the succession of forced marches across sandy deserts devoid of water, and to the great heat of the day which was succeeded by cold damp nights. Later, in 1800, when the French were cut off in the peninsula of Alexandria by the English landing at Aboukir, they had more than three thousand cases in the space of two and a half months. The English suffered no less severely, and at the end of 1810 there were as many as 2,317 blinded soldiers in the military hospitals at Chelsea and Kilmainham. So serious was the problem that the British government provided a special annual pension fund of £100,000 for such men.

Larrey, as I have said, considered the principal causes of ophthalmia to be: "the burning heat of the daytime, the reflection of the sun's rays by the whiteness of so many objects on the Egyptian soil, which fatigues and irritates the sensitive structures of the eye; the immoderate use of spirits and of women; the dust which becomes caught beneath the eyelids and produces a more or less severe irritation of the eyeball; and above all, the suppression of sweating by the sudden passage from heat to cold, and the dampness and chill of the nights from which the soldiers in bivouac are not protected. The sudden suppression of diarrhoea has the same result. . . ." Like most medical men of his period he attributed many ills to the suppression of transpiration.

He divided ophthalmia into serous or mild, and inflammatory or severe types. "The outcome of ophthalmia differs. When it is inflammatory and left to nature alone, a number of points of suppuration usually develop by about the sixth or seventh day on the edges and inner surface of the eyelids or at their angles. These ulcers gradually extend over the conjunctiva and attack the transparent cornea and often perforate it. At times the cornea suddenly bursts without being ulcerated, the rupture taking place during the first twenty-four hours of the disease and when the conjunctiva is hardly reddened. It is difficult to explain the cause of this acute spontaneous rupture—we can only relate the phenomena and their effects as we saw them in Egypt. The opening which results is rounded and of about the same size in all the patients so affected: it allows the exit of a part of the aqueous membrane or of the iris, to form a hernia known as a staphyloma. The tumour formed by the membrane has a dull grey colour whilst that formed by the iris is darker: it is sensitive to the lightest touch and to the friction caused by the eyelids. Sight during the first few days is more or less obscured since the pupil is in part or wholly obliterated, but in general the staphyloma slowly diminishes and returns to the anterior chamber of the eye and the membranes resume their original position. Sometimes a part remains outside which becomes strangulated by the closing of the breach in the cornea, and loses its sensitivity and becomes more dense; on other occasions it swells up and divides into a number of lobules and takes on a cancer-like character, this is especially when there is a venereal taint in the case. When the staphyloma regresses spontaneously the opening in the transparent cornea closes by the union of its edges, leaving a small greyish depressed scar which is at first opaque to light.

"In a number of cases the crystalline lens and the vitreous humour follow the displacement of the iris; their membranes are affected and destroyed by suppuration and the eye becomes disorganized and loses its function. This state of affairs is to be seen in many of the natives of the country, especially amongst the most indigent who sleep on the ground in the open air practically naked, and who are exposed during the daytime to the dust and the burning rays of the sun without protection.

"It is unusual for inflammatory ophthalmia, unless it be very mild, to resolve without treatment. It is quite different with serous ophthalmia, which can be terminated by an attack of sweating, or an excessive excretion of tears, and in particular by diarrhoea.

"When ophthalmia is not neglected but properly treated there are no sequelae, but the blind confidence of the soldier in empirical remedies, failure to go to hospital and his neglect of the prescribed treatment in the early stages, too often defeat our best endeavours.

"When the victims of ophthalmia are at the same time subject to some other disease such as the venereal, its course is more rapid and more serious and is marked by special features: the redness of the edges of the eyelids is more pronounced, the pus is greenish as in gonorrhoea and irritates the parts it touches, and the patient suffers much more during the night. One should satisfy oneself as to the presence of this complication. The sudden suppression of an attack of gonorrhoea is a potent cause in Europe of the particular form of ophthalmia we are considering, and the best way to get rid of it is to re-establish the gonorrhoea. . . . As soon as the local irritation of the conjunctiva has been relieved by scarification of the temples and by anodynes, the gonorrhoea should be provoked afresh, either by inoculation or by an alkaline injection into the urethral canal, which acts as a stimulant to the natural inoculation. . . . Inoculation can be undertaken with confidence since we have a specific remedy which will cure gonorrhoea in a very few days: this is the Balm of Gilead or, in its absence, Copaiba balsam in large doses."

The foregoing is yet another example of the belief that the suppression of discharges had ill effects, whilst their promotion by issues and setons would purge the body of its evil humours.

Larrey's treatment for ophthalmia included bleeding from the neck veins, leeching or scarification of the temples, steaming the eyes, and the use of anodyne lotions made from decoctions of poppy-head, linseed and oriental safron. He condemned poultices, but recommended that a dressing of white of egg, beaten up with rose water and a few grains of alum and camphor, should be used at night. As the inflammation diminished he substituted lotions containing a little acetate of lead, oxychloride of mercury, or sulphate of copper, and when resolution began a decoction of pomegranate bark or zinc sulphate. For ulcers of the eyelids he employed an ointment containing red oxide of mercury, oxide of zinc and camphor. He adds: "The English on their arrival in Egypt likewise suffered from this disease. After a short time they adopted the French method of treatment, which they learnt of from a copy of my Memoir they found in our hospitals at Rosetta; from this time they, too, saved the sight of most of their patients."

* * * * *

Amongst his many activities Bonaparte found time to visit Suez and Larrey accompanied him. The crossing of the desert took them three days, along a track marked out by the bones of men and animals which had perished there. The cold at night was severe enough to prevent the travellers from sleeping and no wood to make a fire was available, but after some difficulty they managed to make one from the skeletal remains! At Suez a hospital of fifty beds was set up for the garrison, and the party then crossed at low tide to the Asian shore, like the Children of Israel when fleeing from the land of Egypt, to explore Moses' Springs, where they found the remains of an ancient aqueduct built by the Venetians to water ships. The return to Suez was adventurous, as some of the party were cut off by the tide like the hosts of Pharaoh and narrowly escaped drowning. Whilst at Suez Bonaparte explored a stretch of the ancient canal, said to have been built by Ptolemy and restored by Trajan in the second century, but which became finally silted up at the end of the eighth century. This exploration no doubt stimulated the revived interest in the canal which led to the European Commission in 1847, which reported adversely on the project and in this was largely influenced by Robert Stevenson. The matter lapsed until de Lesseps obtained his concession in 1856, but the canal he built cut straight through the isthmus and does not follow the old one which connected the Gulf of Suez with one of the branches of the Nile.

Back in Cairo, Larrey had to face a new anxiety which was to dog the expedition until its final expulsion from Egypt. News came from Alexandria and other places in the delta of the outbreak of a pestilent fever associated with boils and buboes, which was making rapid progress. Soon a soldier of the 32nd demi-brigade was admitted to a Cairo hospital with a blackish boil on his lip and died in three days. Larrey, who was certain that this was plague, concealed the matter from everyone but Desgenettes and had the body removed with great precaution and the man's bedding and effects burned and his room fumigated. He nevertheless sent a circular to all the surgeons of the first class, urging them to give every care to any who might be attacked by this disease, whilst at the same time taking all precautions to avoid contagion.

* * * * *

Chapter 5

Syria. el-A'rych. Jaffa. St. Jean d'Acre. Retreat
from Syria. Poisoning of wounded at Acre.
Return to Cairo.

Meanwhile the campaign in Syria (Fig. 12) was in active preparation and
Larrey's immediate problem was to provide transport for the wounded
who, in view of the length of the army's communications, would need
protection from attacks by Arabs, and in any case be exposed to the
horrors of hunger and thirst unless their evacuation were prompt and
speedy. The only animals available were camels, which were useless for
draught purposes, and so his mind reverted to an earlier idea of pack
transport. He devised light panniers to be carried as cradles slung on
each side of the camel's hump, and long enough to take a man lying at
full length (Fig. 13). A hundred of these were prepared, but unfortunately
the animals were all commandeered by the transport agents on reaching
Syria which greatly aggravated the problem.

The army marched on February 9th, 1799, and the advance guard
under Reynier had a sharp engagement before the fort of el-A'rych
where the wounded amounted to nearly three hundred. Larrey at the
time was with headquarters at Salehyeh but he immediately obtained
permission to go forward. He had an uncomfortable journey of three days
on a camel and on passing through Catieh saw a second case of plague in
a man who had come from Damietta. At el-A'rych he found the wounded
in wretched conditions, lying on palm leaves and covered by a few
miserable tents or palm branches without shelter from rain or damp, the
weather at the time being very cold and wet. Most had serious wounds,
many were attacked by tetanus, and almost all required operations. There
was no light food or meat to make broth, so Larrey obtained permission
from the commander to slaughter such camels as were injured and no
longer of use. This source of meat did not last long and soon they were
compelled to eat horse flesh which he found inferior to camel's.

With the arrival of Bonaparte and the artillery park the siege was
opened and the fort speedily capitulated. Larrey was ordered to inspect
its interior and to do what was required to render the quarters healthy.
"I first sought out the sick or wounded whom the defenders had left
behind, and discovered some fifty of these in subterranean apartments
lacking both light and air and lying on dirty rotting mats, without bedding
and covered with vermin. These unfortunates had received no medical
help at all, and in almost every case their wounds were undressed,
gangrenous and full of worms. Many of them had the symptoms of

malignant fever: one had a plague buboe in the right groin and a plague boil on the leg of the same side.

"All this shewed clearly that plague was present amongst the troops of the enemy garrison, and I reported this to the General and his Chief-of-Staff. Having separated and isolated these luckless individuals within the fort, in such a way that they could have no communication with our troops, I dressed their wounds and then turned to the second of my duties. The courtyards were filled with the corpses of men and animals, more particularly horses, already in a state of putrefaction. Scattered about the soldiers' living rooms were masses of rags and nauseating and infected objects of every kind. I began by having the bodies carried as far from the building as was practicable and buried in one of the bays of the trench. I then collected all the contaminated materials into a large heap in each courtyard and burnt them. I also lit small bonfires in the different apartments to purify the air and burn the contents, as well as the numerous insects which were present everywhere. The entire fort was cleansed, and before allowing our troops to take up their quarters the necessary repairs were made and every part whitewashed.

"A suitable place was made ready for the reception and treatment of our wounded. M. Valet, whom I put in charge, looked after them and they rejoined the army not long afterwards, except for some who died of plague."

Jaffa was reached on March 3rd and after four days' siege was captured by assault. The horrors of this surrender, culminating in the cold-blooded murder of 4000 of the garrison who had surrendered on condition that their lives would be spared, are well known. The French wounded did not amount to more than two hundred and forty-two who were taken into a large convent in the town, whilst a second was set apart for fever cases, most of whom were either already suffering from plague or contracted it in hospital. Amongst the wounded were about twenty women who had escaped with their lives from the sack of the town and came daily to the hospital for treatment. The seriousness of the plague increased, and the troops were kept in bivouac as a precaution and forbidden to wear Turkish clothing.

The advance to St. Jean d'Acre was resumed on March 15th, and in three days time the army was encamped opposite Mount Carmel and Mount Tabor and the plain of Estrelon. Haifa was captured and following the mountain chain to gain shelter from the fierce heat the heights of Acre were reached on the 20th, after an exhausting march and severe privations which produced many problems in the transport of the wounded and sick, whilst the deaths from plague increased daily. The position occupied was on a ridge to the north of the town, from which runs the road to Sour, the ancient Tyre. Larrey considered this unhealthy, on account of the frequent mists arising from stagnant lakes formed during the winter inundations and the bad quality of the river waters, which he thought the cause of "obstinate diarrhoeas, colics and nervous putrid fevers." Later the aqueduct which carried water to the city was tapped and a better supply obtained. The principal ambulance was established in Djezzar's stables, the only place where shelter from the weather for the more seriously sick and wounded could be found. They lay without covering on rush leaves which were only infrequently changed, and there was a general dearth of medicaments of any kind. Stationary and convalescent hospitals were set up in the castle of Chefamer and the hermitage of Mount Carmel, and an evacuation hospital formed at Haifa.

The siege trench was opened on March 21st and the works pushed forward with the utmost activity. Larrey had a first-aid post within sixty yards of the town and directed it himself during the assaults. As soon as sufficient preparations had been made and a breach effected the main assault was launched, but failed. The defenders took courage, and the French suffered a further severe setback by the loss of their heavy artillery which was being brought up from Jaffa by sea, but the convoy was captured by English ships and the guns were an invaluable asset to Sidney Smith and Phélippeaux in the defence of the town. Thirteen assaults in all were made and were repulsed before Bonaparte had to admit failure and abandon his grand plan. The military operations of the invaders were by no means confined to the siege, for they were harassed by an attempted British landing at Haifa and by a serious attack by the Syrians and Ibrahim Bey's Mamelukes on the plain of Esdrelon, where a force under Kléber was surrounded and threatened with extermination. They were only relieved after many hours of desperate resistance by Bonaparte's arrival, and had about a hundred men wounded who were taken to the Convent of the Holy Land at Nazareth which was converted into a hospital. Later, the Commander-in-Chief visited Nazareth with Larrey and according to the latter was received as a new Messiah.

As the siege of Acre progressed towards a stalemate, what with the repeated assaults on the town and the increased amount of disease the state of the French troops became parlous. Larrey tells us that he had not a moment's peace or rest, being constantly on the move between the trench and camp, or visiting the divisions where there were almost as many sick and wounded as at the ambulance, which had about two thousand, many of them very severely injured from fighting at close quarters. Seventy amputations were required, two being through the hip joint and six through the shoulder joint (of whom four survived). Seven cases required trephining, five of whom recovered.

Amongst the casualties, the senior officers were General Caffarelli, who was shot through the elbow and underwent amputation but died nineteen days later of pyaemia. Duroc, then an aide-de-camp to Bonaparte, received a large bomb wound on the outer side of his right thigh which Larrey debrided and averted the threatened fatal issue. Eugène Beauharnais had a superficial wound on the side of his head. General Bon was killed by a bullet through the pelvis which lacerated his bladder. Lannes was hit in the face by a ball which buried itself behind his ear and could not be extracted, but later the suppuration brought it to the surface and Larrey removed it. Berthier's aide-de-camp, Arrighi, was hit in the neck by a ball which severed the external carotid artery close to its origin. As he fell a gunner in the breach battery saw the blood spurting from the two openings and had the presence of mind to thrust a finger into each. "I was called for at once and ran to his assistance amidst cannon balls and bullets. A methodically applied compressive bandage to my great astonishment arrested the threatening death and saved the officer." Years later, in recalling this event, Larrey mentions that he only knew of one other survival from a similar wound. This was a young English soldier he saw at Brussels after the battle of Waterloo, in whom the left external carotid had been partially severed and who had further severe haemorrhage on the removal of the first dressing. An English surgeon had rapidly exposed the common carotid artery and doubly ligated it and the patient recovered.

In spite of the extreme scarcity of every form of medical or surgical equipment and the insanitary state of the camps, which it is not difficult to imagine, most of the wounds progressed normally. Many however became infested with maggots from the bluebottle flies which were everywhere, and though these revolting parasites appeared to have a favourable effect in promoting the inevitable stage of suppuration and the separation of sloughs, they gave rise to intolerable itching, and so rapid was their development that they were fully formed within twenty-four hours. The best method of destroying them was found to be by a strong decoction of rue and small sage which was easily procured. The presence of gentles and their beneficial effect in some severe wounds was noted on the Western Front in the 1914–18 war[1] and their deliberate use has even been advocated since to promote the separation of sequestra.

The evacuation of the wounded was a major problem. Larrey states that during the siege and subsequent retreat eight hundred were evacuated to Egypt across the desert and twelve hundred by sea, most of them being embarked at Jaffa. "The complete absence of every means of transport left the wounded with the cruel alternatives of being left behind in our ambulances in the desert, either to die of hunger and thirst or to have their throats cut by the Arabs. General Bonaparte ordered all the horses in his headquarters, not excepting his own, to be used to carry them. As a result each demi-brigade was made responsible for transporting its own wounded, so that all those brave fellows reached Egypt and I had had the satisfaction of not leaving a single one behind in Syria." The accuracy of this statement is open to doubt and later it seems contradicted. Bourienne, not a very reliable witness in any case, says that it was on reaching Tentoura that Bonaparte made the decision to use all the transport animals for the sick and wounded. Many had already been abandoned between this place and Acre. Larrey wrote the above in 1812, during the apogee of the Empire, and in doing so he eulogizes the "heroic qualities of this great man". Perhaps he told less than the truth, though it well may be that few if any living wounded were left behind on the road *between Acre and Kanounès*, just beyond Gaza, which marks the geographical border of Syria.

[1] Basil Hughes. *British Journal of Surgery* 1916–17, Vol. IV, p. 754.

The army broke camp on May 21st, 1799 and set out for Egypt. "The second march was as full of trials as our first. The troops, who were worn out by disease, hardship and privations, were obliged to help or take turns in carrying their wounded brothers in arms. The heat was great and became progressively worse as we neared Egypt. We took the route along the shore, by way of Caesarea. . . . Our entrance into Jaffa was anything but pleasant. The town was dilapidated and had been largely abandoned by its inhabitants. Those of our sick and wounded who had made their way along the coast filled the hospitals, the port, and the neighbouring streets and provided a most heartrending spectacle. We spent three days and nights in attending to them, after which I put the worst cases on board ship for Damietta and sent the rest across the desert into Egypt. It is difficult to give any idea of the strain and exhaustion endured by the army surgeons."

It was at Jaffa that the much discussed, and often denied, order is said to have been given by Bonaparte for the poisoning of the incurably sick who could not be evacuated, and who if left alive would be tortured and murdered by the Arabs. Bourienne states that on May 28th a conference was held between Bonaparte, Berthier and several physicians and surgeons, and that the incurably sick were poisoned before the army resumed its march. Thiers says that such an order was given to Desgenettes, who refused to carry it out. Sir James McGrigor, in his *Medical Sketches of the Expedition to Egypt*, which Larrey certainly had read before he wrote his account of the retreat, says: "The *Pharmacien en Chef* to the French army often related to me the order which Bonaparte gave him to poison the wounded with opium."[2] In the copy of this book in the library of the Royal Society of Medicine there are two marginal manuscript notes to this, which it would appear are roughly contemporary. The one reads: "The same thing was repeatedly told by the Chief Physician, Desgenettes, at Lord Hutchinson's table after the surrender of the French Army and heard by the whole British Staff. Yet this *supple sycophant*, afterwards, when Bony was Consul, happening to meet at Turin Dr. Joseph Franck of Wilnar, and learning that he was coming to England, desired him to contradict this, and deny that he ever said so!" The second note, in a different hand, says: "Sir Sidney Smith told me that on entering St. Jean d'Acre not a French (sic) was found in the hospitals alive. They had not been poisoned —but had died of natural disease. Their case was hopeless when the rear guard left them and Bonaparte did suggest that opium might be given

[2] If this was the pharmacist, Royer, who served in Syria, his testimony is certainly suspect, since he betrayed the trust reposed in him by using the vehicles and animals allocated to the conveying of medical supplies for the carriage of wines, spirits and other luxuries, which he sold for his personal profit, and thus had some part in the responsibility for the general shortage Larrey complained of at St. Jean d'Acre. His fraudulent transactions were reported to Napoleon, who had the pharmacist tried by a court-martial which condemned him to be shot. Larrey pleaded for his life and Napoleon gave way, with the words: "Very well, Larrey, you may have him. But let me never see him again." This Royer must have been an undisciplined scamp, for earlier he had smuggled himself aboard the flagship *Orient* without Napoleon's permission and was put off at Malta.

them that they might not be tortured by the Turks into whose power they must fall in a few hours—Desgenettes has told me that these men were *in articulo*—Baron Larrey said the same—I therefore leave it to others to decide—what was the most humane conduct—to allow them to be put by torture to death by the Turks which was certain, or to accelerate their death without torture." I have not been able to trace the authorship of these interesting contemporary comments. Larrey himself does not mention the matter and Napoleon at St. Helena flatly denied it.

"After this we marched on and once more entered the desert without halting at Gaza. We left behind at el-A'rych the cases of plague which had followed us and others who had fallen ill on the march. This crossing was extremely arduous, but it became even worse when on reaching the sandy plain which stretches from the Roman bridge to Salehyeh we were overtaken by pestiferous winds. It was here that we first learnt the terrible effects of the *Khamsyn*—the burning south wind from the desert. . . . After a few minutes of torture I collapsed in a faint without hope of reaching Salehyeh. Many of our animals were suffocated, especially the horses, and the whole army suffered a great deal. This day saw the death of many of the convalescents from plague who were following us.

"The sight of the fertile fields of Salehyeh with the shade of immense palm forests, the waters of the Nile, the good food we found and the pure air we breathed, quickly restored our strength so that our march through the province of Charqyeh, then covered with harvest and presenting a magnificent spectacle, was little more than a pleasant walk.

"We left behind us in the hospitals of el-A'rych, Quatyeh, Salehyeh and Belbeys the sick and wounded we had brought with us, who remained there until they had recovered. A large number were sent by water across lake Menzaleh to Damietta to join the wounded who had come direct from Syria; later they were all moved up to Cairo where we completed their treatment.

"The army rested for two days at Matharieh, where orders were given for the soldiers to wash their uniforms and underclothes and to burn such of these as were past cleansing. Following this permission was given for the troops to enter Cairo without going through quarantine.

"General Dugua came out to meet us at the head of the troops which had been left under his command. With what pleasure we saw our old and brave companions once more! Worn out by the toils of a long campaign, our bodies weakened by constant privations and long burnt black by the burning desert sun, we fell on the necks of these friends and brothers, united to us by glory and our common cause in this land where we had created a new country in the midst of a foreign race."

*   *   *   *   *

Chapter 6

The plague in Egypt. Death of Masclet.
Leeches in the throat.

It has been mentioned that at the time of Bonaparte's expedition to Suez Larrey received news of the occurrence of plague in Alexandria and himself encountered a case of the disease in Cairo. It was the policy of the French authorities to keep the presence of this fell disease a secret and in this Larrey played his part. But subsequently he criticized it very adversely, arguing that the soldiers were so inured to dangers of all kinds by the hardships of the campaign that they were proof against further emotions. "Had the true nature of the disease been made known and presented in the least unfavourable light the number of its victims might have been diminished. Instead, the soldiers, who had been imbued from the outset with the idea that this illness was not plague, did not hesitate in their need to take and wear the clothes of their companions who had died of it, so that the germ speedily developed in them and they often suffered the same fate." Like others of his time Larrey was very exercised about the question of a disease being *contagious* or not—the word then meaning conveyed by touch in the literal sense. With an appreciation of the bacterial or viral nature of infection this old problem has lost its meaning, but it was very real in the 18th century and influenced most views about disease transmission. Larrey, who knew nothing of the *rôle* of rats or fleas, believed plague to be an epidemic and contagious disease, but not at all stages, and that the infection might be spread in different ways. "I do not think that it is infectious when it is mild and in the first stage. Neither do I believe that this is to be feared from feeling the patient's pulse with the finger tips or from opening and cauterizing his buboes or sores, or in the quick application of dressings, or from the contact of small surfaces with his body or clothing, or from going into his room, provided that there is abundant through ventilation. A long stay in ill-ventilated rooms of plague cases must be avoided, as well as the exhalations from the dead bodies or from cases in the third or fourth stages of the disease; that is to say during the periods of eruption or nervous prostration. Contact of large areas of the skin with such patients should be avoided, as well as the use of clothes which have been worn by victims of plague."

He also had some astonishingly modern views upon the presence of a virus in the body. "A number of observations has led me to believe that the virus of plague can exist for a long time in the living body when the disease has only partly declared itself or the crises have been incomplete, above all when the buboes have failed to suppurate or their suppuration has been suppressed by some cause or other. It is also probable that the plague germ acts in a similar way to certain other viruses, such as those of small-pox, measles and scarlet fever."

The success of inoculation against smallpox, then a wonderful novelty, led to various attempts to inoculate against plague. The whole problem was rather confused by arguments about the "contagious" nature of the disease and a suggestion—which Larrey upheld on epidemiological grounds—that there was an antagonism between plague and smallpox. There were a number of experiments on inoculation. Desgenettes inoculated himself very lightly in the axilla with pus from a convalescent patient's buboe, rather to encourage the morale of the soldiers than to experiment. He subsequently washed the area with soap and water. Two small inflammatory spots developed which persisted for three weeks. The most tragic essay was that of Dr. White, a surgeon with McGrigor's Indian contingent, who holding strongly that plague was not contagious inoculated himself in the thigh by friction with pus from a buboe, and on the following day in the forearm by incision. Three days later he was siezed with rigors and at the end of three more days died of plague. Larrey mentions this as evidence of the uselessness and danger of inoculation. He believed, however, that running sores, issues, or wounds in full suppuration, gave a measure of protection and mentioned that smallpox vaccination might confer this. This opinion had considerable currency and Clot-Bey[1] refers to Valli's experiment of inoculating himself with a lancet dipped in a mixture of variola virus and plague pus. He experienced a local and general reaction but recovered. This fortunate outcome Clot-Bey generously suggests was probably due to the "immense quantity of coffee, brandy, wine and opium, which he had for some time been accustomed to take." Valli also inoculated twenty-four other persons in the same way, none of whom contracted plague.

On the matter of treatment there is little that is said, but there is a good deal about preventive measures. Larrey observed that the disease was endemic on the coast of Syria—the French lost more men from plague before St. Jean d'Acre than anywhere else—as well as in Alexandria, Rosetta, Damietta and Lower Egypt generally. He attributed this local prevalence to the crowded character of the towns, and their narrow, tortuous, unpaved streets, with middens at every crossroads liable to be sodden in winter since they were below sea level, and inundated by the overflowing of the adjacent rice fields. Putrefaction from bodies—as at el-A'rych, where out of a garrison of three hundred, seventy died—and the unburied corpses at Jaffa and Acre he thought to be potent causes, especially during the season of the Khamsyn. As precautionary measures he recommended exercise, the use of clean linen and a good diet: excess of spirits was to be avoided and the body washed frequently with water and vinegar; the under-linen and clothes were to be changed often, and the bed to be in a dry well-ventilated place. To concert more general hygienic measures a commission was set up in Cairo which included the chief

---

[1] A. B. Clot-Bey: *La peste observée en Egypte.* Paris 1840.

physician and surgeon, and sub-committees of this were established at Alexandria, Rosetta and Damietta. An observation post on the delta challenged all vessels coming up the Nile and directed them to a quarantine station at the island of Roudah. Sufferers from plague were taken to the isolation hospital which was divided into a number of small reed huts, and contaminated belongings were burnt or disinfected. Daily reports were sent to the commission, which had its authority extended to all camps, barracks and towns throughout Egypt.

Whilst the returning army rested for two days at Heliopolis Larrey received a number of reports on the plague which was raging at Alexandria from his young assistant, Masclet. This courageous and energetic young man, though only in a subordinate position, had shewn great energy and commonsense in his endeavour to institute effective measures of isolation and hygiene. "As I cannot communicate with both the hospitals and the town," he wrote, "and as my wish is to direct the service generally, I propose to renounce the latter and to live in a hut in the middle of the hospitals. From there I shall be able to visit each of them with the escort of an orderly, and so avoid the inconvenience of my continual absence. I hope that my personal sacrifice may be of use to those whose lives are our responsibility. As for the dangers, I don't consider these; the best thing is not to fear them. . . ." With the eye of a born observer he supplied vivid details of his cases which Larrey was glad enough to use in his own clinical descriptions, and he inspired in others a like devotion to this dangerous service. A few months later the older man was to write: "Masclet, animated by a noble enthusiasm and an ardent love of his profession, set an example to his colleagues by shutting himself up in the hospitals, where, without a thought of the dangers he was exposed to, he was unsparing in the skill and love he lavished on numerous victims of the plague; consoling some, encouraging others, and saving the lives of many of these unfortunate men who without doubt would have been carried off by the disease but for the fight which he put up against it. Out of every ten patients he cured five, six or seven. Masclet, whose zeal and courage were above all praise, relying on his strength and the methods of protection he used, and without fear of the insidious and contagious torrent, operated upon and dressed all those attacked by the disease with the same confidence with which he would have treated an intermittent fever in France. But his courage did not triumph for ever over this formidable malady: in the end he was stricken, after having seen all his young colleagues die one by one, including eventually his cherished pupil M. Niel who contracted the plague for a second time. We had the unhappiness of losing in him the most devoted friend of humanity, the most zealous of colleagues and, perhaps, the wisest.

"Worthy companion of my labours, receive with thy pupils the tribute of my eternal regrets and the assurance that thy name and memory will live in my mind for ever."

*   *   *   *   *

Leeches in the throat and nose

"On our way to Sâléhyeh we came across several small freshwater lakes, similar to those we had previously seen in the deserts on the Lybian border, which were full of small insects, amongst them leeches of a variety akin to those found in the island of Ceylon, and only a few millimetres long! Although generally no thicker than a horse-hair, when gorged with blood they can swell to the size of an ordinary leech. They are blackish in colour and there is nothing special about their shape.

"Our thirsty soldiers threw themselves down at the water's edge and drank freely, without suspecting any new enemy. Many of them felt almost at once a prickling sensation from the leeches they had swallowed. The immediate effect of the punctures was to produce a painful tingling in the throat and a desire to vomit, with much coughing and the bringing up of glairy mucus slightly tinged with blood. This irritation to the sensitive parts of the throat was followed by swelling and haemorrhages. Swallowing became difficult and breathing embarrassed, whilst the constant cough and irritation of the lungs and diaphragm caused considerable pain in the chest. The cough was made worse by the leeches' tails touching the epiglottis or edge of the glottis (this could also have been caused by blood trickling into this opening). The victims became visibly thinner and lost their appetite and sleep; they were restless and anxious, and if not properly and promptly treated the condition was capable of proving fatal as it did in a number of cases.

"Zacutus Lusitanus[2] gives an account of a woman who died in two days from the punctures of a leech which had been introduced by an error into the nasal fossae, and there are many examples of deaths from the introduction of leeches into the urethra, vagina or rectum.

"The Egyptians are well aware that leeches attach themselves to horses' noses when they drink from these particular lakes. They recognize it by the animals' restlessness and bleeding from the nose the same day or on the day following. The local farriers are very skilled in removing them by the use of special forceps or, if they are without these, by the injection of salt water into the nostrils, but they have no record of a like condition in men. The first case we saw was a soldier of the 69th demi-brigade, who on returning to Sâléhyeh from Syria, complained of a painful prickling sensation in the throat, with coughing, blood-stained expectoration, and weakness from loss of blood.

"Gargles of vinegar and salt water generally sufficed to detach the leeches from the back of the throat but at times it was necessary to use polypus forceps or inhalations of tobacco and squill bulbs; at others injections of salt water. Two of the patients, who only came to hospital some days after swallowing the creatures, were very weak and in some danger.

"Brigade-Commander Latour-Maubourg, who commanded the 22nd Regiment of Mounted Chasseurs, left Alexandria during the blockade to

[2] *De Medicinae Principiis*, Lib. I, p. 5.

rejoin his regiment in Cairo, and crossed the Saint-Macaire (Skiahiat) desert which is on the border of Lybia. As he could not carry enough fresh water with him he used the muddy water of small fresh-water ponds which are at a day's march from the Pyramids. The men of his escort, who had kept sufficient water in their bottles, did not drink from these and escaped the consequences which affected M. Latour. Two leeches he had swallowed tormented him during the rest of the march, and reduced him to a state of extreme weakness and emaciation. His cough and blood-stained expectoration persisted during his first few days in Cairo, and as their cause was not recognized the treatment prescribed only made him worse. He was in actual danger, when the tail of one of the leeches which was gorged with blood was seen at the back of his throat. The patient himself pointed this out to his doctor and it was pulled out with strong dressing forceps, whilst the second was dislodged from the nasal fossae by injections of salt water. M. Latour's convalescence was long and tedious from his exhausting march and the very large quantity of blood he had lost."

*   *   *   *   *

Chapter 7

Turkish landing at Aboukir. Fugières' sword. Turkish invasion from Syria. Battle of Heliopolis. Recapture of Cairo. Assassination of Kléber. Torture and death of the assassin. Command assumed by Menou. Prostitution and syphilis.

The army had hardly established itself in camp in the vicinity of the Pyramids (Larrey climbed to the top and cut his name there—a boyish act shared with William Wittman who came two years later with the Grand Vizier's army!), when the Turks landed in force at Aboukir, capturing the fort and its protecting redoubt and killing the garrison. Bonaparte at once marched to Alexandria where he concentrated all his troops and attacked on July 25th, 1799.

The result was the total rout and destruction of the Turkish force. Larrey says that they left more than ten thousand dead on the field whilst three hundred were taken prisoner. Many of the latter were men who had taken refuge in the fort, where they had held out for six days before surrendering at discretion. "As they marched out the wretched prisoners threw themselves into the cisterns at the sides of the road. Many died with their bellies blown up from the effects of their thirst and the large quantities of water they swallowed." Wilson[1] put the Turkish strength at not quite 8000, a half of whom were killed or wounded; nearly 2000 escaped in boats and the remainder surrendered in the fort. The French lost Brigade Commander Cretin; Guibert, the Commander-in-Chief's aide-de-camp who was killed at his side, and General Leture. Amongst the wounded were Lannes, Murat and Fugières. Lannes received a bullet wound in his right leg and developed symptoms which made Larrey fear tetanus. He recovered, however, and returned to France with Bonaparte. Murat's wound was more extraordinary. He was engaged in a hand to hand combat with Moustapha Pasha, the Turkish commander, and shot the latter through the hand just as the Turk was aiming a blow at him with his sword. Almost at the same moment Murat was shot through the throat, the bullet entering on the right side near the angle of the jaw, and emerging near the upper attachment of the opposite sterno-mastoid muscle. In its course it passed behind the tongue and severed the top of the epiglottis, which the wounded man spat out. No important vessel was injured and there was no haemorrhage. For the first few days Larrey

[1] R. T. Wilson. *History of the British Expedition to Egypt.* 1802.

fed the patient on fluids through an oesophageal tube; and on a starvation diet, antiphlogistic measures and complete rest the General recovered, though he was voiceless for about twenty days. In recounting this Larrey also records the similar case of a grenadier, Michel by name, who was shot through the angle of the jaw at the British landing at Aboukir twenty months later. The bullet grooved the base of the tongue and severed the glottis, which the wounded man spat out and shewed to the surgeon who attended him. He could barely speak and each attempt to swallow ended in a fit of choking. It was in this parlous state that he was seen five days later by Larrey and the nature of his lesion confirmed. A gum-elastic oesophageal tube was passed and his immediate thirst relieved. For some time he was kept alive by this means, although difficulty was experienced in telling whether the tube had entered the oesophagus or trachea, for the larynx had lost some of its sensitivity. So much was this the case that before feeding him it became customary to make a preliminary trial with a small amount of fluid; if this entered the oesophagus all went well, but if it passed into the trachea a violent paroxysm of coughing and threat of suffocation resulted. After about six weeks effort the man gradually acquired a limited knack of swallowing, mashing his rice into small balls which would pass into his oesophagus. He was eventually returned to France and entered the Invalides, where he gradually regained the power of speech and swallowing: "doubtless because the arytenoid cartilages have partly taken over the function of the epiglottis, by their development along with that portion of the base of the tongue which is opposite the glottis."

Murat's opponent, Moustapha Pasha, was taken prisoner and attended by Larrey until he was well. He rewarded his benefactor generously.

General Fugières' arm was shattered by a ball and Larrey disarticulated it on the battlefield behind the central redoubt of the Turkish entrenchments. Hearing that the wound was mortal, Bonaparte came to take a last farewell. Fugières handed him his sword, a valuable weapon ornamented in gold. "Perhaps, General, you may some day envy me my fate. Take this weapon: I shall never use it again."

"I accept it, but I give it to the man who will save your life." And so saying he handed the sword to Larrey.

Napoleon's prognostication was correct. After the operation Fugières was evacuated to Alexandria by water and thence to Cairo where he speedily recovered and in later years became governor of the branch hospital of the Invalides at Avignon. To commemorate his skill Bonaparte had Larrey's name engraved on the sword in letters of gold along with the name of the battle in Arabic characters. Larrey carried it at Waterloo, where he was robbed of it by the Prussians when he was wounded and captured.

In the Aboukir battle the mobile ambulances were stationed at three chief points in the line to give first-aid, and we are told that not a man had to wait more than a quarter of an hour to receive treatment. All the more seriously wounded passed through the central ambulance, where Larrey himself operated and supervised their dressing. Over forty amputations were required which had "surprisingly good results". The wounded were afterwards carried on collapsible stretchers to barges, which by the foresight of the Chief-of-Staff had been collected in the roadstead of the Port Neuf and were then taken by sea to Alexandria, Larrey accompanying them with Fugières. At Alexandria he supervised their treatment during the first fifteen days and by degrees they were evacuated to Cairo where he himself had gone to set up a large hospital at Ibrahim Bey's farm, and also to re-establish the School of Anatomy and Practical Surgery which had suspended its teaching during the Syrian campaign.

It was at this time that the turn of events in France decided Bonaparte to quit Egypt. Under the pretext of inspecting the coastal defences between Lake Burlos and Alexandria he embarked on board ship on August 22nd, 1799, leaving the army under Kléber's command. But much was to happen to the discouraged and disconsolate troops, now more than ever conscious of their isolation in a strange and hostile land, before the story of the Army of Egypt was concluded.

The Grand Vizier had been slowly assembling a force on the Syrian frontier, and in December it attacked and captured the important key position of el-A'rych and massacred the garrison. This was at a moment when negotiations between the French and British were in progress through the intermediary of Sir Sidney Smith, whom the latter government had put in the anomalous position of "Joint Minister Plenipotentiary" with his brother Spencer Smith, the British minister at Constantinople. It was a strange post for a relatively junior naval officer; very annoying to his seniors Lord St. Vincent and Nelson, and was to be a factor in much of the misunderstanding that followed. The negotiations were in any case slow and hampered by difficulties of communication and the oriental mentality of the Grand Vizier with his *entourage* of relatively undisciplined and uncontrolled hordes. Kléber, not unnaturally, regarded the attack on el-A'rych as a breach of faith and his reaction was to advance his troops to Sâléhyeh, but here, after the gesture of reviewing them, he announced his intention to return to France. In the meantime General Desaix and M. Pousielgue, in the *rôle* of French plenipotentiaries, had reached el-A'rych and after long discussions concluded the famous convention of that name, which provided for the departure of the French from the country with the honours of war. The thing being done, the French soldiers hailed with delight the prospect of leaving the foreign land and whilst Kléber, in fulfilment of his side of the bargain returned to Cairo and withdrew a part of his force to the west of the Nile, the Grand Vizier followed close upon him and occupied Catieh, Sâléhyeh and Belbeys. But now a number of complications arose. Sidney Smith, in assenting to the convention of el-A'rych, had assumed powers he did not in fact possess, and the British government sent orders to Lord Keith, the admiral in command in the Mediterranean, that the French must surrender as prisoners of war. Moreover, newspapers supplied by the British brought the French the exciting news of Bonaparte's appointment as First Consul, and of the favourable changes in their country's fortunes in the struggle in Europe. The cumulative effect of these events was to steel the hearts of the French against an ignominious surrender and to bring Kléber to the sticking point. He promptly issued orders for the reoccupation and rearming of the Cairo forts, recalled the troops which were on the march for Alexandria, and demanded of the Grand Vizier, who by now had reached Heliopolis, an assurance of the safe passage of his troops to France, the provision of hostages as a guarantee of this, and the withdrawal of the Turkish army to a distance of ten leagues from the town. The Grand Vizier replied that he could not retire his columns which were already at the gates of Cairo, where he was expected. The position of the French was critical. Strong defences had been abandoned under the convention of el-A'rych and they had behind them the threat of a popular rising in Cairo, where a grenadier had already been assassinated and French shopkeepers insulted. Kléber reacted swiftly. He seized Moustapha Pasha, the Commandant of Cairo, collected the French civilians within the protection of the forts, and during the night of March 20th marched out with about thirteen thousand men to attack the Turkish army which was encamped near Heliopolis, where they had entrenched and fortified the village of Matharieh. The Grand Vizier's army was no match for the French squares with their murderous fire of grape and after a lively action broke and fled, in part towards lower Egypt and in part to Syria, except for the force which had earlier out-flanked the French and had already infiltrated into Cairo. This was the end of the Grand Vizier's army; many of them, fleeing from Sâléhyeh without water or provisions, died of hunger and thirst in the arid deserts between Syria and Egypt, whilst many others were slaughtered by the Arabs who hung on the outskirts of both armies awaiting their chance to kill or plunder. The force which retreated towards Damietta was pursued by General Belliard, who destroyed or captured it without losing a man.

From this engagement, which is known as the Battle of Heliopolis, Larrey received only fifty wounded, who were dressed and sent to the fort of Berket-el-Hadj. Amongst the enemy wounded was a Mameluke of Mourad Bey's (Mourad had held off during the battle and subsequently allied himself with the victors), whose arm had been carried away by a cannon ball and on whom Larrey performed a successful amputation at the shoulder joint. Whilst in pursuit of the enemy the headquarters staff, to which Larrey was attached, was surprised by a body of two thousand hostile cavalry near the village of Coraim. They escaped with difficulty, and Larrey's servant was decapitated at his side. His head, with those of twenty gunners or hussars who were lost in this affair, was found exposed at Sâléhyeh when it was entered on the following day.

The main army returned to Cairo by forced marches, suffering a good deal of hardship as their transport had been left behind at Sulkouski during their hurried advance, and on reaching the city they were un-pleasantly surprised to find it strongly defended, and its gates barred by the Mamelukes with the help of that part of the Turkish army which had made its way in and was now supported by the inhabitants. The French managed to reoccupy their headquarters, which had meantime success-fully maintained a defensive, but were faced with the difficult problem of the reduction of the great warren of this large and tortuous city, and the prospect of prolonged and costly street fighting against perhaps 50,000 armed men and nearly 300,000 hostile inhabitants. Kléber endeavoured to negotiate with the Turkish leaders, whose position was sufficiently precarious since any capitulation they might have been disposed to make would be opposed by the populace, who realized that the withdrawal of the Turks would leave them at the mercy of the French. As a preliminary to an attempted reduction by force an attack was made upon Boulaq, a small suburb of Cairo which was well defended, though the farm where their own sick were quartered, with whom were Desgenettes, who had received a slight wound in the head, and the unfortunate hostage Moustapha Pasha, were still in French hands. The assault under Belliard was completely successful, achieving great slaughter of the defenders and but few casualties to the French. Amongst the wounded was General Almeras who was shot through the pelvis, with damage to the bladder and extra-vasation of urine: he recovered so well that he subsequently participated in the German, Russian and French campaigns.

Immediately after the capture of Boulaq the main assault on Cairo was attempted but failed. The French lost a number of men and had over two hundred wounded, including Belliard himself who was hit in the left side of the abdomen by a musket ball which damaged the sigmoid colon. He too lived and served again, only to lose a part of his left calf at the Borodino. The horrors of this assault, to which night put a temporary stop, decided the people of Cairo against continuing their alliance with the Turks and negotiations were again opened and on April 25th the latter set out upon the road back to Syria. In a campaign lasting little over a month the Grand Vizier had been driven in disastrous retreat back over the frontier, and with the submission of the towns of Lower Egypt the French were once again complete masters of the land (Fig. 11).

Their possession was not long to remain undisputed. For a while they might imagine, as did Larrey, that a period of settled occupation under Kléber was to be their reward for over twenty months of strenuous fighting, against foes, disease, and the forces of nature. But any such optimistic complacency was shattered by the murder of Kléber on June 14th by Soleyman el-Hhaleby, a young Philistine fanatic. The assassin whilst pretending to ask for alms stabbed the General several times, the fatal thrust piercing the right auricle of the heart. Larrey was away at the time examining the surgeons attached to the different army corps at Alexandria and Rosetta, but he hurried back to Cairo and on embalming the heart found a wound of about fifteen or sixteen millimetres in length in this cavity. The fate of the assassin was terrible: "Hhaleby was seized and condemned by a special tribunal to suffer the penalty customary in this country for such a crime. The cool courage with which he suffered the burning of his right hand and empalement by a stake astonished all men of sensibility, and shews the degree to which firm resolution can dominate the physical senses. He survived for about four hours amidst the most cruel suffering without uttering a cry. The burning of the hand was continued down to the bone and the stake, after lacerating the viscera and vessels of the abdomen, fractured the sacrum and two lumbar vertebrae and lodged in the spinal canal. I discovered these facts from the examination I made of the body some time afterwards, although it was rather dried up. I sent the skeleton to the museum of Natural History."

The day of Kléber's death also marked that of Desaix, who had accompanied Bonaparte on his return to France and fell at the battle of Marengo, where his arrival in the afternoon changed defeat into victory. This was a severe loss to Larrey since Desaix, one of the ablest of the Republic's generals, had been his close friend since the days of the Army of the Rhine and they had been together in Italy. A solemn parade was held in his honour and Fournier, permanent secretary of the Institute of Egypt, pronounced an eloquent funeral oration, typical of the times with its oblique tributes to republican feeling and rather sycophantic praise of the First Consul.

The command on Kléber's death fell to Menou, a man of little distinction and mediocre parts, who displayed no great qualities of leadership and who as chief of an army which, in spite of recent successes in the field, found itself in uncertain isolation in a strange land, was faced with many difficulties from the disloyalties and jealousies of those under his command. Nevertheless, he seems to have been a painstaking and conscientious administrator who was unfortunate to encounter circumstances he could not control. "He set up a number of useful organizations, reformed the administration, and gave orders for the organization of the hospitals and field ambulances. He rewarded the courage and zeal of all the medical officers by creating new appointments and set up various important commissions, as well as a private council which included the Physician and Surgeon-in-Chief. . . . The situation of the army was better now than it had ever been: it was at peace, re-equipped and re-clothed, pay was no longer in arrear, the barracks were healthy and well sited; workshops of every kind were full of activity and the soldier lacked nothing and was no longer a constant prey to the desire to return to his own country. During this period of respite we were able to appreciate the advantages and disadvantages of the Egyptian climate, and indeed it was the only time at which we had any sort of happiness."

Larrey himself commenced courses of instruction in surgery at Cairo and busied himself with the organization of the field ambulances, "so that everything might be ready in case of an emergency".

There were other local problems. "The itch, gout and a number of diseases common in France entirely disappeared in this climate, but the free intercourse which grew up between our soldiers and the local women encouraged syphilis, and in a short time there were many men in the hospital with this disease. It was far from easy to prevent its spread, for to deprive the seasoned soldier who had recovered his strength and vigour of the society of women was to engender boredom and homesickness. To meet this difficulty, and to arrest the spread of syphilis, I proposed to the Commander-in-Chief that we should set up a civil hospital for the prostitutes suffering from venereal disease and also for women of this class who were pregnant, so as to prevent the abortion which they

F<small>IG</small>. 13. Larrey's camel ambulance with personnel. Note on left method of bandaging an amputated thigh.

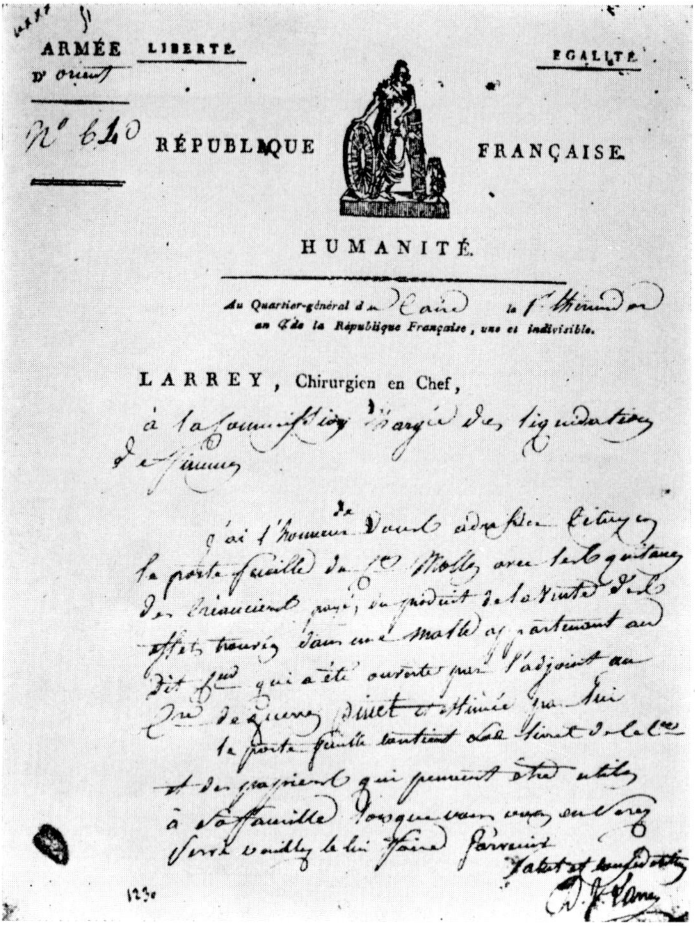

ARMÉE D'Orient LIBERTÉ ÉGALITÉ

N° 610

RÉPUBLIQUE FRANÇAISE

HUMANITÉ.

Au Quartier-général du Caire le 1er Thermidor an 8e de la République Française, une et indivisible.

LARREY, Chirurgien en Chef,

Letter from Larrey.
(Translation)
French Republic

Army of the Orient. *Liberty* *Equality*

Humanity

At the Headquarters at Cairo
1st. Thermidor of the 8th. year of
the French Republic, one and indivisible.

LARREY, Surgeon in Chief,

to the Commission charged with the liquidation of affairs.

I have the honour to send you, Citizen, the portfolio of Cn. Molles with the credit payable from the sale of the belongings found in a trunk the property of the said Cn. which has been opened by the assistant to the Cre. of War Pirret and valued by him.

The portfolio contains the pay-book of the Cn. and some payments which may be of use to his family, when after having finished with it you kindly send it to them.

Greetings and Regards
D. J. Larrey.

Fig. 14. Letter from Cairo with translation. (By the kindness of Signor Julio Lobo, of Habana, Cuba.)

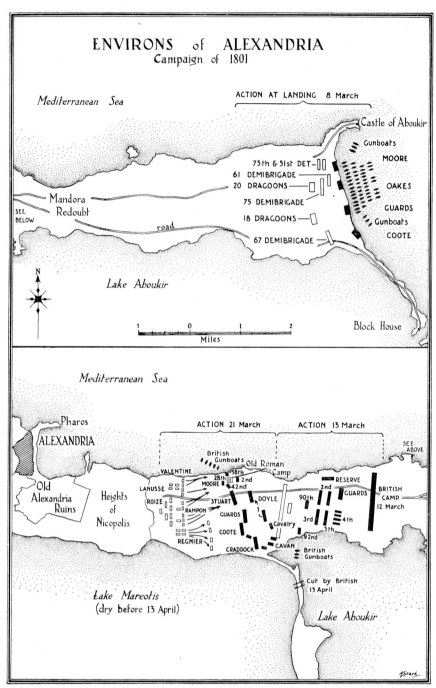

FIG. 15. Map of Alexandria. (Reproduced with permission from *Sir John Moore*, by Carola Oman, published by Hodder and Stoughton, London.)

commonly induced and to ensure the survival of their children. In consequence an order was issued by General Belliard, the commandant of Cairo, for a suitably situated large house to be provided for this purpose, to which were brought without distinction all the women suspected of having had commerce with French soldiers. Those who were not infected were sent home, the others were kept and treated with the greatest care. At the same time a rigorous inspection was instituted in the barracks and all suffering from venereal disease were sent to the military hospital and detained until they were cured. These different measures produced the effects we had anticipated and before long the victims of both sexes were cured.

"I have noticed that in Egypt syphilis only rarely has serious symptoms and in general is readily cured. But if it be carried to Europe, and in particular to the western countries, it becomes extremely obstinate and difficult to eradicate: this has been proved by a number of soldiers who brought the Egyptian syphilis to France and were only cured with the greatest difficulty and after a considerable time. The treatment which gave us the best results in Egypt was the use of mercurial preparations by the mouth, together with tonics and diaphoretics, the effects being assisted by vapour baths. Mercurial inunctions were bad; they failed to cure the disease and caused fits of violent frenzy in some patients, and in others convulsive spasms and obstinate ptyalism."

*   *   *   *   *

Chapter 8

English landing at Aboukir. Siege and Capture of Alexandria. Scurvy. Return to France. Larrey's report to French Government.

The short Egyptian honeymoon was at an end. An Anglo-Turkish fleet was blockading Alexandria and threatening a landing, whilst on the eastern border the forces of the Grand Vizier were reassembling. Here was Dr. William Wittman of the Royal Artillery, serving with the British Medical Mission attached to the Turkish Army, who has left us in his *Travels* (1803) a contemporary account of this extraordinary army as well as his observations on the plague which affected it. Finally, Baird's force of British and Indian troops of the Honourable East India Company, which had come by sea from Bombay and landed at Kosseir in the middle of May, was making its way down the Nile. This force also had its medical chronicler in a surgeon of the Royal Regiment of Horse Guards—one James McGrigor—who published his account in *Medical Sketches of the Expedition to Egypt from India* (1804). McGrigor later became the head of the British Army Medical Service and a friend of Larrey's.

To meet these converging threats the French made preparations for a new campaign. This opened abruptly on March 8th, 1801, with Sir George Abercrombie's landing at Aboukir. Menou divided his force, sending a part of his army to reinforce Alexandria, with which went Larrey with five ambulance divisions, and leaving Belliard to cover Cairo, which he eventually surrendered on June 27th.

"We marched through the fertile plains of the province of Baheira, then covered with a magnificent harvest ready for reaping. When we reached Rahmanieh we were greeted by a violent storm as we entered the town, followed by very heavy hail, the first we saw during our stay in Egypt. Here we had several cases of plague, which I had treated in the nearby isolation hospital under Dr. Sotira.

"From Rahmanieh we marched to Alexandria by the dry lake Maréotis, to avoid the English whose gunboats on lake Ma'dyeh covered the usual road (Fig. 15). Headquarters arrived on the evening of March 19th after a forced march, and the main body of the army joined us on the 20th. The general commanding the province at once informed us of the enemy's advanced positions and of the nature of his defences. He also realized that no time was to be lost before giving battle if he were to sustain the courage and confidence of his men which was beginning to be undermined by the exaggerated reports which were spread regarding the strength of the enemy. A council of war was held the same evening and the attack ordered for the next day.

"I used the twenty-four hours grace to hurry on the work of preparation, by all the naval and military surgeons in Alexandria, of dressing materials and suitable places for hospitals. Quartermaster Sartelon greatly assisted me with his zeal and energy throughout the subsequent siege by requisitioning bedding, utensils, and everything that was necessary for the care of the wounded. As soon as I had ordered all the preparations within my province, and put their execution into the hands of M. Mauban, a surgeon of the first class, I returned to the camp during the night of the 20th to settle the position of the ambulances in the line of battle. I was back at general headquarters before daybreak to join the Commander and direct the ambulance of the centre, which I had placed in the rear of the Corps of Guides. I distributed my light ambulance wagons amongst the divisions, so that the wounded might be removed with the least possible delay. This transport as events proved was of the greatest value.

"The enemy was entrenched on the Roman lines, a natural fortification formed by the old walls of Caesar's camp and the formation of the land, and protected on his left by the lake Ma'dyeh and on his other flank by the sea. The principal positions were strengthened by some redoubts bristling with cannon: flotillas of gunboats flanked the two wings of their army, whilst their camp was covered by the fleet which was anchored in Aboukir roads.

"At half past four on the morning of March 21st, the signal to engage was given and our troops advanced boldly and steadily upon the English entrenchments. The intrepidity and courage which they shewed at the initial encounter promised us victory, and our brave men would doubtless have achieved this had not a series of misfortunes, upon which I am unable to pass judgement, supervened to upset our order of battle and check their impetuous attack at a time when they had already made themselves masters of a part of the defences. General Roize was spreading terror in the rear ranks of the enemy when a cannon ball stretched him dead in the midst of his men. This misfortune forced our cavalry to retire, and before long the whole army was in retreat.

"From this battle we had about 1300 wounded, who with those of the engagements of March 8th and 13th filled our hospitals. Many of the wounds were serious and required extensive operations. They included all ranks of the army; generals, officers and soldiers. Amongst the former were Lanusse, Baudot, Destaing, Sylly, Morangié and Boussard.[1]

"General Lanusse had a small cannon ball through his right knee. The articular ends of the bones were injured, the popliteal artery and nerve severed, and the femur fractured some distance away. There was considerable haemorrhage and a great deal of trauma. I at once suggested that I should amputate his thigh as the only means of saving his life but this he refused, saying that he 'did not wish to survive this disastrous day'. Eight hours later, suffering terrible pains and entreated by his friends, he

---

[1] Destaing was struck in the right arm by a shell, Boussard in the right axilla.

asked for my help. By now hiccough and the signs of inflammation were present, and the anxious state, clammy coldness, the insensibility of the wounded limb and the feeble pulse warned me that the operation could no longer save him. However, there was this much in its favour, that the removal of a limb which was becoming gangrenous would relieve pain and help the morale of this brave warrior. The operation was completed in under three minutes and produced the state of calm I anticipated, but the vital forces were wholly spent and the General died without suffering during the night of March 21st.

"General Baudot was wounded in the leg by a similar missile. The calf was shot away and the bones fractured. Immediate amputation was again indicated, but he would not submit to the operation and died of gangrene after a few days of terrible suffering.

"These two cases, and the one which follows, illustrate the first principle (the necessity for early amputation) which I have laid down in my Memoir on Amputations.

"General Sylly had his left leg almost completely shot away at the knee joint, the limb being attached by only a few strands of ligaments and tendons. He was carried behind the line of battle to the ambulance of the centre, but did not realize the seriousness of his wound on account of his state of extreme collapse from loss of blood. The operation was done at once, and he did not know until afterwards that he had lost his leg owing to the numbness and loss of sensation. In spite of his age (he was over sixty) and our critical condition he was cured in a very short time without any complication, except a discharging sinus which formed along the course of the femoral vessels owing to the violent stretching they had undergone. There is no doubt that but for this operation the General would have suffered the fate of his two colleagues."

In recalling this in 1841 Larrey added: "I performed the amputation in three minutes amidst the fighting, and had just finished when we were charged by a body of English cavalry. I had barely time to hoist the patient onto my shoulders and carry him as quickly as I could towards our army which had begun to retreat. I crossed a series of holes or ditches used for the cultivation of capers which saved us, since the cavalry could not follow over the broken ground, and I was fortunate enough to gain our rearguard ahead of the English dragoons. I ultimately reached Alexandria with my honourable patient on my shoulders and effected his cure there. The General has been living in France in retirement for many years. . . ."

Larrey added a manuscript note in the margin of his own copy of his *Mémoirs*: "Like so many soldiers who owe their lives to me, Sylly left me nothing to mark his recollection of this."

"Even though I have said a good deal on this subject I must describe the unhappy end of a Captain Duvilars of the 85th demi-brigade, and I make this digression to emphasize the necessity for immediate amputation in similar cases. This officer resolutely refused to undergo the operation, having been persuaded by a surgeon of his unit who had dressed him in the line that he could be cured without it, and who had thought it sufficient to cut away with scissors some disorganized shreds of flesh which were attached to the stump. My first examination favoured the views of Bilguer and his adherents, for the bone appeared to have been taken off cleanly without fragmentation and the contusion and laceration seemed limited to the severed parts; there was no haemorrhage and the wounded man did not appear in danger. But on further examination, and on reasoning the matter out and drawing on my previous experience, it was not difficult to realize that the portion of the limb which had escaped the immediate violence of the cannon ball was in such a state of disorganization—for some distance at any rate—that without the resection of the whole bone above the site of injury, together with the adjacent soft parts in which the circulation of the fluids was only partial, the patient must die after great suffering.

"It is true that there are some persons who have lost a limb and have survived without amputation; but is it not wrong to base a principle of practice upon exceptional cases—which have been cured through some extraordinary circumstances on which the practitioner cannot count—when we see so many others which have ended disastrously?

"Good surgeons know very well that the amputation or extirpation of a limb is not the simple and easy operation it is made out to be, especially when it is carried out on the battlefield. A lack of courage and a fear of being overtaken unawares by events in a crisis help to sustain the opinion of those who follow Bilguer.

"Moreover the wounded rarely live for more than a few hours after such wounds. They are found dead on the road, or they die as they reach hospital. Humanity will always reproach the man, whose duty is to serve it, if he does not forgo his prejudices and personal interest to preserve the lives of the many citizens whose wounds demand immediate amputation.

"The day of March 21st, 1801, and the eight or ten following, were terribly hard ones for the surgeons. Our first nights and days were entirely occupied in attending to the wounded who were scattered throughout the hospitals in the different parts of the town."

The siege of Alexandria tightened and the cutting by the British of the revetment between lake Ma'dyeh and the dry lake of Maréotis completed its investment.

The beleaguered French were not actually in the town of Alexandria but encamped behind the ruins of the Old City, within a circular perimeter running from Pompey's Column to Cleopatra's Obelisks; one of which is now a feature of the Thames embankment[2] whilst the other, then lying in the sand, is in the Central Park, New York.

It was hilly, sandy country, covered with fragments of ruined ancient buildings. At the beginning of May more than a thousand of the wounded from the earlier engagements had been returned to duty, but there were still six hundred in the hospitals. The inundations caused by the overflowing of lake Ma'dyeh lapped the camp, and to the miasma arising from

[2] The transport of "Cleopatra's Needle" to England was financed by Sir Erasmus Wilson, the dermatologist, and made in a metal cylinder constructed under the supervision of Mr. Dixon, the engineer. (Vide *Cleopatra's Needle*, W. J. Erasmus Wilson, 1855.)

these Larrey attributed a particularly severe outbreak of ophthalmia which caused over three thousand men to be admitted to hospital. In many cases a pterygium—a thick dense membrane at the inner angle of the eye—developed, on certain of which he operated, and he also stimulated a veterinary surgeon to do the same to some horses which were similarly afflicted. A more serious malady was scurvy, which first attacked the wounded but later became so widespread that it came to be looked upon as a contagious epidemic. Larrey described it in great detail, refuting the view of its contagiousness and attributing it to the circumstances of the blockade.

"The soldiers were soon without fresh vegetables or meat. Owing to our lack of wheat we were forced to make bread from equal parts of rice and corn; the former is naturally indigestible when taken in large quantities, and was saturated with salt (it is prepared in this way for sale). The bread was therefore excessively salt and this had an effect on the digestive organs and system generally.

"The soldiers lived on this bread for almost two months and also ate large quantities of fish which they bought at an extortionate price from the people of Alexandria. They drank cistern water, which was contaminated by the infiltration of sea water or water from the lake which in many cases had risen above this level, or was vitiated by the putrefaction of the slime in these cisterns, which had not been properly cleansed for a long time. . . ."

"The chief predisposing cause was the almost continuous humidity to which the soldiers were exposed after the overflowing of lake Ma'dyeh. This brought large quantities of mephitic gas, in part coming from the decomposition of the great quantity of animal and vegetable matter present in lake Mareotis, and in part from the numerous stinking drains of Alexandria. The latrines, which contributed these gases in proportion to the size of our force, and the twenty-five to thirty hospitals which we had set up in the town, also made the place a dangerous one to live in. Finally, the salt air from the sea, and the necessity to be always on the *qui vive* and almost constantly in bivouac owing to the nearness of the enemy, all played a part in affecting the troops' health.

"At the outset, although scurvy attacked a considerable number of the men, its symptoms were mild, viz.: a reddening and superficial ulceration of the gums, vague pains in the limbs, torpor and anxiety. A change in the bread, in which we reduced the amount of salt by washing the rice before it was ground, together with some rations of vinegar, dates, molasses and coffee, appeared to cure it or at least to minimize its effects, but as we were entirely without fresh meat the disease progressed again and took on the proportions of an epidemic. A large part of the army and the civil population were affected simultaneously, so that at the beginning of Fructidor (August 1801) there were between fourteen and fifteen hundred cases of scurvy in the Alexandria hospitals and the deaths averaged about two to four or five a day. The civilians' deaths were about six or eight, which suggests that the cases were more numerous amongst them and that they suffered more from the causes of the disease;

in point of fact they often lacked fresh water and their only food was bad quality rice.

"The officers suffered less than the soldiers as their diet was better, but apart from this the disease attacked persons of all ages. Its results were more rapid and generally more severe when the patients were already suffering from some other malady, such as severe wounds or ophthalmia. I saw many cases in which the lower limbs were threatened with gangrene, but in which by the help of the measures I shall mention we secured the resolution of large ecchymoses and in most cases ultimate recovery.

"As the cavalry horses were useless in our besieged state and forage was lacking, I asked the General-Commanding to let them be killed to provide food for the troops and for the patients in hospital. From my previous experience I had found on more than one occasion the flesh of these animals to be excellent,[3] especially when they are young as were our arab horses, and very suitable for soup and pleasant to eat if well prepared. An order was issued providing for a daily ration of such meat.

"This innovation at first caused some murmuring amongst faint hearted and ill-informed people, who thought the flesh dangerous to the health of the men. It was fortunate that by the force of my own example I was able to get it accepted, as it was the only form of fresh food we had. The sick were greatly benefited, and I am convinced that it was the most effective of all the measures we used to arrest the disease.

"Our treatment varied according to the stage of the scurvy, the constitution of the patients, and a number of other circumstances; though up to the time of the capitulation we were without many of the things we needed.

"However, in the midst of this penury, we had the good fortune to receive several cases of medicaments from France, including in particular some excellent quinine, ipecacuanha and cantharides. At almost the same time two more were thoughtfully sent from Rosetta by M. Boudet, which contained a complete set of medicines of all sorts. We also found several hundredweights of tamarinds in Alexandria, and a small Greek vessel with a cargo of lemons went aground in the harbour, though it is true that the lemons were already over-ripe and only lasted a few days. In consequence, as was stated in the report of the Chief Officers of Health on the state of the troops and hospitals, we had enough medicaments to see us through to the following Vendémiaire (September, 1801)...."

"From the outbreak of the disease in the beginning of Thermidor (July 1801) until the re-embarkation of the sick with the remainder of the army on the 18th Vendémiaire (October 10th), two hundred and seventy one men died out of the three thousand five hundred cases of scurvy in the hospitals of Alexandria. More than two thousand rejoined their battalions before or during the embarkation. About seven hundred were transported back to France, and except for six or seven who died on the voyage all were cured or on the way to recovery by the time they reached the quarantine station. Rather over a hundred of the worst cases were left

---

[3] All the asiatic tartars eat this meat. (This passage suggests that the *Boucherie Chevalerine* dates from Napoleonic times.)

behind at Alexandria: they returned home shortly afterwards, having suffered proportionately no worse than the others.

"At the capitulation the English provided us with wine and fresh bread and vegetables, which very much assisted the recovery of our patients.

"On the 29th Thermidor (17th August) the allied army attacked our line from all sides, and although they outnumbered our troops they were strongly repulsed with loss. Lieutenant-General Rampon directed the operations. This initial engagement was followed during the first fifteen days (sic) by many partial attacks in which we sustained a large number of casualties. These were treated on the battlefield by the ambulances which I had attached to the rear of each division, and thence transported to the drill ground inside the first line of defence, where I had had a large shelter made.[4]

"Nevertheless, the main force of the enemy army broke into the Alexandria peninsula from the Débarkadère (west) side, opposite to the old port (the weakest point of our line), and dispersing the troops which opposed their passage advanced upon the ramparts of old Alexandria. Our soldiers strongly resisted this bold attack and in falling back disputed the position foot by foot, but a part of the English fleet which was anchored before Alexandria entered the old port and by their enfilading fire, together with that of the ships upon lake Maréotis, drove our men back upon the second line. Fort Marabou was bombarded and breached. Its resistance brought honour to the besieged. Two naval surgeons whom I had stationed there perished with its defenders, and a third, M. Faure Moro, had one leg shot off and the other fractured. This brave medical officer owed his life to the amputation I performed through the condyles within a few hours of his being hit.

"We were hemmed in and blockaded on every side with our hospitals crowded with sick and wounded. The difficulty of the position, the bad state of health of the troops, the lack of the prime necessities of life, and doubtless other considerations not known to me, caused negotiations to be opened between the chiefs of the opposing armies on the 10th Fructidor (August 28th). . . ."

"A council of war of all the generals was called by Menou, the General-Commanding, at which it was decided that it was impossible to sustain the siege any longer. The two Chief Officers of Health were summoned to advise on the state of the hospitals, the current diseases, the health of the troops and the quantity of provisions available. We produced a report on this matter which was annexed to the Act of Capitulation which was signed on the 13th Fructidor (August, 31st 1801). The chief condition of this capitulation was that all the French should return to their country with the honours of war.

"It is difficult to describe all the trials and difficulties, or what we endured in the way of fatigue, danger and privations in this siege. In these critical times I owed much to my colleagues, whether medical

---

[4] Our eighteen to twenty hospitals were insufficient: it therefore became necessary to build these shelters to receive the sick and wounded.

officers of the ambulance, surgeons to the fighting units, or to the navy. The latter were directed by M. Leclerc, a Surgeon-in-Chief, who encouraged them in maintaining the zeal and activity they had already given proof of after the battle of Aboukir. I shall mention no one in particular: all deserved equally well of humanity.

"I made the most of the opportunity which the capitulation afforded us to visit the English camp and hospitals. M. Yonck[5] the Inspector-General of the Army Medical Service, who was responsible for directing the whole medical and administrative arrangements, accompanied me without any intermediary. I found their ambulances were well equipped and provided with all necessaries and the medical work appeared to have been carried out successfully. But I was much astonished to find only three cases of amputation who had recovered, though a large number of soldiers had been submitted to this operation. I have described the cause of this lack of success in my Memoir on Amputations. This is yet another proof of the superiority of French surgery over that of other nations, even the most civilized. . . ."

"A thousand three hundred and thirty-eight sick and wounded departed with the army, excluding the permanently disabled whom we had to regard as patients for the period of the voyage. To embark the former was no easy matter, as a lot of ignorant or timid people were frightened of a contagion which did not exist, and wished to leave the cases of scurvy behind at Alexandria with the seriously wounded; but in the end all reached France in good health or well on the way to it. We lost only eight of our patients on the voyage, two of these from an accident."

It is related that when certain of the French negotiators wished to leave the sick and wounded behind in Alexandria, Larrey replied: "What you want is to avoid a long quarantine at Toulon, and to arrive with a fine army in good condition! The possibility that scurvy is contagious, which you put forward is without foundation. The disease is not contagious and in any case the sick will be embarked separately. *I* shall decide who are unable to make the voyage and who would be endangered by it. As for the others, I demand not merely their re-embarkation but that the best ships be put at their disposal and that they leave the first." "Not a French voice," writes Triaire, "supported Larrey, but the powerful one of Lord Keith caused his proposal to be accepted." He himself wrote later: "I owe to General Stewart and Admiral Keith, members of the superior council of the two armies to which I had been summoned by General Menou's orders, the advantage of embarking the wounded before the healthy troops, in opposition to the pretensions of the French generals."

Larrey left Egypt on October 18th in the frigate *Dido*[6] in company with his Commander-in-Chief, Menou. Although during the siege there had been only a few cases of plague it would appear that Menou developed a plague sore at the very moment of embarkation—if Larrey's diagnosis was correct. In this quandary he took the bold course of embarking the general: "Since I had been able to arrange for the isolation of his cabin

[5] Dr. Young was Inspector-General of hospitals for the British army.
[6] *Dido* was a 6th rate, built in 1784 and sold in 1817.

on board the frigate, and should the disease develop further I would isolate myself there with him and attend to him without any contact with the ship's company." It may be presumed that he kept his knowledge from the Captain! Menou's condition improved during the voyage and at the end of the period of quarantine in Toulon he was convalescent.

On submitting his customary report on reaching Toulon, Larrey received the following letters:

Paris
3 Nivôse Year IX

The Minister of War to D. J. Larrey, Surgeon-in-Chief to the Army of the Orient.

"The General Commanding the Army of the Orient has informed the Government, Monsieur, of the unlimited devotion and the success you and your colleagues have displayed in the preservation of the health of this invaluable army. The Government, which watches over it lovingly, has through your care seen the realization of one of its dearest wishes, the protection of so important a part of the French forces from the dangers of a climate which differs so much from our own. In praising your efforts, as splendid as they have been successful, it can only ask you to continue your endeavours, which will bring you the ever growing appreciation of the army you will have saved and of the Government which places the highest value on its safety.

I salute you.
(Signed). Al. BERTHIER."

The patent propaganda and the pressing and exculpatory anxiety of the civil government to publicize its care for a defeated and greatly diminished army is in marked contrast to the soldierly character of the letter from Bonaparte:

Paris,
18th Nivôse, Year IX.
(8th Jan. 1801).

"*The Minister of War, to D. J. Larrey, Surgeon-in-Chief of the Army of the Orient.*
You, Sir, have rendered to the wounded of the Army of the Orient services too distinguished to have escaped the notice of the First Consul. He is satisfied with your devotion to duty, and it is with great cordiality that I fulfil the order he has given me to inform you of this.

I salute you.
(Signed) Al. BERTHIER."

Berthier also wrote in person:

Paris,
8th Pluviôse, Year IX.
(28th Jan. 1801).

"*The Minister of War to D. J. Larrey, Surgeon-in-Chief of the Army of the Orient.*
The Government has up to now used every occasion to make known to the whole of France the services you have rendered and which the army of Egypt, with whose glory your name will ever be associated, has long

proclaimed. Your wife, who is in good health, has received the sum of fifteen hundred francs as a national reward.

For myself, Sir, I have been extremely gratified that the account which I have published of the expedition to Egypt has given me an opportunity to do justice to your devotion. I have not failed to point out *that you were often seen, at the head of your worthy colleagues, attending to the suffering wounded even at the foot of the breech.* In so doing I have undertaken to make known your right to the nation's recognition in all circumstances: this undertaking I shall fulfill.

I salute you.
(Signed). Al. BERTHIER."

Chapter 9

The Empire. Consecration by the Pope and Napoleon's self-coronation. Trafalgar. Battle of Ulm. Vienna. Austerlitz. Embalming. Epidemic at Brün.

On his return to Paris, Larrey was received by the First Consul with every kindness and, indeed, affection. He was nominated to the position of Surgeon-in-Chief to the Consular Guard, his Commission being dated 1st Germinal, Year X (March 22nd, 1802).

Once freed from active duties in the field Larrey settled down to write his *Relation chirurgicale de l'Armée d'Orient*, which he dedicated to the First Consul. At the same time he started a course of experimental military surgery, and sustained a thesis on "Amputations" at the School of Medicine. By so doing he became the first to receive the title of *Doctor of Surgery* under the then newly enacted regulations.

But a new order was being established in France, which it was hoped would bring her institutions into harmony with those of the rest of Europe and give permanence to the destinies of the country. On May 18th, 1804, the First Consul was elected Emperor of the French with the title of Napoleon I. One of his early acts was the institution of the Legion of Honour, and at the inauguration ceremony at the *Invalides*, on July 15th, 1804, Larrey was created an Officer of the Legion. A few days later he was appointed Inspector-General of the Health Services of the Armies.

The consecration by the Pope, and Napoleon's self-coronation, took place on the 11th Frimaire, Year XIII (December 2nd, 1804) in Nôtre Dame. On returning from the ceremony Larrey said to his wife: "I was very moved when I saw this famous soldier take up the sceptre of Kings. Everything tells me that this instrument of tyranny will lead to his downfall and France's ruin." He was as good a prophet as he was republican.

But the much longed-for era of peace eluded France and her Emperor. The Treaty of Amiens had collapsed in 1803, and the obstinate island of Albion across the Channel stood forth again as a hostile and tenacious foe. In the circumstances Napoleon decided upon the invasion of Britain, and work was commenced on a huge camp at Boulogne for the 480,000 men destined for this undertaking, and thither Larrey proceeded. But Napoleon's naval plans to gain command of the Channel for forty-eight hours miscarried, and while Villeneuve lingered in Cadiz a new danger threatened from beyond the eastern frontier. As the autumn drew on the Emperor drastically revised his strategy and decided to march into the valley of the Danube, and by breaking the power of Austria to seek peace in the destruction of the coalition.

"In the midst of these great preparations a new continental alliance was formed, and France in her turn was threatened by the armies and considerable pretentions of Austria. At this juncture the combined fleet, when on its way to its destination, encountered that of Admiral Nelson and the terrible and memorable battle of Trafalgar was fought. From this moment everything was changed, but the great genius of the Emperor instantly comprehended the situation and a new campaign was at once resolved upon. The disembarkation of the troops was ordered, and our columns marched so quickly across France that they had passed the Rhine and entered Germany before the enemy was properly aware of the movement."

The Austrian commander, Mack, was surprised and out-manoeuvered by the speed and surge of the French envelopment, and allowed himself to be trapped in Ulm. "Whilst their generals were concerting a plan of attack our columns, which had advanced considerably further, cut off their retreat, surrounded them and forced them to fall back into the town, which they did with some confidence as they felt themselves well able to defend it. But they failed to find a sufficient supply of provisions and at the same time were dominated by the powerful fire of our artillery, which had set up batteries upon the very heights they had abandoned and could thus command the place.

"The first few cannon shot made them realize the danger of being besieged and they asked to be allowed to capitulate. This was accepted on condition that the whole army should become prisoners of war, and lay down their arms on the glacis of the ramparts. Only the generals and officers were permitted to return to their homes on parole.

"The capture of Ulm is one of the most astonishing and remarkable of military events.

"The march out of the captured troops in the presence of the *Grande Armée*, was the most extraordinary sight imaginable. (Fig. 16). There were two different parties to this veritably picturesque tableau. Our troops in battle array, were drawn up upon the slope of the hill which encircles Ulm like an amphitheatre, with the infantry filling the tiers. In the centre, on an isolated hillock below which the enemy army defiled, was His Majesty. The various corps of cavalry and light artillery were stationed on either side of him close beside the road. The brilliance which was reflected by the arms and streaming flags, and the air of satisfaction and joy on every face in this part of the picture were all eloquent of success and victory. The other was very different: a large body of infantry, defiling before the French army in serried ranks and laying down its arms on the glacis; the cavalry, dismounting and delivering its horses to our unmounted dragoons. What a contrast between the troops of the two nations! The result of this engagement spread terror amongst our other enemies and produced a lively effect throughout Germany.

"General Headquarters and the Imperial Guard re-crossed the river at Elchingen and returned to Augsburg. We cleansed the Ulm hospitals and brought to them the wounded from the different engagements which had been fought on both sides of the Danube, and we also took possession of some large hospitals at Augsburg. This is a rich commercial town where we found plenty of everything required for the army and the wounded. From its situation, its warehouses, and the canals surrounding it, it appeared a very suitable place for fortification, and in fact it was afterwards so used."

The capitulation at Ulm opened the road to Vienna, and on November 14th, less than six weeks after leaving Mayence, Napoleon established Imperial Headquarters at Schönbrunn. The going had been bad as well as swift, and Larrey had more than a little to say about it.

"Snow and rain had been our constant companions on the march to Vienna, and the speed of our advance had given the soldiers no chance of drying their clothes; furthermore they had been without any of the comforts requisite for the trials they had sustained, as our wagons had been outdistanced and a regular distribution of rations had only been made in the larger towns.

"In spite of these unfavourable circumstances we had hardly any sick: it appeared rather that the men's health had become more robust by the time we reached Vienna. This may explain the successes achieved by the Greeks and Romans in the face of the greatest obstacles at the end of their long expeditions. In fact the soldier who is accustomed to bear arms, and is imbued with the spirit of his profession and in full physical fitness, will not become ill whatever degree of cold and fatigue he has to put up with, provided he is not too much deprived of his food. No doubt the functions and activity of his organs are increased, but this excessive activity is not injurious to his health as long as he has regular intervals of a few hours rest.

"His morale is not lessened by this increased activity and his short periods of rest are not disturbed by mental anxieties. There is even some risk in allowing him too much relaxation at the bivouac after he has been marching all day in rain or snow. He then becomes plunged in deep sleep brought on by the cold and fatigue he has experienced and his animal forces become enfeebled and suspended. The mucous secretions and cutaneous exhalations are also greatly reduced, whilst on the other hand the interior absorption is as active as ever. The damp from his garments penetrates more easily, the nervous sensibility is altered, the capillary system becomes engorged, and little by little, by sympathy or by the action of heterogeneous principles, the organs are affected: this derangement gives rise to maladies which shew themselves almost at once, and in particular to rheumatic affections.

"It is good for the soldier's health when he reaches his place of bivouac, wet and hungry, to have to search for or cut the wood for his fire, to forage for meat and vegetables for his soup and to cook this for himself. Whilst thus employed his wet clothes do him no harm and they soon dry at the bivouac fire. His animal forces sustain him: he gets a short period of rest and may even snatch a few moments' sleep, but not so much that the motion and normal activity of his organs are suspended. He has his meal and is soon fit to march again.

"Unless the troops find shelter, a fire, a bed or some good straw and soup ready prepared, when they reach their halting place, it is better that they should perforce undertake the healthy exercise we have just described and bivouac. The interest of the inhabitants of the country, and the safety of the soldier himself, more especially in the face of the enemy, imperiously demand this.

"This system of campaigning is assuredly the best for the troops' health, especially when they overrun countries as fertile as Germany, where the soldier has never lacked bread, flour, vegetables and beer, which is a much healthier drink in the field than spirituous liquors he so habitually abuses."

It may well be that Larrey is making a virtue of necessity in this argument. He is singularly silent about the surgical arrangements at Ulm, but his less exalted contemporary, d'Heralde complained that on the day of the battle not a single set of instruments was available. He, however, was writing a diary for himself, whereas Larrey was very conscious that his record would reach the eyes of the Emperor.

The remnants of the Austrian army retreated into Moravia to join forces with the Russians. Although they abandoned Vienna, which was difficult to defend, they had every intention of standing behind the Danube, but Murat and Lannes by pretending that an armistice had been signed deceived the defenders of the main bridge into allowing their men to infiltrate across and so to capture it intact. By a like act of deception the Russians were able to delay the advance of the French marshals and make good their retreat into Moravia, though Bagratian had to fight a severe rearguard action at Hollabrün on November 16th. The French entered Brünn, which was undefended, three days later. Here they captured large quantities of stores and equipment, including sixty cannon and over a hundred tons of powder. The convent and civil hospitals were taken over for the needs of the army and Larrey appropriated the *Hôpital de la Charité* for the Guard. Percy, the Director of the Medical service, was still in Vienna organizing the hospitals there, and the responsibility for the medical arrangements for the coming battle of Austerlitz devolved upon Larrey.

"After I had visited all the ambulances I was at great pains to instruct their surgeons, and the chief surgeons of the corps and regiments, on their duties for the next day, and to site the ambulances relative to the divisions. In conformity with His Majesty's orders I wrote to the Commandant of the hospitals at Brünn, to request him to furnish the means of transport, stretchers, etc., to the central ambulance, which I had previously estab-lished at the mill of Paleny.[1] I was admirably assisted in every way by the commissary of war, M. Dagiaut, who was charged by the Commandant with the execution of these measures."

Well may Larrey have sent to Brün for supplies! There seems to have been a dire deficiency in both these and in the arrangements, if we are to believe Surgeon d'Heralde who was in charge of the ambulance of the

---

[1] The name of this mill is blank in the mémoirs.

4th Division of Soult's 4th Corps. He recorded in his diary, which has only recently come to light,[2] that at nine o'clock on the evening before the battle Larrey had not a single dressing at his disposal and actually asked d'Heralde, who had sufficient materials for only 400–500 wounded and two cases of amputation instruments, to join him and pass the night beside him. The Guard's ambulance equipment did not arrive until eleven o'clock at night on the day after the battle.

It may be that a knowledge of this failure of organization was the reason for Napoleon's order, which d'Heralde heard read before his unit moved off to take up its battle position, that the wounded were not to be collected until the engagement was over. An order, he comments, which may have been either heroic or barbarous, but was in no case reassuring!

Subsequently there were no facilities in Brün for dealing with the large number of wounded. Every house became a hospital, and typhus destroyed impartially the victims, vanquished and civilians.

"A proclamation that the battle was to be engaged the next day having been made in general orders, each soldier knew the Emperor's decision and great joy was shewn that they were about to measure themselves against the enemy. General enthusiasm broke out when His Majesty passed along the lines, and electrified by his presence, in a spontaneous and unanimous movement, the soldiers lit torches made from twisted straw. In an instant more than twenty thousand men produced a unique illumination, which was all the more brilliant and systematical from the clearness of the sky and the fact that the troops were lining the hills as though in an amphitheatre. The Emperor was met with the most enthusiastic acclamations, which at the same time commemorated the anniversary of his coronation.

"Such scenes of enthusiasm might well suggest a happy augury of the events to come: the weather had cleared after the constant rain and snow, and a fine spring day was promised for the morrow.

"At sunrise the imminence of battle was obvious everywhere, since the enemy had decided to attack on the same day. The first encounter was extremely hard fought but our success was never in doubt, and the most complete victory crowned this brilliant and memorable day, which has been called *The Day of the Three Emperors* or the *Battle of Austerlitz*. The enemy lost more than forty flags or standards, more than a hundred and twenty cannon, twenty generals, more than thirty thousand men taken prisoner and ten to twelve thousand either left on the field or drowned in the lake, as well as a considerable number of wounded whom we afterwards collected and sent to Brün during the following days. The French wounded were almost all treated on the spot, as the weather was favourable.

"The Inspector-General, M. Percy, having rejoined the army, I returned to my post with the Imperial Guard during the course of the battle. The first wounded we received were from the terrible charge made by this unit against the Russian Imperial Guard. All were operated on

[2] "*Relation historique des campaignes du Chirurgien-Major d'Héralde Dominique.*" Médecin-Colonel Hassenforder. *Histoire de la Médicine.* 1959, No. V, p. 8.

and dressed on the field, and carried back as soon as they were ready in the wagons of our light ambulances which I had organized at the mill.

"The speed with which these vehicles could move enabled us also to transport the wounded of the Line. I myself followed the Guard with my ambulance, halting wherever our presence would be of use.

"No field of battle ever presented a more amazing picture of destruction than that of Austerlitz. It was covered with dead, dying, wounded, and an immense debris of arms and equipment and every kind of *matériel* abandoned in disorder by the Russians in the early stages of the fight.

"On returning to our central ambulance, four hours after midnight, we attended to those who had not as yet received first aid. The next day I had them all evacuated with Surgeon Paulet to Brün, for admission to the convent I had bespoken before I left the town. In addition his Majesty sent me an order to remove and preserve the body of Colonel Morlan of the Mounted Chasseurs, who was killed in the first charge.

"The Emperor pursued the remnants of the Austro-Russian army for many leagues beyond Austerlitz. He halted at the bivouac of his advance guard at Saruschitz to receive the envoys of the Czar Alexander and the Emperor Francis II, who had requested an interview.

"After this meeting the Emperor Napoleon and the Imperial Guard returned to Brün, where negotiations were entered into and continued until the final conclusion of peace which was signed at Presbourg. I went on ahead of the Guard to visit the wounded and to embalm the body of Colonel Morlan."

Larrey as an embalmer

It was Napoleon's desire to give Morlan, who had played so conspicuous a part in the great victory of Austerlitz, full funeral pomps in Paris so he instructed Larrey to embalm the body. The surgeon was no stranger to such matters, as he had studied and described the Egyptian procedure and had unwrapped a considerable number of mummies in both upper and lower Egypt, in particular at Sakhara, but for this purpose he relied upon his own chemical knowledge. Morlan's body was found with some difficulty amongst the many corpses on the battlefield, and was taken to Brünn where Larrey had the help of his friend Ribes, an experienced anatomist. Although decomposition had set in it would appear from what follows that they were very successful in their gruesome task.

In describing his method Larrey states that he did not open the abdomen unless the subject were very fat or the weather very hot, but flushed out the stomach and large intestine by a tube and syringe aided by manual compression, and then filled the organs with a melted bituminous compound. The arterial system was injected through the aorta with "fine red material" which he thought reached as far as the capillaries, and this was followed by a coarser suspension of the same stuff to fill the larger vessels. Where it was necessary to remove the intestines a semilunar incision was made in the lumbar region, through which the contents of the abdomen and thorax were extracted. All the cavities were then sponged out and plentifully powdered with oxychloride of mercury, and afterwards stuffed with horsehair.

The skull was opened with a trephine at the junction of the saggital and occipital sutures and the membranes pulled out by a blunt hook, after which the brain substance was washed out by a stream of cold water. Finally, the whole body was immersed in a large volume of a strong solution of the mercury salt for 90–100 days, and was then placed on a hurdle and exposed to moderate heat in a dry airy place. As the drying progressed the body and features were remoulded and the limbs placed in whatever attitude was desired. Enamel eyes were inserted between the lids to cover the sunken globes, the hair dyed to an appropriate colour and the whole body coated with a slightly tinted varnish which gave it an appearance of freshness . . . "and thus we are able to preserve for thousands of years the features and the memory of great statesmen." So successful was the embalming that seven years later Larrey was able to write that Morlan was still perfectly preserved. His body, clad in uniform, was exhibited in one of the rooms of the Guard's Hospital where it was recognized by many of his old friends. Indeed, one female relation believed him alive and was about to embrace the corpse! The shock of the discovery caused her to faint, "which might have proved fatal had she not received prompt treatment". Baron Marbot (1892) has a cock and bull story that the surgeons, having neither time nor materials to embalm the General's body on the battlefield, put it into a barrel of rum in which it was transported to Paris. But events having delayed the construction of Morlan's monument, the barrel was left in one of the rooms of the School of Medicine where it still was when Napoleon lost the Empire in 1814. Not long afterwards it broke open through decay, and people were surprised to find that the rum had made the General's moustaches grow to such an extent that they fell to below his waist. Marbot goes on to say that to obtain possession of the body the relatives were obliged to bring an action against a scientific man who had made a curiosity of it!

Larrey also embalmed Lannes, who was mortally wounded at Essling, and Colonel Barbnègre of the 7th Hussars who fell at Jena, as well as the eccentric Lord Egerton,[3] who left specific instructions for this. The embalming of Lannes must have been not only a most unpleasant but a difficult and dangerous task, for the weather was hot and Lannes appeared to have died from sepsis and his body was well advanced in decomposition.

The bodies of Morlan and Barbnègre eventually found a lodging in the anatomical museum of the School of Medicine in Paris and after the restoration were claimed by their families to whom they were handed over. This roused Larrey's wrath and he sent a letter of dignified protest to the Dean of the Faculty, but he was overruled.

The brilliant victory of Austerlitz was followed by an outbreak of disease, unusually severe even for that period, in the temporary hospitals of Brün, crowded as they were with French and Russian wounded. Larrey described this as: "a putrid fever with nervous, malignant and

[3] Helenic authority and débauché—" a sink of science and vice." One of his last acts was the charging of Larrey with his embalming.

nosocomial (adynamic-ataxic) characters, or the 'contagious typhus' of the older nosologists." Today we should be content with the older name, for there is little doubt that the disease was typhus, although typhoid may have been present as well.

Simultaneously hospital gangrene appeared and many of the unfortunate men contracted both infections. Hospital gangrene is a disease of the past, and its clinical characters are unknown today: "When this condition shows itself the purulent effusion takes on an ashen-grey colour; it is thick, glutinous, and has a nauseating smell: the edges of the wound swell and become blackish and warmth and sensation in the part are lost." In Brün, "the wounds assumed a truly gangrenous character and gave out a very foetid odour which could be smelt a long way off. The miasma of the discharge, or the purulent exhalation from these ulcers, was extremely contagious, and the patients who lay near to those affected by the epidemic, and even the doctors who attended them, had every reason to fear that they might contract the disease. The other wounded in the same ward were quickly attacked; the disease spread step by step and infected the hospitals and the nearby houses from the frequent coming and going of persons. . . ."

"The movement or transportation of the patients also contributed to the spread of the contagion, which developed so rapidly that in less than a month the hospitals of the Line had lost more than a quarter of their wounded. . . . The fever hospitals were soon overcrowded and the mortality was proportionately great. At the same time the (typhus) epidemic broke out amongst the Russian prisoners, whom we had been forced to collect in great numbers in the churches and other large buildings, and before long spread amongst the local inhabitants and then throughout the whole line of evacuation as far as France in consequence of the movement of the prisoners and sick of the two nations."

The Russian prisoners suffered badly from being overcrowded in inadequate camps and their general lack of hygiene. Larrey had sensibly suggested that separate routes of evacuation should be used for the Russians and the French, and that the clothes of the convalescents and soldiers who had recovered should be disinfected. But this sane advice was not acted upon: "No doubt the circumstances did not allow of it."

It is clear that Larrey had an excellent understanding of the dangers of hospital infection of wounds, its mode of spread and, indeed, of the *rôle* of carriers. His personal responsibility was to the Guard, and as was his wont he made special provision for them by reserving the *Hôpital de la Charité*, which "was at some distance from the other hospitals and isolated from the populous parts of the town, as well as being well sited, airy and kept in perfect order. The hospital service was assiduously carried out by the medical officers and orderlies from our mobile ambulance, with the result that we only lost a very few of our wounded and fever cases."

He must have had considerable liberty of action, for he goes on: "The evacuation of the wounded of the Guard, which began on the day following Austerlitz and went on uninterruptedly down to the last man, was very successful. We brought them all to the hospital of the Dominicans in Vienna—a place which left nothing to be desired in its internal arrangements and hygiene—so that they might have the best treatment and receive the personal attention which was the responsibility of our ambulance, and also that their effects might all be disinfected in the one place."

Gradually the epidemic worked itself out, and with the coming of cold weather, the gradual dispersal of the prisoners and the passage of time, it became only a memory. But the impression made on Larrey by this comparatively early and disastrous experience in a major European campaign remained with him throughout his life. It was one of the factors which from that time on made him so insistent on the dispersal of his battle casualties, and sometimes caused him to advise such of his patients who were capable and resolute to make their own separate way back to their homes after an operation on the battlefield.

The French took the opportunity of their occupation of Vienna to send to France the cannon, arms and armour of the arsenal—one of the famous collections of the world, and including the armour of most of the crusaders and many of the great captains of the middle ages. Soon after the signing of the Peace of Presburg Larrey left to inspect the hospitals of the line of evacuation. On reaching Paris he resumed his practice at the Guard's hospital.

*   *   *   *   *

Chapter 10

Jena. Berlin. Asphyxia. First Polish campaign.
Marie Walewska. Battle of Eylau. Commandant of
Legion of Honour. The Polish Plica.

The overwhelming defeat of the Austrian and Russian armies at Austerlitz was followed by the treaties of Presburg, which humiliated Austria almost unbearably and deprived her of four million subjects, and that of Schönbrun which bound Prussia to France as the price of her perfidy. But already behind the scenes the Prussians were scheming to free themselves from their formidable partner and making overtures to both Russia and Austria. The rumour that Hanover, which Prussia had acquired as a reward of her alliance, was to be restored to the King of England as part of a settlement, which for a moment seemed possible after the death of Pitt and his replacement by Fox and a Whig ministry, was the last straw at the court of Frederick-William, and in an upsurge of patriotic zeal the Prussians presented Napoleon with an ultimatum, demanding the evacuation of Germany within a fortnight. In October 1806 Prussian troops began to invade Saxony. The reaction was swift and devastating!

The French army was still quartered in Franconia, but on October 8th orders were given to cross into Saxony. A brisk action, in which the French advance guard routed the Prussian cavalry in the neighbourhood of Schleitz, was the first they knew of the presence of the *Grande Armée.* The main advance was in three columns, the centre one being led by the Emperor and including the infantry of the Guard which had been brought up by post from Paris. The cavalry of this division, to which Larrey was attached with his mobile ambulance, had not moved so quickly and consequently was still at the rear at Géra at the time the battle of Jena was fought, and to his chagrin he could not obtain permission from his commanding officer to be present on the battlefield. However, there were plenty of casualties brought to the chateau of Géra, where he and the other surgeons of his ambulance treated them.

The medical arrangements of Jena, which was fought on October 14th, aroused his criticism. "The more seriously wounded," he wrote, "could not be attended to until some time after the battle; either because the ambulance divisions were too far away, or because the lightly wounded, who were able to walk, occupied the whole of the surgeons' time on the first day. The best procedure, and one I have always followed, to ensure that those who are gravely wounded shall be the first to receive attention, is to set up the ambulance as near as possible to the line of battle, and to form a headquarters to which all the wounded who require the more difficult operations can be brought and operated upon by the chief surgeon, or by experienced surgeons under his eye. The most seriously wounded should always be treated first, regardless of rank or distinction. The more lightly wounded can wait until their more gravely mutilated brothers-in-arms have been dressed and operated on, who otherwise would either be dead within a few hours or only survive until the next day, even if for so long. It is, on the other hand, always easy for the lightly wounded to get to the hospitals of the first or second line, especially the officers who usually have means of transport; moreover the lives of such men are not in danger."

Jena decided the Saxons, in any case unwilling allies, to quit the coalition and make a separate peace, but Prussia continued in the field and the Guard was ordered forward to join the Emperor at Nuremburg. Some of the heaviest fighting had been near this town, which was full of wounded, but the Guard not having been engaged pressed on to Halle, which had been obstinately defended, and two days later was in Wittemburg, the birthplace of Martin Luther. The fertile Saxon country was now exchanged for the sandy lands of Prussia, and before long they entered Potsdam, with its magnificent park and château full of souvenirs of Frederick the Great, including his sword and military decorations which Napoleon appropriated and dispatched to the Invalides, remarking how delighted these old soldiers would be to see in French possession the sword of him who beat them at Rosbach. The Emperor took up residence in the royal palace of Charlottenburg, whilst awaiting the concentration of his forces which had been pursuing the enemy, and on October 27th, 1806, made his triumphal entry into Berlin. It was a fine autumn day and Larrey, watching the magistrates delivering the keys of the city to the conqueror and preceding him to the palace, admired the splendid avenues of limes and plane trees and the magnificent quadriga surmounting the Brandenburg Gate—a famous group destined soon to be torn from its site by Napoleon's orders and sent as a trophy to Paris, only to be returned on the fall of the Empire. Destroyed when Berlin fell to the Russians in 1945, it was recast from the original moulds, which fortunately had been preserved—with minor modifications to suit it for communist eyes—and since 1958 it has stood once more over the restored gate.

The effective Prussian resistance was now at an end and with the fall of most of the remaining cities which had resisted an armistice was sought; but so severe were the proposed terms that Frederick-William refused it, and retreating to Königsberg, resolved to join the Russians on the Vistula and continue his resistance. In the meantime Prussia became occupied territory.

Larrey remained in Berlin throughout November and was flatteringly received by the German scientists, amongst them Humboldt, who shewed him his biological specimens, and Walther, who had sold his anatomical collection to the King of Prussia for 400,000 francs. In return he made a present of a copy of his book on Egypt to the Royal Academy. He found much in Berlin to admire, but was critical of the interior of the houses which he found meanly provided, and of the furniture which was mostly of poplar or walnut with very little mahogany. This lack of opulence he explained as being due to the fact that threequarters of the populace were in the pay of the government and the remainder engaged in the arts or professions: "There is very little industry or commerce, since the national pride does not encourage this."

The health of the army in this short autumn campaign of barely a month had been excellent, and little more than a hundred sick had been left in the towns through which it had passed. In Berlin itself Larrey appropriated a part of the Hôtel Dieu for the needs of the Guard and personally directed the surgical service there. At the end of December, however, the weather suddenly became intensely cold and this resulted in the asphyxiation of numbers of soldiers who had shut themselves in rooms heated by the cast-iron stoves usual in that part of the country.

"Since carbonic acid gas is much heavier than air it accumulates on the floor of a room and reaches to a height determined by its mass or quantity; thus in one of the places where the cases of asphyxia occurred, the soldiers who were closest to the stove, lying on the tiles with a very small amount of straw which is always scarce in large towns, were the first and most severely asphyxiated. The corporal and three other soldiers of the detachment to which these unfortunate men belonged escaped the danger, as they were either on beds or on tables near to the windows and farther from the stove. They awoke at the drum beating the reveille, half-stupefied and with aching heads.

"One man succeeded in getting up and opening a window; the fresh air revived him, but he was terrified when he saw that none of his comrades answered his calls, and those lying in the straw on the floor did not move. He shouted for help, and though very weak shook the men on the beds and without much difficulty roused them from their lethargy. In the end in reply to his cries the people of the house and other soldiers rushed in. They hurriedly opened the windows and doors and sent for the doctors, whilst giving the unfortunate men such treatment as occurred to them. Five were brought to our hospital as I was making my morning round. In spite of our efforts we could do nothing for three of them, and finally could only leave them under observation in a well-ventilated room for forty-eight hours, after which a post-mortem examination was carried out in the presence of all my pupils with findings I have already spoken of. The treatment we gave the other two, who shewed hardly any signs of life, restored their organic functions, albeit imperfectly. Rubbing the whole body with snow and alkaline and alcoholic lotions, dry cupping, scarification, limited bleeding from the jugular veins to reduce the venous congestion in the head, acidulated drinks, stimulating cordials, and in some cases emetics, followed by bitters, quinine and cinnamon, were all employed with benefit; but one of them developed gangrenous plaques over the sacral region and shoulder blades which greatly hindered his recovery. The convalescence of his comrade was also slow and tedious, and for a long time his speech and intellect were affected.

"As these asphyxial accidents occurred in a number of other places in the Guard's cantonments I took precautions against their repetition, and at my instance instructions were issued in the routine orders which had the desired effect.

"The first intense cold of winter was succeeded by heavy rains and thick fogs which produced a large crop of sick, most of them suffering from low catarrhal infections and diarrhoea, which readily yielded to appropriate treatment. The most serious disease was syphilis, which quickly spread amongst our men and in many took on serious characters. We found it necessary to combine febrifuges and tonics with our anti-syphilitic remedies, as indicated by the special symptoms. Apart from this we lost only a few of our sick, and as far as the health of the Guard was concerned the outcome of the campaign was favourable. Our departure for Poland put an end to inroads of these diseases, and in general the men quickly recovered their strength and customary vigour as soon as they were on the march again. . . ."

*   *   *   *   *

With Austria and Prussia prostrate Napoleon developed his megalomaniac ambition of universal European dominance, and from Berlin he promulgated the famous *Decrees* of November, 1801, opposing to the maritime blockade of England his "continental blockade". But to make this effective he required to subordinate Russia. Russia, who had been driven from the field at Austerlitz but had as yet escaped irretrievable disaster by retreating into her vast and frigid lands beyond the Vistula and Niemen. The campaign in Poland, upon which he was about to embark, was to be the first tactical move in this wider strategic effort.

The defeated but still indomitable Frederick-William had been pushed with the remnants of his army into Königsberg at the farthest extremity of his kingdom and had joined forces with 100,000 Russians who had advanced to the Vistula. Napoleon, with his enormous numerical superiority, intended to strike an immediate and severe blow at this force so as to cripple and disperse it, and then to go into winter quarters on the Vistula in preparation for a systematic spring and summer campaign. The operation opened in the second half of November, 1806, the Emperor leaving Berlin on the 25th, and reaching Posen on the 27th, where he was loudly acclaimed as the bringer of Polish independence. In the meantime the army had been ordered to advance to the Vistula and had seized a number of places on both banks.

The Russian commander, Benningsen, tried to cross the river to the north of the French who were at Modlin, so as to cut their communications with Berlin, but was stopped by Lannes at Czarnova, and on the 24th of December Napoleon took the offensive. The battles of Goldmin and Pultusk, fought in terrible conditions of rain, snow and mud, were of a slogging deadly character, and in the end the Russians were forced to retreat but disengaged themselves without being routed. This determined opposition, together with the winter weather and the dreadful state of the roads which clogged all manoeuvres, decided Napoleon to withdraw his army into cantonments before the Vistula, there to await better conditions and the reinforcements which were being called up from every part of France and her subjugated countries. He himself returned to Warsaw on January 1st, 1807, to find relaxation in the arms of Marie Walewska. But the Russians did not remain passive. As soon as the ground had been thoroughly hardened by the first frosts they attempted a wide outflanking movement against the French left wing, where Ney and Bernadotte were posted on the lower Vistula. The marshals, however, resisted sufficiently strongly to give time for Napoleon to take the field with the main mass of his force and to drive the Muscovites back beyond Landsberg, where they turned to fight the battle of Eylau.

"We left Warsaw on the 1st February: there was about three feet of snow on the ground and the temperature was six or seven degrees below freezing point. We crossed the Vistula with difficulty as the ice had broken the bridges. Imperial Headquarters made for Wittenberg, where the advance guard of the Grand Duke of Berg (Murat) was already in contact with the Russian outposts which fell back after a short resistance. In spite of the severity of the weather our troops pursued and endeavoured to overtake the enemy with the utmost ardour. The Imperial Guard marched immediately behind the advance guard. Administrative headquarters followed at a short distance, but halted at Liebstat to set up various establishments. My colleague, M. Percy, was responsible for organizing the hospitals and for the reception of several hundred wounded from the first engagements whilst we, for our part, dressed a very considerable proportion of the casualties on the battlefield. By the 6th the cavalry of the Grand Duke of Berg found the enemy at Hoff and made the most brilliant charge ever seen."

The Emperor had arrived before Hoff with Murat's cavalry, and not wishing to wait for Soult's infantry to come up ordered an attack by several regiments of light cavalry. These were met with heavy musketry and grape fire and driven back in disorder. A division of dragoons was no more successful, so Napoleon called on General d'Hautpoul's cuirassiers, who fell upon the Russian line with such strength that they exterminated or captured nearly the whole of the eight battalions who were defending the position. To testify his satisfaction with this brilliant exploit Napoleon embraced the general before the whole division. D'Hautpoul exclaimed: "The only way to shew myself worthy of such an honour is to get myself killed in your Majesty's service!" He died the next day on the field of Eylau.

"We had only a few wounded, who were at once dressed and evacuated to the first-line hospitals. The Russians, on the other hand, left on the field a large number of dead and dying. This success seemed to promise the complete defeat of the enemy when he should halt to give battle."

Although it had been Napoleon's intention to wait until the 8th, by which time his wings should have come up, the battle of Eylau actually commenced on the evening of February 7th, when the Guard and Soult's corps entered the village of that name. By the morning of the 8th the Russian left was at Serpalten, their centre at Auklappen and their right at Schloditten (Fig. 17). Ney, on the French left, and Davout on the right had not arrived when the attack was opened by a violent Russian cannonade. Soon Davout's corps appeared advancing through Rothenen and drove the Russian left back upon Klein Sausgarten. A tremendous fight developed between Eylau and Rothenen as the Russians counter-attacked Davout's left flank and two of Augereau's divisions which had been sent to support him. Although they lost 12,000 out of their 15,000 men, and Augereau himself was wounded, their sacrifice enabled Davout to capture Klein Sausgarten and by advancing on Kutschitten to threaten the whole Russian left. At this point Napoleon threw in Murat's ninety squadrons of cavalry between Eylau and Rothenen and broke the Russian centre. This decided the battle, and with Davout in Kutschitten and Ney advancing upon Schmoditten as the evening drew on, the Russian commander gave orders for a retreat, leaving the French the masters of this frightful battlefield on which the Russians had some 25,000 casualties and the French 20,000.

"The enemy had formed a *point d'appui* at Prussich Eylau, an advantageous position strengthened by redoubts and batteries of siege guns, with their rearguard drawn up on the heights in front of the town, behind a village which lies rather less than half a league on the road from Eylau. We did not delay in reconnoitring and before mid-day a preliminary skirmish began which lasted into the night but did not involve the Guard. However, as I was the only one of the Army Medical Service of the rank of Inspector, I was ordered by H.M. Major-General the Prince (Berthier) to move all the wounded to the aforesaid village and take charge of them. I collected them in the main room of the largest house in the place which had hurriedly been made ready, and we spent the rest of the day and the whole of the night in attending to them. There were a number of cases which required amputation, some at the shoulder joint, others at the leg or thigh. I learnt subsequently from news I had of these patients that their operations were in most cases successful.

"In the belief that the enemy had halted on the hill which dominates Eylau, at the entry to the forest, the Guard and the corps behind it passed the night in bivouac. In the meantime the cold increased, the thermometer falling from eight degrees to thirteen or fourteen degrees below zero ($-14°–17°$F.). At daybreak our troops ascertained the enemy's position, but being ignorant of his strength descended the hill which faces the low ground of Eylau, which is reached through a narrow defile. This ground, which was at the time covered with snow and ice, forms a fresh-water lake in summer.[1] The advance guard and the Imperial Guard, with a number of divisions from other corps, deployed here.

"The Russians, being in force and favourably situated, began a general attack on our troops. Soon a heavy cannonade broke out in various places, the two armies clashed and the battle became murderous. Victory

[1] Marbot says that neither side knew that they were on ice and so no ricochet shots were fired to break it: had this been done there would have been a second Satschan (Austerlitz) disaster.

was in the balance, when a furious charge by the Imperial cavalry at the end of the day settled it in our favour. This was one of the most terrible battles ever fought. Although the infantry of the Guard was not actually engaged it suffered a good deal from artillery fire. Early in the day I had set up an ambulance in some barns, on the left of the road just outside the town, but unfortunately these were open to the weather on all sides and their straw had been taken for the horses. The wounded, including numbers of men of both the Guard and the Line, were brought to this miserable shelter where they had to lie on the remnants of straw partly covered with snow. I first attended to the men of the Imperial Guard, but faithful to my principles I began with those who were most severely wounded without regard to their rank or distinction. So great was the cold that the instruments frequently fell from the hands of my pupils who held them for me during the operations. Happily I myself was sustained by a supernatural strength, due no doubt to the intense interest aroused in me by these honourable victims.

"The burning desire which possessed us all to save the lives of these brave men sustained us in the exercise of our difficult tasks. Night arrived, and we had not even had time to satisfy the needs which nature requires. And amidst what heartrending scenes did we perform our sad but necessary ministry! Whilst I operated on one wounded man I heard from all sides the urgent appeals of others for the same assistance. It is true that after the operation the dolorous cries of these brave soldiers gave place to a state of profound tranquillity and a sort of internal satisfaction which they shewed by their expressions of deep gratitude. They seemed no longer concerned with their own misfortunes, and not only vowed the safety of the Emperor and the success of our arms, but encouraged each other to submit to the operations which their wounds made necessary.

"In the midst of this infinity of obstacles due to our situation and the intense cold, I performed a number of delicate and difficult operations, such as the disarticulation of the arm at the shoulder, and amputation of the lower limb at unusual levels as the nature of the case required, as well as extensive sutures of the face for complete division of the soft parts of the mouth,[2] or of large areas involving the nose and ears: all of them were carried out as promptly as if the conditions and season had been favourable.

"Just as a general restoration of the morale of our wounded had been achieved, the unfortunate men were greatly alarmed by a sudden movement of the enemy's right wing in an attempt to turn our left, at the very point where the ambulance was stationed. Some, who could walk, at once took to flight and others made vain attempts to escape this unexpected attack. But we were their support, preferring to die at their side rather than to seek an ignominious safety. I hurriedly completed the amputation of a leg on which I had been engaged, and in front of all the remaining wounded vehemently declared my resolve not to abandon my post. I assured them that whatever might be the result of this alarm, which I believed to be false, they need have no fear for their lives. All my

---

[2] It is remarkable that none of these was followed by salivary fistula.

pupils rallied to me and swore not to leave my side. At this difficult juncture M. Pelchet, the military director of the ambulance, displayed all his qualities of character, burning zeal and rare intelligence. With a handful of his orderlies he stopped the flight of the most terrified wounded, and in a time of the greatest scarcity he managed to procure the meat we needed both for our own men and the wounded from the Line regiments. Here, as on many other occasions, we made great use of horse flesh for our soup.

"A timely and impetuous charge against this enemy column, made in the midst of thickly falling snow by the cavalry of the Guard, removed the threat which so terrified our patients. Tranquillity was restored, and we were once more able to continue with our operations. All the severely wounded guardsmen and many of those from other units were treated and operated upon during the first twelve hours, and only then were we able to obtain some rest and to pass the remainder of the night lying on the frozen snow around the ambulance bivouac fire. Never have I experienced so painful a day and never had I been so moved. I had even been unable to keep back my tears at moments when I was trying to sustain the courage of my wounded. I had the sorrow of seeing several unfortunate men, whose wounds demanded amputation through the hip joint, die because the wretched conditions we were in—the great cold and the lack of proper accommodation—made it impossible for me to perform these difficult and essentially dangerous operations. The death of these brave fellows strengthened the opinion I had formed earlier on the necessity of operating on such cases.

"The next day, as soon as it was light, we returned to our work amongst the wounded guardsmen and to seeing to the needs of many other men and the Russian prisoners. I concerned myself particularly with the evacuation of our own men, and began by having the most serious cases taken to a large house in Eylau, especially those with amputations of the leg and thigh, or with dangerous wounds of the head and chest, including a number I had trephined.

"The impossibility of bringing all our wounded as well as those of the enemy into this small town, which also had to accommodate the entire headquarters of the army and of the Guard, made evacuation urgently necessary. Further, the risk of an epidemic from the crowding together of patients and from the abundant suppuration of their wounds which would be present after the third day, and finally our extreme state of want in a country covered with snow, abandoned by its inhabitants and lacking every kind of resource, made the evacuation imperative. H.M. the Emperor had foreseen this, and had decided in his wisdom that it was better to expose the wounded to the vicissitudes of a long, difficult and painful evacuation than to see them die from causes we could not remedy. Moreover we did not know what the enemy's movements would be. A general evacuation by stages was ordered, and I succeeded in getting away all the less severely wounded of the Guard within the first twenty-four hours.

"I wrote to M. Paulet, the Assistant Surgeon-in-Chief whom I had left behind in Warsaw with a part of the ambulance, to move at once to Inowraklaw, to a large château designated by Marshal Bessières for the reception of the wounded I was sending, and at the same time I sent him all necessary instructions. Once again the conditions made us appreciate the great advantages of the lightness and design of our ambulance vehicles: they were able to follow the cavalry of the Guard across the muddy roads of Pultuska, for the fifty-five leagues which separate Eylau from Inowraklaw, which lies beyond the Vistula, and to cross the snow, ice, and the floods due to thawing.

"I shall try to make clear the advantages gained by the prompt evacuation of the wounded after a battle when circumstances do not allow us to treat them during the early stages in security and in suitable hygienic conditions somewhere near the field of combat. In this opinion I draw upon my own experience, and in ordering it H.M. no doubt remembered the successful evacuation of our wounded at the siege of St. Jean d'Acre in Egypt. I was equally successful when with the armies of the Rhine and Eastern Pyrenees.

"One cannot pass lightly over the grave inconveniences which arise from the crowding together of many seriously wounded men in a hospital after a battle. The adynamic affections and hospital gangrene, due to the abundant pus from the wounds and the presence of other animal excretions, the anxiety and fears of the patients who by dwelling on their condition and the state to which they have been reduced mutually depress one another so that they become obsessed by their sufferings, are influences which tend to make even simple wounds, and much more the serious ones, take on grave characters which are too often fatal. On the other hand their state is very different when we are able to evacuate them quickly after the battle. The external and internal movement occasioned by the transportation excites and sustains the functions of the organs; the muscles are all in play, the circulation is quickened, the secretions are maintained, the suppuration remains within proper limits and the sloughs separate more quickly on account of the increased oscillation of the underlying vessels. The wounds become clean, their edges grow and come together from the gradual expansion of the vessels, and under this general stimulation they meet and adhere with but little inflammatory swelling. The outside air, which is always purer than the air of closed dwellings, activates the secretions, the cutaneous transpiration in particular is continuously absorbed by the free currents of air and the wounded have nothing to fear from its suppression. Being less preoccupied with the dangers or results of their wounds, and more concerned with their own immediate preservation, their thoughts dwell less on their unfortunate state. Their minds being constantly concerned with passing matters they do not suffer from the chronic affection of their morale, and, finally, however great the vicissitudes of the evacuation, these can never be as harmful as the innumerable secondary diseases to be found in buildings where large numbers of sick and wounded are housed. The extremes of temperature also are less harmful to the wounded in movement in the open than when they are lying in rooms which are usually unsuitable, by reason of the situation of their doors and windows, for the purpose for which they are used. In the first case the changes of temperature occur gradually and hardly perceptibly, especially if care be taken to provide ample covering during the night and to avoid damp. In the second such changes are sudden and it is impossible to obviate them.

"In addition to these hygienic considerations, there were political reasons behind the evacuation. It lies with the Commander-in-Chief alone to weigh these matters and to give such orders as are best for the safety of the wounded and the preservation of the soldiers' morale. It was thus that after the terrible assaults and battles at the siege of St. Jean d'Acre, being faced with the alternatives of abandoning our wounded on the shore, without food, without shelter and without resources and liable to be butchered by the Arabs, or of marching eighty leagues on foot or with our indifferent transport across arid country completely lacking in fresh water, with one or two kegs of biscuits and a small leather water bottle which barely lasted a day, we did not hesitate to accept the latter. And although many of these soldiers were seriously wounded or lacking a limb, they reached Egypt either cured or in process of being cured. We did not lose the fifteenth part of them, although the heat of the desert was very great and they were exposed on their march to the *khamsyn*, a burning wind I have described in my writings on the campaigns in Egypt and Syria.

"In Poland, in spite of the great cold and the difficult roads, in spite of the insufficiency and imperfection of our transport, and of being forced to augment our sprung vehicles by sledges and miserable carts whose progress became more and more difficult with the recurring frosts and thaws—in a word, in spite of our lack of victuals and of exposure to every kind of fatigue inseparable from a long march, my wounded reached Inowraklaw for the most part in good condition, and once there their progress was rapid and complete. We hardly lost an eleventh part of them, although there were many with serious wounds or with wounds which became serious from superadded complications,[3] including certain wounds of the chest and head, and cases of amputations of the thigh who had contracted typhus which had already broken out in the hospital at Eylau. It is highly probable that if these patients had stayed behind in the town they would have died from this disease, which no doubt would have become epidemic as it did at Brün. I well remember placing a number of wounded men onto the vehicles myself; they could barely move in their beds and I feared to see them expire within twenty-four hours: nevertheless they reached their destination free from fever and with their wounds clean and in good condition. So fortunate an outcome justified measures which some described as an act of barbarism, giving vent, as was only natural, to the pity which the wounded aroused from their condition and their obvious repugnance to being sent away. These circumstances confirmed the truth of the aphorism of the prince of physicians: *Ad morbos extremos extrema remedia*, etc. It is true, indeed, that

[3] The only complication which did not affect the wounded in the Guard was tetanus, and I learnt that amongst the Line regiments also there were very few cases of this.

the transport of the wounded was carried out with the greatest care, each convoy being accompanied by a sufficient number of health officers, non-commissioned officers, and medical orderlies to attend to them during the march. Their billets and soup were prepared in advance at each halting place by the non-commissioned officers who went ahead of the convoys. All these men owe a great deal to the zeal of the Chief Commissary, M. Dufour, who energetically assisted us in all matters of administration. I must also praise the devotion of my colleagues, the surgeons of the ambulance and of the Guard's regiments, to these honourable victims throughout the whole of this difficult evacuation.

"The 6th, 7th, 8th, 9th and 10th of February were extremely trying days for the whole army, and especially for the Guard which was continuously in bivouac, with the result that almost all the men and very many of the officers suffered to some extent from the consequences. Many who felt the cold most and had been foolish enough to expose their feet to the bivouac fires, and others who were taken unaware during their sleep on the night of the 9th and the morning of the 10th, when the temperature changed and the mercury rose above zero and a thaw set in, suffered from gangrene due to frost-bite. Our own wounded were saved from this by having no means of warming themselves. A memoir on this form of gangrene comes later (p. 91).

"Those who escaped this misfortune were stricken with diarrhoea or dysentery, and catarrhal and rheumatic troubles due to sudden changes of temperature, poor food and the Eylau water, which like all the water in Poland is not suitable for drinking. These affections of the mucous membranes lasted until our return to the Vistula, and as long as the winds continued in the west or south-west. In many patients they were complicated by ulceration of the gums and aphthous patches in the mouth.

"Doses of ipecacuanha,[4] initially as an emetic but later as an infusion, the use of opium, bitters, wine, together with vinegar and brandy which we were able to get from the towns on both banks of the Vistula, lotions of weak mineral acids to the ulcerated area and the return of the north-easterly winds caused these troubles to disappear and restored the troops to health.

"After this battle His Majesty conferred on me and on my honourable colleague, M. Percy, the cross of a Commandant of the Legion of Honour. He also bestowed that of Chevalier on a number of surgeons who had merited it by their energy and devotion to the wounded. Amongst these were Dr. Ribes and his colleague M. Jouan, Surgeon to the Imperial Household, who had worked in our ambulance during a number of battles and also helped us to attend the wounded on the field.

"Imperial Headquarters and the Guard remained at Eylau whilst the army pursued the enemy through the vast forests which stretch as far as the Plegel, behind which the Russians had rallied and taken up new positions. The advent of a thaw which made the use of the roads impracticable, and the exhausted condition of our troops doubtless decided the Emperor to

---

[4] Ipecacuanha was used in the treatment of "trench mouth" in the 1914–18 war.

bring us back to the Vistula into winter quarters. In consequence we left Eylau on the 17th February. For the first eight days following the battle the army surgeons under the command of M. Percy were occupied with dressing the wounds of both French and Russians, whom it had not been possible to attend to during the first twenty-four hours, and progressively evacuating them to the hospitals set up in the towns on the left bank of the Vistula. We also had to see to the burial of the dead who covered the battlefield; the majority being Russians.

"We passed through Lamberg and Liebstat and reached Osterode on the 28th of the month. The Imperial Guard took up its quarters there and in the adjoining villages. The army corps took up positions behind the Passargue, on the line Liebstat, Morninghen, Elbinghen.

"For the first few days we continued to suffer from a great scarcity of food and forage, but thereafter we found abundant supplies in the towns along the Vistula, and in particular an excellent wine of which we were in great need.

"It would be difficult to put into a few words the hardships, privations and exhaustion which we endured in the course of this short but very arduous campaign."

*   *   *   *   *

The Polish Plica

During his stay in Poland in the early part of 1807 Larrey carried out some important researches upon a reputed disease known as the Polish Plica; defined in Fox's Medical Dictionary (1808) as: *An enlargement of the hair of the head so as to be painful and to bleed, common in Poland and Lithuania.*

This was widely accepted as a peculiar regional malady and included in most of the dermatological books of the period. The Polish physicians maintained that the condition of the hair and scalp was the final consummation of a general chronic disease which had as its symptoms lassitude, debility, pains in the bones and joints, and various local manifestations such as buboes, exostoses, ulcers and pustules on various parts of the body; all culminating in an affection of the hairs which became matted together and contorted into a painful mass like a cap. In the belief that this *plica* marked the crisis of the disease, and was the receptacle for the evil humours causing it, the hair was kept confined within a woollen bonnet and the mass carefully preserved for a certain length of time. Plicas which formed in the winter were not cut off until Holy Saturday or Easter Day and their ultimate removal was believed to take away the evil of the disease. By the same argument the premature removal, or the prevention of the formation of the plica, was thought to "drive the disease in" and to be dangerous.

Larrey quickly concluded that the plica was a factitious condition, produced by dirt and prejudice in sufferers from syphilis, which was very prevalent in Poland, and he pointed out that the roots of the hairs were healthy which would not be so were they really the seat of disease. He was also able to satisfy himself that the plica might be removed without ill effect. ". . . it is nothing more than an inconvenient incubus; tiresome and highly insanitary which may in the long run affect the proper action of the body's functions. . . . We should educate the populace as to the true nature of diseases. These have been too long hidden from them from motives of personal interest and by prejudices, the offspring of fear and charlatanism. But the laws which have just been made in their interest get rid of these by destroying the serfdom in which two-thirds of the Poles exist. We shall put a stop to the cupidity of quacks, and establish amongst these people that spirit of emulation which will ensure their survival and the perfection of their physical and moral education."

*   *   *   *   *

Chapter II

Courland to Tilsit. Meeting of Napoleon and Alexander.
Larrey made Chevalier de la Couronne de Fer.

"On its return from Eylau the army spent the whole of the month of March in cantonments between the Vistula and the Passargue. A certain number of army corps were sent to take possession of the principal towns at the mouths of the rivers or on the Baltic coast of Pomerania; some, like Danzig and Stralsund, demanded large-scale military operations and a more or less prolonged siege.

"For the first eight or ten days of March we had rain or fog. Such misty humid weather caused a persistence of catarrhal and putrid affections, but the continuous and uninterrupted evacuation of the sick and wounded, from the hospitals to as far as Thorn and other towns on the left bank of the Vistula, prevented an epidemic and also maintained the patients' strength, so that their disease pursued a normal course without setbacks or complications. The mortality was not great; the severe cold and snow which reappeared towards the middle of March contributed not a little, as we had previously found, to keeping down sickness and promoting the recovery of the wounded and the re-establishment of the men's health.

"The exhaustion of all the resources of the Osterode cantonments, as well as those of the advanced positions occupied by the Guard and the army generally, together with the proximity of rivers and marshes so common in Poland which the threatened thaw would uncover, decided His Majesty to move a number of army corps and the Guard nearer to the Vistula. In consequence the Emperor shifted his headquarters to Finkeinsten, and the Guard went into cantonments in the neighbouring towns and villages, such as Rosemberg, Reysembourg, etc. I myself took up quarters with my ambulance in the latter village, where we found all the supplies we required. The cold weather lasted all through April, but soon afterwards the sun rose higher above the horizon, and as soon as the snow which covered the fields and the ice on the ponds had melted it became prudent to move the troops from these unhealthy localities, and H.M. had camps formed for the Guard and the army corps in more salubrious places. The change which this involved and the business of constructing barracks gave the soldiers some very healthy exercise, and from this moment we had very few sick. The Imperial Guard's camp, built on a high plateau near Finkeinsten, was noteworthy for its splendid barracks, their uniform mode of construction and their excellent interior arrangement: every soldier seemed all of a sudden to have become an architect, carpenter or bricklayer!

"We passed the whole of the months of April and May, which were very fine, in these cantonments. During this time Danzig and a number of other fortified places were either taken or surrendered.

"Negotiations were at the point of reaching definite proposals for a general peace, when the Russians unexpectedly attacked our outposts. At the news of this onslaught, which was followed by a number of partial attacks, the Emperor marched out with the Guard. We passed through Custadt and advanced to Heilsberg, where the enemy had taken up a position on a hill which encircles the western side of the town and was protected by rivulets and deep ditches and here we made contact with their army on the evening of June 10th. A brisk attack by several of the leading regiments and by the fusiliers of the Guard took place towards the end of the day, but bad weather and the difficulty of the terrain robbed us of complete success. We had some two hundred wounded amongst the fusiliers, whom we brought to the huts of a nearby camp which the Russians had abandoned the day before. In this engagement General Roussel, Chief-of-Staff of the Guard, was killed by the explosion of a shell. The projectile fractured the right temporal bone and caused such damage to his brain that all the functions of sensitive life were destroyed. He became unconscious, all his limbs were paralysed and his sphincters relaxed, although internal life remained for another twenty-four hours. This unhappy event, which deprived us of a general and which was regretted by the whole Guard, well illustrates the relative independence of these two forms of life. One of my pupils, M. Juville, who was attached to the fusiliers' corps, was struck on the temple by a fragment of the same shell whilst going to the assistance of another general officer. I went out to look for them and brought them both back to my ambulance. We spent the whole of the night and of the next day in caring for our wounded, about forty of whom required amputations, either at the shoulder or through the arm or thigh. One of these was M. de Segur,[1] an aide-de-camp of the Grand Duke of Berg (Murat), whose wound was most unusual. A cannon ball took off his forearm below the elbow-joint and at the same time struck the side of his chest. As it was travelling at its full velocity the effect of the projectile was entirely the opposite to that at the end of its parabola; the skin was excoriated over a wide area and the *lattisimus dorsi* muscle bruised, but the ribs were left intact and the organs within the chest did not suffer even a moment's derangement. The officer did not lose consciousness and was brought to the ambulance without having dismounted from his horse. It would have been quite different had the ball struck him towards the end of its course; then the skin would have remained intact whilst the ribs would inevitably have been fractured and the lungs lacerated, resulting in his prompt demise.[2] In the present case the wound was entirely recovered from before the twenty-fifth day. The colonel of the fusiliers, M. Vrigni, also received a very curious wound as

[1] Louis-Philippe de Ségur (1753–1830). Ambassador to Russia and Grand Master of Ceremonies under the Emperor. His son Philippe-Paul was the author of *l'Historie de Napoleon et de la Grande Armée*: a book bitterly resented by the Emperor at St. Helena.
[2] See my views upon the course of a projectile (*Memoir on Amputations*) (p. 119).

a result of being struck in the chest by a cannister shot. This iron ball penetrated the right pectoral muscle obliquely for a matter of about three inches and struck and fractured a part of the sternum, but the fracture was not very extensive and the elastic resistance of the sternum repelled the projectile so that it rebounded and came out by the same hole as in it went, some pieces of the officer's clothes being left in the wound. This wound was serious and took a long time to heal, as the fractured part of the sternum formed sequestra which required to be exfoliated.

"The wound of Colonel Jeannin of the 12th Light Infantry (son-in-law of the famous painter David and today a Brigadier-General) was also unusual. A grape shot broke his lower jaw and so disorganized the soft parts of his left cheek that his features were unrecognizable. I only knew who it was from the men who brought him to the ambulance, although I was well acquainted with the colonel as I had treated him in Egypt for equally serious wounds. In spite of the disruption of the parts and the appearance of his wound I had hopes of curing him without leaving too great a deformity.

"After excising some shreds of badly torn tissue and extracting the detached fragments of the jaw bone, I put in about a dozen sutures and brought the parts together by an appropriate bandage and evacuated the colonel to Thorn with the other wounded. As I advised, he and his companions did not have their dressings changed for five days, by which time a large part of his wound had united and he speedily became perfectly cured, being ultimately very little disfigured. Had he remained for only a few hours without attention he would have been in danger of losing his life, or at the best he would have been left with a fistulous wound and frightful deformity.

"A soldier of the line was at the point of death from an enormous wound at the apex of the shoulder and loss of all signs of life in the shattered arm. Against the advice of my colleagues, who feared to see him die in my hands, I had the courage to undertake an amputation at the scapulo-humeral joint. The operation was performed in less than a minute without loss of blood and I evacuated the patient with the others: to my astonishment I found him well two months later when I was at the hospital of Marienwerder. Success of this sort is an example which should encourage surgeons, and it has helped me to save the lives of a number of other wounded men who have been in danger as great as this man's. The spasm of the heart and other organs ceases when the causes of irritation are removed.

"For a second time I was in the position of having to make a counter-opening in the cranium. A ball penetrated the left parietal eminence of one of our men and passed obliquely along the inner surface of the parietal bone, following its parabolic course and came to rest about a centimetre from the occipital suture. The introduction of a small gum-elastic sound, the information given by the patient, and the presence of a slight ecchymosis at the point mentioned decided me to expose this bone by a cruciform incision. A small split was then seen but the symptoms of cerebral compression continued to increase. These facts induced me to apply a trephine to the spot so as to include the crack. Beneath the circle of bone removed I at once discovered a flattened part of a ball whilst another portion was embedded in the bone. The dura mater was detached from the vault of the skull over the whole track of the missile, which had followed the concavity of the cranium. There was considerable haemorrhage from both of the openings. The patient was evacuated the same day to Marienwerder where he remained for fifteen days without further mishap; but he eventually contracted hospital fever which robbed me of the success of this operation.

"I performed amputation of the leg through the condyles at the level of the tibial tuberosity on three of our guardsmen, though the damage according to most writers would have required an amputation through the thigh. The three wounds were rather slow in healing, but this was a small matter compared with the great advantage to the patient and the much greater inconvenience which results from amputation at the higher level.

"After the battle of Heilsberg the enemy seeing himself threatened, with envelopment, abandoned his position during the night of the 9th and hurriedly retreated into Friedland. At daybreak the next day we occupied Heilsberg, where we found food and supplies for the men, and then pressed on through the forests to Eylau which we now saw for a second time. The battlefield was no longer recognizable, since the ice with which it was formerly covered, and the hillocks of snow against which the dead and dying shewed up in relief,[3] were now transformed into a superb lake, bordered on one side by the town and on the other encircled by beautiful gardens and fields covered with crops. We quickened our pace and our leading corps rapidly advanced into the Friedland plain to prevent the enemy's crossing the river by the bridge near the town of that name and to bring him to a full-scale battle. As matters turned out the engagement occurred as soon as the two armies met, the number of combatants increasing continuously as the different columns emerged from the forests they had been marching through. The action soon became general and resulted in the almost total defeat of the Russian army without the Guard being fully engaged. More than six thousand of their dead were left on the field and a large number of prisoners were taken. Their wounded, the greater part of their artillery, and many flags, fell into our hands: this was one of the Emperor's most brilliant days. M. Percy was able to accommodate and deal with the wounded of the army in comfort in a nearby village, consisting almost wholly of barns of great size in which we found an abundance of stores and cattle. Here the men were protected from the ill effects of the weather, and it was possible to prepare their soup and to organize the vehicles for their evacuation.

"I learnt subsequently that the operations performed on the battlefield were generally successful. The progress of some of the wounds, and especially those with fractures of the limbs, was complicated by tetanus induced by the sudden change from the heat of the daytime to the damp cold of the night.

"After this battle, which decided the fate of the Russian army, we continued the pursuit of its remnants as far as the Niemen. The Imperial Guard followed the trail of the enemy cavalry which re-crossed the river at Tilsit where the Grand Duke caught up with the Russian rearguards, but they succeeded in crossing, burnt the bridge and insistently demanded a suspension of hostilities and peace. An armistice was agreed, and the

[3] This has been faithfully reproduced in the picture by Gros.

armies occupied the banks of the river on which the meeting between the two Emperors and the King of Prussia took place.[4]

"A raft, on which a room with windows had been built, was moored in the middle of the river. The monarchs accompanied by their staffs arrived there at the same time. The two armies were arrayed in battle order on the opposite sides of the river, all eyes being fixed on the movements of these august sovereigns. On each side the result of the interview was awaited with unexampled impatience.

"The appearance of the two lines of troops with their varied uniforms; the picture of the river and pontoon on which the three monarchs met, attended at a distance by their chief officers and facing the castle and fortress built by the Teutonic knights, made the most animated and interesting spectacle ever to be seen, and one which the painter of the Panorama of Tilsit, lately on view in Paris, has faithfully and accurately portrayed.

"The preliminaries of peace were decreed at this first conference and the armies immediately informed. Communications at once became established between the French and the Russians. The sovereigns visited each other in turn and Alexander, Frederick-William and the Queen of Prussia took up their residence in the palace of Tilsit.

"I took advantage of this freedom of intercourse to visit the Russian army. The Cossacks and the Kalmucks particularly interested me. The latter were armed with bows and arrows, and some with spears or javelins; they were very skilled in the use of these arms, and could kill a bird with an arrow from a considerable distance. None of our soldiers was wounded by these weapons. The Cossacks, who might be called the Arabs of the North, are armed like the latter with lances, which are less dangerous but more unhandy. As Tilsit is 55° and some minutes north of the equator the nights are almost absent at the spring equinox which was the time we were there, so that when I visited some French people in the evening I was able to read the addresses written on the outside of their houses as easily as in full daylight."

*   *   *   *   *

"After I had finished the evacuation of our sick, each convoy being accompanied by the requisite number of medical officers, sub-officers and medical orderlies, I left for Berlin with our ambulance quartermaster, M. Pelchet. It was a pleasure to see the fertile and smiling country along the Vistula and the Warta which we had left in such a sorry condition in our first campaign. Our short stay in Berlin at the beginning of August was no less enjoyable. The walks along the great canal, bordered with poplars and plane trees, are fresh and delightful; they are the rendezvous

[4] Secret articles of the Treaty of Tilsit, between France and Russia laid down that the Danish fleet was to be demanded by the former for use against Great Britain. These articles, through means never exactly known, were communicated to Canning and led to Great Britain's immediate request for the temporary surrender of the Danish ships of war and naval stores. This was refused by the Danes and led to the bombardment of Copenhagen by Nelson and the capture of the Danish fleet.

of the fair sex and the youth of Berlin, who gather there at sunrise and after sunset. It is a strange habit, by comparison with Paris, to see the elegant women of Berlin promenading at five o'clock in the morning along the canal, or afloat in the numerous boats: they take a light breakfast at eight o'clock and then go home to rest during the heat of the day. This sensible habit seems to contribute a great deal to keeping the people of the capital, and especially the women, in their remarkable state of freshness and good health.

"From Berlin the Imperial Guard and ambulance moved to Hanover, and remained there during the rest of the fine weather. I left M. Paulet in charge, and on the orders of H.E. Marshal Bessières I returned to Paris by way of Wittemburg, Leipsic and Jena, stopping for a few days at the last two towns which are famous for their universities. At Leipsic I saw with veneration the amphitheatre where the immortal Leibnitz taught. Other famous men adorn its University today, where everything inspires meditation and study. Leipsic is moreover surrounded by lovely scenery with charming walks and fertile fields. Saxony in general is a rich and very beautiful country.

"From Leipsic I went to Jena which I reached a few days later. I at once visited the hospital, which still held some of the soldiers who had been wounded in the battle near this town. I was very honoured and flattered by the distinguished and affectionate welcome given me by the Jena professors. They insisted that I should spend a few days amongst them and I took advantage of this to become a Doctor of Medicine of their University. After I had undergone the customary examinations and sustained my thesis the diploma was accorded me.

"From Jena I passed through part of Hanover and returned to France by way of Westphalia. These countries are very fertile, well cultivated and varied: their people have the pleasant social manners which we encountered generally throughout Germany.

"I reached Paris at the end of October, and at once resumed my duties at the Guard's Hospital. The Emperor had gone to Milan for his coronation as King of Italy. It was during this journey that H.M. conferred on me the honourable title of *Chevalier de la Couronne de Fer*, and I received the decoration of the order at the beginning of January, 1808."

Larrey's stay in Paris was short, for a little over three months after his return he was ordered by Bessières to join a column of the Guard destined to serve with Murat in Spain. He left on February 11th, 1808, in the company of Frizac, one of the best surgeons of his ambulance.

*   *   *   *   *

Chapter 12

Napoleon's first Spanish Campaign. Intrigues in the Spanish Court between Godoy and the Royal Family. Bull fighting. Madrid hospitals.

Napoleon was led into his disastrous Spanish adventure, which marked an early turning point in his hitherto spectacularly successful career, by the decision to deal with England's ally Portugal, which was a perpetual irritant and one of the remaining gaps in his continental system. By the Treaty of Fontainebleau, of October 27th, 1807, France and Spain secretly agreed to invade and partition that country, and Junot was given orders to march on Lisbon. Soon the north of Spain was full of French troops. This foreign army was at first well received, but the troops were of poor quality, largely very young ill-trained and ill-disciplined conscripts who straggled raggedly along the Spanish roads, creating a bad impression with the populace, and in the end only 4,000–5,000 of them succeeded in reaching Lisbon which the Portuguese rulers had abandoned without a struggle.

But in the meantime the intrigues of the Spanish court in which Godoy played a leading part, suggested to Napoleon the thought of turning out the Bourbons, and with this in mind he despatched further troops the following February under the command of Murat: it was this force which Larrey joined. Believing that the French had come to free the king from Godoy's influence the Spaniards made them welcome. However the Spanish sovereigns and Godoy fled from Madrid to Aranjuez, from whence they hoped to escape to Cadiz and ultimately to South America. Their intentions were divined by the populace, and on March 17th the Madrib mob rushed on Aranjuez, burst into the palace and seized the wretched Godoy, who was thrown into a dungeon. Charles IV abdicated and the Infante Ferdinand was acclaimed king, as Ferdinand VII. Murat, who was only a few miles away, hastened to occupy Madrid with his troops. He rescued Godoy, with whom he had secret relations, and promptly proceeded to play a dubious personal rôle in the hope that as the Emperor's brother-in-law he might be able to seize the Spanish throne for himself. There followed the involved and degrading proceedings at Bayonne, where at the end of April Charles IV, his wife and Godoy were joined by Ferdinand, and Napoleon induced both the king and his son to relinquish the crown, which he promptly bestowed on Joseph Bonaparte.

The turn things were taking was not long in being perceived in Madrid, and when it was realized that the Royal Family had been entrapped by Napoleon insurrection broke out on May 2nd. This Murat crushed out of hand, but it marked a turning point in Franco-Spanish relations and the War of Independence began. Thenceforth the running sore that was Spain was not only an ever-present irritant to Napoleon but continuously drained his resources, until the wheel came full circle and in the spring of 1814, as his Empire was falling in ruins, Wellington crossed the frontier from Spain into France.

* * * * *

"On reaching Burgos my first care was to visit the hospitals and improve the lot of the patients. We stayed there for several days, whilst the Prince's (Murat's) troops advanced on Madrid, and we heard the news of the revolution of Aranjuez and of the accession of the Prince of Asturias to the throne of Spain. To celebrate the occasion the magistrates gave a bull-fight which was seen by the people with transports of joy. I saw this spectacle, about which I was very curious, for the first time and noted all its details, so that I am able to attempt a short description of it here.

"In each important town in Spain there is an amphitheatre or circular arena devoted to these fights. The spectators occupy the boxes, balconies and platforms which surround it, being separated from the arena by a double barrier. The *tauradors*, whose part it is to fight the bull, bring it into the arena: some of them are on horseback wearing a cuirasse and armed with a very long and extremely sharp lance. As soon as the bull arrives it is excited from all sides by the horsemen and by others on foot, who wave red flags in front of it. The animal becomes infuriated, it immediately charges the object of its anger and attempts to gore whoever exposes himself to the chance of its menacing horns. We saw two horsemen thrown from their mounts, the horses eviscerated and the men escaping only by their skill and agility. One of the unmounted tauradors also was seriously injured and left as dead on the arena. At these horrible sights the Spaniards made the air ring with their applause and acclamations. Finally the tauradors ended the event by a rapier thrust into the bull's heart. If the stroke is exact, which is usually the case, the animal falls and dies almost at once: this is an occasion for renewed shouts of joy from the spectators. When the taurador is particularly skilled he thrusts his blade into the animal's neck, to sever the spinal cord and kill it instantly, but this manoeuvre is very dangerous.

"If the bulls are sluggish and not readily roused they are attacked with darts garnished with favours, which pierce the skin and flesh: they then become furious and try to break down the barriers. Sometimes hounds are set at them which promptly seize them if they escape the animal's murderous horns at the first movement of encounter.

"When the requisite number of bulls has been killed the conqueror obtains a great ovation and the most marked proofs of appreciation and satisfaction, especially from the women. It is greatly to be hoped that the day will come when this sort of entertainment, which lovers of quiet disapprove and humanity condemns, will be forbidden."

* * * * *

"On my arrival at Madrid I received instructions from the Intendant-General, together with a copy of the order which H.E. the Minister had already addressed to me personally, appointing me to direct and inspect the medical service of the army. I commenced my duties by visiting the hospitals of the capital and such other places as were suitable for this purpose. First of all, I set aside a number of wards in the main city hospital for the sick of the Imperial Guard and Line. This hospital, which lies at the north-east part of the town, at the end of the Prado, is very well constructed, being four stories high, symmetrically built, light and well-ventilated, and internally conveniently and commodiously laid out: it can accommodate 3,000 patients. The wards only communicate with each other by externally placed corridors or galleries. There is a lecture theatre with the necessary accessories for teaching all branches of the healing art.

"However, two very important things are lacking: latrines, and cisterns to hold the water for the wards and services. The nurses are obliged to carry the *vases de nuit* down several times a day to a sort of pit in the base of the hospital, which is very inconvenient and insanitary. In consequence this is not done as often as it should be and the wards are polluted from these vessels being left for a long time by the bed of each patient. I proposed to H.I.H. the Prince and Commander-in-Chief, that instructions should be given for making latrines at the end of each corridor. It was equally easy to bring water to the second and third floors, and once these improvements were effected they would make this a very efficient hospital of its kind. . . ."

"To organize the health service of the entire army I formed a Health Committee, including my colleagues the chief pharmacist, Laubert, and the head physician and surgeon, Bardol and Talabère. Together we drew up a series of regulations for the service of the stationary hospitals and the ambulances which received the approval of the Intendant-General and the Prince. This committee met regularly three times a week at a place appointed for the purpose. These matters being settled, we turned our attention to the general regulations for the medical officers, their classification and the organization of the ambulances. We set up a School of Army Medicine and Surgery at General Headquarters in Madrid for the benefit of the considerable number who were able to attend. Each member of the committee professed some part of the Art."

*   *   *   *   *

"The departure of the Royal Family for Bayonne had caused considerable unrest amongst the populace and there were fears of a rising; in fact numerous incidents had occurred in the towns I had passed through. These caused me to bring my inspection to an end and I arrived back at the gates of Madrid at eleven o'clock on the morning of the actual day of the revolt (May 2nd). This happened to be at the most dangerous time, and musket and cannon fire were to be heard on all sides. However I did not hesitate to enter the town, where I had left my nephew (Auguste Larrey) in the house of my host, the Marquis of Belgida, Porta Sarrada; further, I had work to do in the hospitals. I therefore urged my horse through both our own troops and the insurgents and without thinking of the dangers around me I reached my quarters with my pupil, M. Frizac, and M. Fabar, a surgeon of the artillery whom I had met at the entrance to the town.

"Having made sure that my nephew was safe and well protected by the worthy marquis, I remounted my horse and followed by my two companions rode to the hospital, which we knew to be menaced by a mob that had evaded our soldiers' swords. We passed through a number of groups of insurgents, whom I should not have recognized as such had it not been for the shots which greeted us, and eventually reached the hospital in time to have the doors closed and to arm the surgeons and such of the convalescent patients as were fit to fight. We arrested several Spanish orderlies, who in collusion with the rebels outside had already attacked some of the sick and two or three of our medical officers. Dr. Houneau, one of the best of our French doctors, was the worst used.

"This bold front, and a few shots from the windows and from above the door, drove off the rebels who had established themselves under the walls of the building. In the meantime our troops, pushing their way through the whole town, succeeded in putting an end to the fighting and calm was re-established.

"Before long the wounded of both nations, for whom I had hurriedly made the necessary preparations, began to arrive. Their number grew rapidly, and by night we had taken in about three hundred, seventy of them from the Imperial Guard. Amongst the latter were several sabre wounds of the head with fracture of the skull. In one man the whole of the right parietal eminence had been obliquely shorn away, together with its coverings, the dura mater, and a part of the surface of the cerebral cortex. The piece of bone was removed, the membranous coverings put back in place, and healing resulted without mishap. We also successfully treated penetrating wounds of the chest and abdomen, the latter with the extrusion of undamaged loops of the intestines, and amputated a number of limbs, two of them through the shoulder joint. The first of these was quite successful, but the second patient died of Madrid colic, which he contracted one very cold night.

"A just, though severe, proclamation by the Prince-Generalissimo restored order and brought the people of Madrid to a state of submission."

*　　　*　　　*　　　*　　　*

"The extremely hot weather and rainstorms which now occurred affected our men's wounds adversely, and gangrene suddenly broke out amongst those of the Line regiments who occupied the wards on the ground floor at the south-east side of the hospital. Almost all with wounds of the larger joints or fractures of the thigh died of this complication. Fortunately I was able to prevent similar grave results in the men of the Guard, whom I had lodged on the third floor, although they were equally involved.[1] Mineral acids, with bitter diaphoretic drinks, aetherated quinine, together with external antiseptic applications rid them of the gangrene in most cases, but it was necessary to perform amputation on two in whom these measures failed to arrest it.

"The special study I made of the character and progress of this disease, and the surprising success I had in a number of similar cases of amputation, induced me to write the following Memoir on the subject.

* * * * *

[1] Here and elsewhere it is very obvious that Larrey paid special attention to the needs of the Guard. Line regiments were his secondary consideration and had to wait their turn until those of the Guard had been provided for.

Chapter 13

Gangrene. Case of Antoine Barre. The Madrid colic.

In Dante's first canto of his *Inferno* he wrote:
> "Nel mezzo del camin di nostra vita
> mi ritrovai per una selva oscura,
> che la diritta via era smarrita."

Which surely was the maze in which Larrey found himself in writing of gangrene. Today we know of simple ischaemic gangrene, gas gangrene, gangrene from arterial embolism and a host of others. But when we come down to clinical bedrock we must admit that there are really two varieties: the gangrene in which the part becomes cold and turns black, after which a line of demarcation forms and the dead part is sloughed off—and the rest: and surely this is as good a rough and ready clinical description as any; handy for practical purposes, since in the former the outcome is usually satisfactory—in the rest doubtful.

There must have been gas gangrene in the French and Allied armies, since they had tetanus, but with us it only became a recognizable entity when the 1914–18 war was well under way. Larrey knew of "Hospital Gangrene", which we no longer see, but what lights were there for the differentiation of all the other confused, and perhaps overlapping, types?

In this *"salva oscura"* he wrote:

"When no distinction is made between the different varieties, causes, and modes of development of a given malady, there will be confusion about the correct method of treatment. Thus a remedy which is useful in one form may be useless and even harmful in another. The efficacy of the treatment is then called in doubt, and the failure or ill effects of its misuse influence the judgement of the physician, so that either he contents himself with palliative measures or else leaves the case to nature, which is generally insufficient. The disease pursues its course, death supervenes, and no advance is made in our Art. Hence the slowness of the progress of medicine and of so many other sciences towards perfection.

"In general, the medical men who have written on gangrene or sphacelus of the extremities, advise that amputation should never be done before the dead area is demarcated by a zone of reddening, which indicates a true line of delimitation between the healthy and the dead parts. This state of affairs only occurs in cases of spontaneous gangrene due to an internal cause; or in the rare instances in which it does occur in gangrene from wounds which pursues an altogether different course, it would be very imprudent to wait for it, since such traumatic gangrene almost always continues to progress: the infection becomes general and the patient dies. Before going into details about this form of the disease I shall indicate briefly the causes, varieties and general features of gangrene.

"When a portion of the living body is deprived of its circulation, sensation and the other properties which are characteristic of life, it is dead or gangrenous. Gangrene then, as all writers agree, is the partial or general mortification of a part of the body. Hence anything which at one and the same time will extinguish the vital functions of a limb causes gangrene. The condition is characterized by coldness, a dead weight of the part, loss of sensation and movement, and the total disappearance of arterial pulsation: soon spontaneous putrefaction sets in, which is obvious by the foetid nauseating smell, the black colour of the part and the decomposition of its tissues. We shall endeavour to explain this phenomenon which has been much neglected by writers on the subject.

"Gangrene assumes different appearances and pursues a different course according to the causes which produce it. When these are external mechanical ones which attack the vitality of organs directly, it is always preceded by inflammatory engorgement, erethism, and capillary dilatation over a considerable area. The parts swell from the reaction of tissues in which life is as yet only partially extinct; the epidermis is detached and forms bullae filled with the serous fluid which should supply the material for transpiration; the *cutis* softens, takes on a blackish colour and putrefies; the subcutaneous tissues and membranes decompose, and the result is a superabundance of juices from the vessels and cells of the adipose tissue, on account of which this type of the disease is called *moist gangrene*. Such are the principal phenomena of gangrene due to injury, which I have called *traumatic gangrene*. We shall shortly give an account of its development and progress, but before doing so I must say something about *spontaneous gangrene*, or that produced by some internal cause or the effects of cold. This usually shews itself in parts which are most distant from the centre of life or in which the vitality is enfeebled, such as the feet, the nose, the ears and the fingers, whereas traumatic gangrene can shew itself wherever the deleterious agent acts. In the one there is a harmful influence which attacks parts furthest removed from the sources of bodily vitality. In the other the injured parts have been partially disorganized. In either case the tissues die; but since in dry gangrene the vessels have not suffered any early alteration they are less engorged than they are in traumatic gangrene, and this is especially so in those individuals who have been exposed to the effects of severe cold, or have been weakened by disease. Here the affected part blackens and instead of swelling as it does in traumatic gangrene, it shrinks, dries, and may become hardened: thus the condition of dry gangrene differs only from the other in that there is no outpouring of fluid. It is altogether different in *traumatic gangrene*, which spreads rapidly through the continuity of the tissue, passing from one part of a limb to another, reaching the trunk, involving vital organs, and bringing about the patient's demise.[1]

"It will be seen from this survey that there is an obvious difference between traumatic and spontaneous gangrene, or, putting it differently, between moist gangrene from an external cause and dry gangrene, which arises as a rule from some internal one.

"The prognosis in both of these diseases is more or less serious; for in either case the patient will lose the affected member, either spontaneously or as a result of operation, and in each life is endangered. What is the correct method of dealing with these two types of gangrene? I refer the reader to my Campaign

---

[1] On this subject Boucher says: "If the mortification shews signs of spreading to a level beyond that at which amputation can be effectively performed, it is clear that there is no resource other than prompt amputation, although the benefit of even this must be very doubtful." See the *Memoirs of the Academy*, Vol. 11, in-4o.

in Poland for the treatment of dry gangrene, or gangrene due to frostbite. Our present problem is to prevent or arrest the grave consequences of *traumatic gangrene*.

"A cannon ball, the explosion of a shell, a grape shot, or even a bullet can, without producing any very great disorganization in a limb, so violently damage the vessels and nerves that their vitality is extinguished and the part mortally injured. We have seen many such cases.

"It is easy to understand that it would be dangerous to wait for this form of gangrene to become limited, or for the formation of the red line of demarcation we have spoken of, since the putrefaction spreads unopposed, not merely by contagion but also by the absorption or transudation to the rest of the limb from the site first affected. We should not therefore hesitate, no matter what writers and practitioners may say, to proceed to amputation as soon as its necessity is clear. There is no need to fear the reappearance of gangrene in the stump, as we do in the spontaneous disease if this has not become demarcated, since traumatic gangrene, being due to a local cause, spreads only by absorption and the involvement of tissues which become inflamed by continuity, and hence amputation at a suitable site will arrest its progress and avert its fatal consequences.

"Supposing that the lower half of the leg becomes gangrenous as a result of a wound from a cannon ball, which has violently contused the parts and seriously damaged the vessels, nerves and ligaments; as long as the skin is healthy we can amputate at the site of election without fear of gangrene reappearing in the stump, even though the subcutaneous tissue extending to the upper part of the limb is already involved. But if the whole skin of the limb is dead it is necessary to go as high as the thigh, and to act with all speed. These considerations hold good equally for the upper limbs. It is important not to confuse a limb which is stupefied as a result of injury with one which is really gangrenous: in the first, warmth, movement, and sensation are retained, even though the skin may be blackish and the parts engorged.

"Amputation above the gangrenous parts and beyond the area of disorganization promptly removes the source of contagion. By their sharp division the nerves and vessels are disembarrassed of the fluids which are beginning to stagnate in them; their action is restored and far from serving as absorbing siphons for injurious materials they become the powerful expellers of these substances and fluids, and once again receive the elements necessary for life. The tissues as a whole become relieved of their engorgement and resume their proper vital activities. These effects of amputation may be assisted by the internal use of quinine, generous wines, tonics, etc.

"I believe that the facts I am about to record will prove incontestably the truth of the principle I uphold, viz: that when gangrene from a mechanical cause endangers the life of the patient amputation must be performed without waiting for it to become limited. It has been my lot to witness the death of many individuals from too slavish an adherence to the contrary doctrine; and being grievously moved by this loss of life I long ago made up my mind to abandon an axiom which I had always believed false. Following the advice of Celsius, I have preferred to use an uncertain remedy than to abandon the patient to a certain death. (*Satius est enim anceps auxilium experivi quam nullum.*)

"I first attempted this at Toulon, in the year IV (1786), on a soldier who developed a gangrenous ulcer following severe crushing wound of the foot, which soon involved the whole limb in necrosis or sphacelus. As the gangrene continued to progress I decided to amputate the leg. The success of the operation exceeded all my hopes; the stump healed and in less than forty-five days the soldier was well. This experience encouraged me to continue.

"A second case, very similar to the first, occurred in Egypt, at the siege of Alexandria in the year IX (1801), in a dragoon of the 18th regiment who was seized with gangrene of the forearm which spread to the upper arm, following a gunshot wound of the left elbow joint. The gangrene was nearing the shoulder and the man's life was in danger when I took the resolution to remove the limb at the shoulder joint. The disease was obviously advancing and already there was evidence of cerebral involvement, for he had the symptoms of ataxia: nevertheless the operation saved his life and he was perfectly well by the time the siege ended.

"After the capture of Ulm, M. Ivan, Surgeon to H.M. the Emperor, amputated in my presence in our ambulance at Elchingen, the thigh of a soldier of the 76th regiment of the Line whose leg was severely damaged by a cannon ball and had become gangrenous. The disease was not limited and was making visible progress: nevertheless the infection was cut short and the man was well by the time we returned from Austerlitz.

"A fourth soldier, an officer of the same regiment, was wounded by a ball in the malleoli at the capture of this town and brought to our ambulance for treatment. Three days had passed since the injury; the foot was gangrenous, the leg swollen and threatened with the same condition, and he was already feverish. I wasted no time but amputated the leg a little above the site of election. Although the cellular tissue of the stump was yellow and blackened, and already the seat of the gangrenous infection, the operation arrested the progress of the disease, suppuration became established in the stump, some gangrenous sloughs formed and separated, and the wound became clean and was scarred over by the fifty-second day. The patient was already able to be about on a wooden leg when he contracted typhus, which was epidemic at Ulm where he had been awaiting his regiment, and to this to my great regret he succumbed after having escaped the earlier danger.

"After the battles of Austerlitz and Jena many of my colleagues, surgeons of the first class, in view of my advice and the successful cases I had told them of, undertook the amputation of similar gangrenous limbs, even though the gangrene had not become limited, rather than leave them to what appeared an inevitable death. In general their success was as great as mine. I am sorry not to be able to quote the records of the many cures of this kind which were sent to me by one of these surgeons, when I was with the Army of Spain where they became lost. However, the case of young Barre, which I give here in full detail, should suffice to determine the opinion of surgeons on the subject of this memoir."

Observation

"Barre (Antoine), eighteen years old, a young man full of courage, of good build and delicate constitution, a fusilier in the 1st regiment of the Imperial Guard, was struck by a missile from an air-gun[2] at the time of the Madrid rising on May 2nd, 1808. The bullet entered the outer side of the fold of the elbow and passing downwards and inwards, after penetrating the pronator radii, was deflected along the interosseous membrane and continued down between the two bones, beneath the flexor muscles of the hand and along the

[2] An air-gun (windbusche) was invented in 1560 by Guter of Nuremberg. The famous huntsman John Peel had one made by Bates of London in 1778.

Carman. *A History of Firearms*, 1945.

course of the interosseous vessels to the wrist joint where it came to rest. The man told us that at the moment of being hit he felt a violent shock which caused him to drop his weapon, and made him unable to move the wounded limb which was painful and paralysed. He was brought to hospital the same evening where I saw him at once. Having searched in vain for the missile, I cleansed the wound and covered it with perforated linen soaked in saline, wrapping the fore-arm in compresses moistened with the same fluid. A low diet was prescribed, with acidulated antispasmodic drinks. The patient was unable to sleep during the night and was restless and anxious; the pale lividity of his face and his haggard eyes seeming to presage grave developments. On the morning of the 3rd the arm was immobile, slightly swollen and threatened with paralysis. Fearing the development of complications I ordered compresses, steeped in warm undiluted wine with camphor and ammonia, to be applied to the whole limb, a dose of theriac antispasmodic at night, and a drink of infusion of camomile flowers. He had a bad night and on the morning of the 4th the hand and forearm were cold and devoid of sensation: the dull hue of the skin and the swelling of the hand left no doubt that gangrene had set in. We applied camphorated brandy at almost boiling heat to the whole limb, with the exception of the wound which was covered with a pad of an active digestive. I added camphor and quinine to the medicines mentioned, but in spite of these measures gangrene was fully evident at half past four. It had already caused the death of the whole of the hand, the epithelium of which was covered with blebs, and of a considerable part of the forearm, whilst the elbow joint and lower third of the arm were inflamed and very swollen. Scarification of the forearm and hand and the application of antiseptics externally and their administration internally failed to arrest its progress, and by 5 o'clock it was up to the level of the wound. The scarification appeared to me only to accelerate the progress of the putrefaction; a fact I had observed on many previous occasions which makes me believe that it does more harm than good.

"At my visit on the morning of the 6th, the sphacelus had passed beyond the joint and streaks of gangrene were extending to the middle of the upper arm. The wounded man was prostrated, his pulse small and intermittent; already he was mentally clouded, his eyes were dull and haggard and his face shewed the pale imprint of death. This imminent peril decided me to proceed at once to the amputation, which I should have performed the previous evening had not my *confrères* been so fearful of the consequences, seeing that the gangrene was not limited. In spite of this I resolved to go to the extreme measure, rather than abandon the sufferer to the death which was inevitable. But before doing so I wished to call in all the most able physicians and surgeons to enlighten me by their knowledge. It was three o'clock in the afternoon before the consultants could be brought together, and in this short interval the gangrene had ascended some millimetres further and was involving almost the whole of the arm. I put my proposal to operate as a last resort, making use of the arguments given in my memoir, my experience, and the maxim of the Roman surgeon. My proposition was rejected by all, with one exception. In spite of this formally expressed and almost unanimous opposition, I knew that I ought to sacrifice my personal interest for the life of a citizen if I saw the faintest chance of saving him, even though it were by an unorthodox procedure. There was not an instant to lose; the ataxic symptoms became more alarming as the mortification advanced with frightful speed, so that within a couple of hours this young man would be dead.

"In a few moments the instruments required for the removal of the arm—

now barely possible at all—were got ready and the patient taken into a private room out of sight of his companions. At the moment of the operation his strength had almost vanished, but nevertheless I proceeded to do it. One of my assistants affirms that it was performed in seventeen seconds, excluding the time taken to apply the ligature. I employed the method of operating described in my article on the Egyptian campaign (p. 121). In ligating the arteries I took care to exclude the nerves—a recommendation more important than has been thought. The fleshy portions of the two flaps were already brownish and flaccid, and the cellular tissue of the axilla diseased. I brought the flaps together but not into actual contact, and covered the wound with fine perforated linen steeped in hot camphorated wine. A number of pads of lint, well powdered with camphor, were applied and held in place by long compresses also soaked in camphorated wine and carried over the shoulder; the whole being covered by a long wide bandage.

"(The amputated limb, which was entirely black, was opened in my lecture room in the presence of a large number of medical officers who had seen the operation. The skin, subcutaneous tissues, membranes and ligaments were black and putrefied, and the muscles softened and full of black carbonized blood. The track of the ball was filled by black foetid secretion. The missile itself lay flattened out beneath the annular ligament of the flexors of the digits; the related articular ligaments were disorganized, and the joint opened.)

"The patient was carried in his bed to the ward reserved for the Imperial Guard. He had not suffered much during the operation, as little sensation remained in the shoulder, and he did not faint since I had not allowed him to lose a drop of blood: on the contrary the amputation seemed to have re-animated him, for his mental aberration was less and his pulse stronger than it had been.

"I sent him a portion of an excellent chicken soup which I had had made at my house for some of my more seriously wounded, and this he swallowed with some good Bordeaux wine. He was less restless, his bodily heat became restored, his pulse improved and he enjoyed two hours of sleep, and for the rest of the night was tranquil.

"On visiting him at five o'clock the next morning I found that there was already an obvious change in his general condition. The dressing, which I did not interfere with, had soaked up a yellowish serum. I prescribed a stomachic potion, composed of suitable proportions of Bordeaux wine, theriac, loxa quinine,[3] and Hoffman's mineral liquor, to be taken in doses of a spoonful every quarter of an hour.

"I covered the stump with a piece of flannel soaked in hot camphorated wine. The patient partook of a good soup flavoured with cinnamon and cloves at frequent intervals, and a stoup of Bordeaux wine after each such meal. I also ordered his whole body to be bathed with very hot aetherated vinegar and wrapped immediately afterwards in warm flannel. In the evening I ordered a clyster made with a strong decoction of camphorated quinine. I again pres-

---

[3] *Loxa quinine.* Towards the end of 1640 the Countess of Cinchona, wife of the Viceroy of Peru, was cured of an intermittent fever by the Governor of Loxa who gave her a powder known to the Indians. This came to be called the *Poudre de la Comtesse* and later the *Poudre des Jésuites.* After its introduction into Europe there was considerable confusion between the different barks: the "loxa" was largely withheld from export on account of its superior qualities.

Dictionaire des Drogues. Chevallier, Richard and Guillemin. 1829.

cribed the nocturnal potion already mentioned and had the patient moved into a bed which had been fumigated with oxygenated hydrochloric acid.[4]

"On the 7th there was marked improvement. The pulse was stronger, the bodily heat better and the face less dusky. He had had several blackish bilious stools which were extremely offensive and this had relieved him considerably: the urine was small in amount but passed without difficulty. The same treatment was continued.

"During the night of the 8th he had some fever, followed at about four o'clock in the morning by a slight haemorrhage, on account of which I was called. I hurried to him and removed the dressings, and quickly found the bleeding vessel which was a branch of the circumflex artery from which the ligature had been pulled off by a movement of the patient in his sleep in which he had dreamt that he was being chased by Spaniards. I ligatured the arteriole and dressed the wound with a lint pad covered with an *animé* digestive. I moved the patient into a fresh bed and prescribed the same remedies as on the previous day, first having myself seen that he took his soup and a little good wine.

"This relapse had brought a return of his weakness and anxiety, but his general condition slowly improved, and in two or three days this was so obvious as to give us great hopes. I dressed his wound daily myself with the materials I have mentioned. Suppuration was well established from the seventh day onward and the young man's strength increased progressively. The consultants could hardly credit this resurrection, and the extraordinary change in the patient's condition aroused the interest of all the medical officers of the army.

"A new misfortune appeared on the ninth day, in the form of a fresh haemorrhage from a more deeply placed vessel than the last, but it ceased on the dressings being removed. As I was unable to find the source I dressed the wound and continued with the usual remedies, modifying them as seemed necessary. He had lost some strength, but speedily picked up and continued to improve until the 13th. The wound was clean, the flesh a rosy-red colour, except for one part below and internally, which was swollen and livid-looking. At this stage, and at the same time as before (at four o'clock in the morning), he had another haemorrhage, which like the former immediately ceased on the dressings being removed; the mere contact with the cold air being sufficient. These repeated incidents at the critical days[5] perturbed me and I made a careful search for an open vessel, but without success. The original arterial ligatures had come away and only that on the axillary artery remained *in situ*, so that I felt confident that none of the vessels I had originally tied was responsible. Since the flow of blood had ceased I waited on events. This time the wound was dressed with colophane and quinine powder, and the stomachic potion repeated. I prescribed a grain and a half of opium in sweetened wine at night. All went well, and Barre was no worse than on the evening before; he took some good broth, several light soups and some Bordeaux wine. A fourth haemorrhage occurred on the twenty-first day, at the same hour as the preceding ones, and once again after a bout of fever: this haemorrhage was more severe and on my arrival I found poor Barre in a dead faint. I was greatly upset, but without losing time I removed the dressings whilst my pupil Frizac made him inhale ammonia. He regained consciousness and I then discovered the bleeding to be from the proud flesh which I have mentioned earlier. I pushed my finger into this, and with a little resistance it entered a very large cavity from whence

[4] Presumably hypochlorous acid in the form of *eau de Javelle*, which was discovered by Berthollet in 1785.
[5] The doctrine of critical days.

came a considerable quantity of purulent matter mixed with shreds of blackish tissue: this focus extended by a long sinus from the apex of the axilla to below the great pectoral muscle. I incised and opened the walls of this pocket and identified the orifice of the artery which had caused the haemorrhage, and ligated it by means of a curved needle. I explored and cleaned the whole area of the abscess and on applying moderate pressure several putrid sloughs escaped through the sinus. I filled the cavity with plugs of soft lint, powdered with camphor and quinine, and applied a suitable dressing and prescribed a cordial. The patient appeared almost dead during the operation and I expected nothing from my efforts; in fact his vitality seemed extinct and we were almost at the point of drawing the sheet over his face. However, and against the feelings of my assistants, I insisted once more on applying both internal and external stimulants. Warm aethereal frictions appeared to me to produce some favourable effect and at length, after persisting in these measures for ten to twelve minutes, he rallied; as the half-extinguished candle is sometimes relumed by a draught. This encouraged us to redouble our efforts, and before the day was ended I once again began to hope that I might save this young warrior. He continued to be very weak, although much better. By slow degrees his strength returned; the suppuration and other secretions continued their normal course and in a few days time I was able to give him a light diet. Happily this was the last of the complications to disturb either our confidence or nature's slow travail.

"The abscess cavity into which the vessel had opened became clean, and its edges fell in and adhered. A scar soon began to form and rapidly advanced from the circumference to the centre. The various symptoms of adynamia which had appeared after each haemorrhage had been successfully combated by the use of mild emetics followed by loxa quinine. The patient's strength steadily increased and he was well on the way to complete recovery when he contracted Madrid colic; the result of having been so foolish as to expose himself to the cold air of a freezing night after abusing his stomach by an excess of cherries and salad. Fortunately his wound was almost healed. I was much grieved by this fresh and perilous complication but I succeeded in curing him, although he experienced two or three extremely violent attacks of colic, which caused him to roll on the ground screaming the while. His convalescence was slow and difficult, but in spite of it all I had the satisfaction of evacuating him to France on the July 20th, ninety days after his wound and eighty-four after the operation. I learnt subsequently that he arrived well.[6]

"This authentic case, with others which we have reported, seems to me to leave no doubt as to the necessity for amputating the limb in cases of traumatic gangrene, even though this be not demarcated, and to assist in solving the general question of the suitability of this method of treatment."

The Madrid colic

"On our arrival in Spain we were warned of the existence of a number of peculiar diseases which most of the doctors and the inhabitants of the country maintained had nothing to do with the climate. Amongst these was the Madrid colic, which aroused our special interest."

Larrey paid much attention to this condition which affected many of the French, amongst them Murat who on account of it was invalided to France. He carefully weighed the evidence for or against its being a form of metallic poisoning, due either to copper or lead, and decided against this; although years

[6] He is today with his family at Castelnaudary, enjoying his retirement.

later it was shewn to have been a form of lead poisoning, due to the cumulative effect of the conveyance of soft water charged with carbon dioxide through lead pipes, the presence of lead in wines, and to the keeping of articles preserved in vinegar in crudely glazed vessels. All these possibilities Larrey rejected, being led into error in part by his lack of accurate knowledge of the chemical changes in lead pipes, and in part by the negative results of analyses made for him by the principal pharmacist to the army. He was also rather obsessed with the idea that metallic poisons were of necessity irritant, and, indeed, he stresses the absence of this feature in the cases he observed as militating against the possibility of lead. With chronic lead poisoning he was perhaps not familiar, and although he refers to painter's colic, and goes so far as to remark on the similarity of the constipation in the two conditions, yet he decides against their identity, saying that "the patients do not suffer from the tremors, convulsions or paralyses of the arms such as we see in sufferers from lead colic."

The thesis of metallic poisoning seeming to him untenable, Larrey turned for an explanation of the symptoms to the hazy views then prevalent on the effects of climate, derangements of the sympathetic nervous system and "transpiration"; believing that the reflux of transpiration caused by nocturnal cold irritated the nervous system and so set up reversed peristalsis in the alimentary canal, made susceptible by errors of diet—hence the vomiting, colic, constipation and the rest. He did, however, mention that an over-consumption of Spanish wines was one of the factors affecting the intestinal system, and though he exculpated these as vehicles for metallic poisons later opinions have concluded that they were probably an important source of the lead intoxication.

His treatment consisted of diet, enemata, emetics and purging; and as might be expected he found that the best restorative in chronic cases was a change of climate and the use of French spa waters, such as those of his own country of Bagnères. Larrey also describes a number of cases of acute coma, or in his phraseology *Stuperose Ataxia*, which was fatal and to which his trusted pupil Frizac succumbed. This he believed to be due to narcotics used to adulterate wine, which most of the victims appear to have drunk to excess. It seems more probable that they were examples of saturnine encephalopathy.

*   *   *   *   *

Chapter 14

Joseph Bonaparte in Spain. Accident to Lannes.

Joseph Bonaparte, the brother of the Emperor, entered Madrid to ascend the Spanish throne in July 1808, following an overwhelming defeat of the best of the Spanish armies under General Cuesta by Bessières. The occasion was one of considerable organized celebrations in the capital, including a grand bull-fight at which fifteen bulls were slaughtered. But Joseph's triumph was short-lived, as on the very day of Bessières' success Dupont was forced to surrender to General Castãnos at Baylen with 20,000 men. This unprecedented disaster to the French armies caused a hurried withdrawal of Joseph and the forces with him to behind the Ebro.

In Larrey's words:

"We were in the midst of all sorts of optimistic conjectures about the total subjugation of Spain, when we heard the news of the surrender of Dupont's division as well as of the rising of a number of provinces and the sudden march of numerous insurgent troops on Madrid. Preparations for a retreat were hurriedly made, and put into operation on the night of the July 31st. A lack of transport and the uncertainty of finding sufficient resources on the road to Burgos forced us to leave a part of our sick in the hospital at Madrid; but we took care to ensure that all their personal and material needs were provided for. All the wounded of the Imperial Guard were moved to Burgos, and thence to Vittoria by our ambulance wagons. We left behind only five who were unfit for the journey and these I put under the direct care of Dr. Hounaud, one of our French doctors.

"On reaching Burgos we met the victorious army of H.E. Marshal Bessières. Almost all the troops of the Guard joined this corps and I was ordered by His Excellency to continue with them. Our retreat across the Summa Sierra mountains was extremely onerous on account of the great heat and the privations we were forced to endure.

"The King set up his headquarters at Miranda and the army camped on the right bank of the Ebro. The corps of Marshal Bessières which formed the rearguard, took up a position between the Port of Pont-Corvo and Brievesca, where we remained for some time."

*   *   *   *   *

"The armies of the insurgents drew progressively nearer to our line and concentrated against two principal points, Saragossa and Bilbao, intending no doubt to advance on the one hand towards Catalonia and on the other into Biscaye to cut our communications with France. The King moved first against an enemy corps which was coming from Madrid to reinforce the Saragossa garrison and to camp under its walls; but on setting out he sent a courier to H.E. Marshal Bessières ordering me to join the Royal Headquarters at Haro, which I reached with some difficulty. We then skirted along the left bank of the Ebro to Logrogno and sent out a reconnaissance party as far as Calahorra without meeting the enemy, who had retired beneath the walls of Saragossa, so that we returned to our first position at Miranda. As we were again threatened from Bilbao it was necessary to move against it with all speed, to dislodge the enemy who had already gained possession of the port. This was accomplished with hardly any resistance and after leaving a garrison behind us we returned to our former positions, headquarters now being at Vittoria. As I was responsible for the general health service of the army I hurriedly took measures for the organization of the active ambulances, which I found lacking in practically all the necessaries which would be indispensable at our first engagement. I purchased sufficient mules and pack saddles to carry the panniers of dressing materials, surgical instruments and medicaments wherever the division might be going. The small Biscaye carts, which go up the mountains and pass through all the defiles, were appropriated for the transportation of the wounded, as being the best suited to this country.

"The armies remained face to face without either deciding to attack, but nevertheless we pushed on with our preparations for the siege of Saragossa and the opening of a second campaign. On his side the enemy fortified the town, and established himself in a favourable position on the Madrid road, where he built redoubts and entrenchments amongst the mountain defiles.

"It was now that we learnt of the imminent arrival of H.M. the Emperor, and in the first days of October we received him at Vittoria, where he had been preceded by the troops of the Guard which had come from Paris, together with a considerable number of divisions. I relinquished my directorship of the medical service to the Inspector-General, M. Percy, who arrived at the same time, and returned to my original post with the Imperial Guard. I sent a report of my work in the first campaign to King Joseph, who expressed his satisfaction, and I also communicated to H.E. the Minister and Director the measures I had taken to improve the hospital and ambulance services.

H.E. the Marshal, Duke of Montebello (Lannes) whilst riding at full speed behind the Emperor fell from his horse on Mont-Dragon, a very steep slope covered with frozen snow. The fall caused very severe compression of his chest and abdomen, which was all the greater as his horse in struggling to rise fell upon him. When brought to Vittoria he was covered with bruises and his abdomen was tense and swollen; he had acute pains in his bowels, difficulty in breathing, and was incapable of making the least movement. His pulse was small and hard, his face pale and wan, his eyes downcast, his voice weak and his extremities cold. The slightest touch on the abdomen caused great pain and increased the sense of oppression. Everything pointed to the onset of inflammation of the internal organs as a consequence of the crushing and the violent trauma which His Excellency had sustained at his fall.

"I knew from experience that bleeding and tonic resolutive embrocations would be insufficient to prevent the complications which commonly accompany violent contusions and trauma to the internal organs. I remembered the marvellous cure effected by the Esquimaux on the shipwrecked sailors from *Vigilante*, when their shallop had been wrecked and they had been thrown up by the seas on the Newfoundland coast. Following their example, and in view of a number of successes I had myself had in very similar cases, I decided to wrap the Marshal's body in the skin of a very large sheep which I caused to be flayed alive.[1] Whilst the animal was being skinned I prepared some very hot embrocation of strongly camphorated oil of camomile. Immediately afterwards I applied the raw surface of the reeking-hot skin, which was exuding an abundant sanguineous fluid, to the whole of his Excellency's body. I wrapped it closely around him and fastened the edges together. Hot flannels were applied to his limbs and I gave him several cups of weak tea with a little lemon juice and sugar.

"At once the Marshal felt distinctly better; his only complaint being of a painful tingling and the adhesion which the sheep skin seemed to cause wherever it was in contact. However, this gradually diminished and ten minutes later the patient fell asleep and remained in a deep and peaceful sleep for two hours. On his awakening I took off the skin and mopped up the copious sweat which was running off his body with warm linen, and immediately made a hot embrocation of camphorated brandy. A number of compresses soaked in this fluid were applied to the parts which were most bruised and I ordered him to be given cooling mucilaginous drinks, aetherated milk of sweet almonds, and camphorated emollient clysters. At eight o'clock the following morning the abdomen had become lax and much less painful; the pulse was full and the bodily functions re-established. The urine, which had at first been suppressed, was thick and bloody. After having applied a number of wet cups to the bruised areas, I plunged the patient into a hot bath. We repeated this treatment with the aromatic embrocations and the other similar medicaments and by the fifth day the Marshal was again ready to set out and follow the Emperor at full gallop. The whole army now marched on Burgos where the insurgents' outposts were established."

* * * * *

[1] To deprive the animal of sensation it was stunned by a slight blow on the neck with a mallet and immediately flayed by a couple of skilled butchers.

Chapter 15

Second Spanish Campaign. Summa-Sierra. Moore's retreat to Corunna. The English wounded. Cure of a case of amaurosis. Typhus in English prisoners. Larrey's typhus.

After the capitulation of Dupont's army at Baylen and Joseph's panic-stricken evacuation of Madrid and retreat behind the Ebro, Napoleon decided that he must see to affairs in Spain himself. To provide an army of 250,000 men it was necessary, in addition to an increased conscription, to recall many of the troops of the Grande Armée from the Vistula and Elbe and some of those stationed in Italy. He also had to look to the security of his Empire against a fresh attack from the East, where the attitude of Austria was threatening. To these ends he decided to accelerate the withdrawal of his occupying troops from Prussia, to strengthen the position on the Rhine, and to give point to his active diplomatic pressure in Vienna by the famous meeting with the Emperor Alexander at Erfurt, where the pledges and goodwill of Tilsit were renewed, and the Russian alliance cemented by the offer to the Moscovite of a free hand for his long-cherished design of the annexation of Finland, Wallachia and Moldavia.

Once arrived with Berthier at Bayonne he formed the plan of pushing out his centre towards Burgos, and allowing his wings to lag, thereby encouraging the Spaniards to advance on either side, with the intention of turning on them with his superior force and annihilating them in detail between his centre and wings, thus leaving the road to Madrid clear. At this stage in the campaign Larrey was attached to Soult's 2nd Corps which led the advance to Burgos.

"On reaching Burgos our advance guard met with obstinate resistance from the portion of the Castillian army which was encamped before it, which turned out to be unfortunate both for the latter and for the populace. The site of the fighting was covered with dead and dying Spaniards from amongst whom we collected the enemy wounded together with seventy of our own men. Rosel, the surgeon of the 4th Light Infantry, had already operated in the field on those who required amputation with the discernment which comes from the widest experience. We dressed all who so far had not received attention and I had them moved into the Burgos hospitals, taking the precaution, however, of separating the French from the Spaniards.

"A few days afterwards we were again on the road to Madrid by way

of Buytrago. I followed General Savary's advance guard, consisting of the
fusilier corps of the Guard with a part of its light artillery and General
Lassalle's light cavalry division.

"On reaching Boussequillas, a village which lies at the mouth of the
Summa-Sierra gorge, we learnt that a force of about six thousand troops
was entrenched on the Spulveda heights and that a second and much
larger one was defending the mountain pass. Before engaging the latter
it was thought necessary to attack the Spulveda encampment, and although
this did not have the success we had hoped the enemy broke up his camp
and promptly took to flight and disappeared. The engagement gave us
about thirty wounded, whom I attended to on the field and then sent to
Boussequillas, from whence we evacuated them to Burgos.

"Our army now advanced into the mountain defile. We met with no
opposition until we reached the enemy's trenches in front of the village of
Summa-Sierra where our difficulties appeared insurmountable. The steep
and narrow road, cut in the sloping side of the mountain, was defended
by masked batteries. The mountainous flanks which bordered the pass
were similarly protected by troops and cannon, and there seemed to be
no way of turning these formidable positions except with much difficulty
and by a prolonged operation. But as things turned out, at the Emperor's
signal and under the fortunate cover of a thick temporary mist, the light
cavalry of the Guard charged the trenches defending the road and amidst
bullets, balls and grape-shot, these brave Sarmatians[1] broke into them,
forced the redoubts, cut the defenders to pieces, and putting to flight
those who escaped their sabres made themselves masters of the road. This
victory was in truth bought with the blood of the many brave men in the
front ranks. It deserves to be regarded as one of the most splendid feats
of the war. The wounded from this brilliant day were all dressed and
operated on at the side of the road carved from the mountain, and our
ambulance wagons removed them without delay to Buytrago and from
thence to Santo Martino, close to Madrid.

"The Spanish troops who escaped our fire dispersed into the mountains
so that we reached Madrid without striking another blow, but here the
inhabitants shut the gates of the capital and resolved to defend themselves.
They discharged a certain amount of artillery and held us at *pourparlers*
for two days, but the completion of the investment and a brisk bombardment of some hours, together with the capture of Bueno-Retiro which
commands the town, caused them to accept the capitulation offered by
His Majesty.

"Being wholly occupied with my own duties I made haste as soon as
we entered Madrid to take over the wards we had previously occupied in
the main hospital, and to prepare them for the reception of the few
wounded we had sustained during the siege, as well as those whom I had
sent to Santo Martino.

"It was not long before we learnt of the arrival of an English army[2] in

[1] This feat was due to a regiment of Polish light horse under Montbran. A full account
of their initial repulse and final success is given by Marbot.
[2] Sir John Moore's expedition. Moore was still advancing on the 23rd to attack Soult,

the province of Zamora, and of the presence of their advance guard at Valladolid. Preparations were accordingly made for a fresh expedition and orders given to be ready to march at any moment. It was clearly of the first importance to cut off the retreat of this army on the road to Corunna, which was the nearest and most favourable port for its embarkation.

"With this intention we left Madrid on December 22nd. We marched to the Guadarrama mountains which we crossed on the 23rd of the month. I noted at the foot of these that the temperature had fallen to —12°F.

"The wind was full from the north and for the last few days there had been a considerable fall of snow; thus the higher we climbed the more intense became the cold, until it reached to such an intensity that men and animals lost their equilibrium and fell, many being swept away on the steep slope by the whirling clouds of snow and sleet, whilst others crippled by cold lay on the edge of the road unable to rise. The light artillery and cavalry were forced to a halt on a large plateau in the midst of the Guadarrama mountains, from the sheer impossibility of climbing the other half, and had to wait here until the next day by which time the temperature had risen several degrees. In this unfortunate situation it was difficult to obtain any wood and the few bivouac fires that could be lighted were of more harm than good. In fact such of our men who failed to take due precaution and warmed their feet and hands as quickly as they could were at once stricken with some degree of frost-bite, whereas the men who did not go near to the fires were not affected by this form of gangrene. One of our ambulance orderlies, who had had his right hand frozen whilst climbing the mountain, rushed to a bivouac fire and held the hand very close to the heat: it immediately swelled up, just as dough does when put into a very hot oven. When he returned to the ambulance a few hours later the hand was completely gangrenous and had to be amputated at the wrist joint. The fact confirms the views I have expressed in my Memoir on gangrene from frost-bite.

"This crossing of the mountains was difficult. Never have I felt the cold so acutely nor experienced such fatigue. After traversing these heights we entered an immense plain which appeared to be very fertile. The bitter cold was followed after the second day's march by rain and thaw. We passed by cross-country roads to Medina del Campo and from thence by similar roads to Rio-Secco and Benevente. The constant rain and heavy going, where many of the vehicles became bogged, made the march very arduous and when we halted we could find neither straw to lie on nor wood to make the fires to dry ourselves.

"However we reached Benevente a day too late; the English army had passed through and had burnt the bridge which spans the river that laps its walls. Our advance guard forded this and soon came up with the

but late that night he received definite news that Napoleon was moving against him from Madrid in force and was already three marches on the road. He at once counter-manded his orders and began the retreat to Corunna the same night or, in the case of his more forward units, on Christmas Eve.

English rear-guard. A bloody engagement took place and although the enemy was in superior numbers our intrepid *chasseurs* made themselves masters of the battlefield, captured some baggage and hastened the retreat of the rest of the enemy rearguard, which was brought to a halt at Corunna by the corps of H.E. Marshal Soult."

*   *   *   *   *

The hardships of this retreat and the sufferings of Moore's army were extreme, but the French suffered almost equally and Marbot relates that he saw three veteran grenadiers of the Guard who could march no further blow their brains out. The account given by Larrey of the engagement at Benevente differs materially from that from English sources. The destruction of the bridge was a difficult feat, successfully accomplished by the engineers, although interrupted by a French attempt to force it which was defeated. After the British had retreated the French began to ford the river but were driven back with small loss to the British, and General Count Charles Lefebre-Desnouettes of the Imperial Hussars was taken prisoner. The British sent an envoy back across the river to obtain his baggage, and that night he supped with Moore. A request from the French for his exchange was refused. Napoleon pushed on as far as Astorga, which is rather more than forty miles beyond Benevente, but receiving alarming despatches concerning Austria's hostile movements, and being anxious about the dubious activities of Fouché and Talleyrand, he handed over the further pursuit to Soult and on January 3rd, 1809, left the army for Paris. He never again crossed the Pyrenees.

"The Imperial Guard relinquished the pursuit at Storga (Astorga) near the Asturias mountains and from there we returned to Benevente and Valladolid, passing through Rio-Secco where I saw where the famous battle had been fought beneath its walls between a large insurgent army and that of H.E. Marshal Bessières. On reaching Valladolid I made the necessary dispositions for the reception of our wounded. In addition to my duties as Chief Surgeon to the Guard I was appointed to the post of Inspector-General of all the Line hospitals in this town. The supervision and treatment of the English sick also devolved upon me and was unquestionably the most difficult part of my service. The fatigues, the cold and wet, which these prisoners had endured whilst crossing the Asturias mountains, the privations they had suffered and the home-sickness with which they were generally afflicted, caused hospital fever to break out and quickly to assume a contagious character. If I had not taken energetic measures to isolate the English sick from our own men, as well as from their own who were healthy, the epidemic would have spread through all the hospitals and into all the houses in Valladolid. The sick prisoners were therefore collected together in a hospital which was isolated from other habitations, and the healthy English placed in a large well-ventilated barracks outside the town. I myself took charge of the treatment of the former and laid down various hygienic measures for the latter. I also obtained for them, through the kindness of H.E. the Marshal and

Governor, some cloaks, shoes and shirts, of which they had great need.

"Baron Denzel, the General-Commandant of the prisoners, shewed a special interest in them and went to great pains to render them assistance, which they surely will not fail to remember. I must also make honourable mention of the Director-General of hospitals, M. Gubert, who was not afraid to accompany me on my daily visits, and filled his post at Valladolid with the same zeal and disinterestedness he had shewn in Egypt.

"In the early days of our reception of the English prisoners we lost a considerable number of the sick of both nations, as the English had been admitted indiscriminately into all the hospitals; but following the adoption of suitable hygienic measures the intensity of the disease diminished and gradually it disappeared. The change of winds and season doubtless also played a part in arresting the epidemic. The excellent quinine and good wine which Spanish agents obtained for us were of great assistance in curing both the French and the English. The case of one of the latter was very singular. This was a soldier of the 12th Regiment of Light Infantry[3] of about thirty-six years old. On becoming convalescent from an attack of noso-comial fever (typhus) he suddenly developed a widespread oedema limited to the right side of his body, the left side being almost normal. This complication persisted for a long time but in the end yielded to the treatment given by our physicians.

"We shall record also the no less important case of the cure of a young English drummer of twelve or thirteen years old, who was a prisoner and the son of a corporal of the same regiment. This child, whose father held him constantly on his knee, was completely blind; his pupils being almost without movement. The blindness, according to the story given by his father, came on suddenly during the crossing of the Asturias mountains in the bitter cold; this no doubt affected him the worse as his hair had recently been cut close to his scalp and he had made the journey from Corunna to Valladolid on his bare feet as did nearly all the prisoners. We readily recognized that the child was suffering from amaurosis, the effect of the two causes just mentioned.

"It would be difficult to paint the father's distress and how deeply he was afflicted by the unfortunate state of his son. Many of his comrades sincerely shared his grief, and I noted with satisfaction that all of these prisoners were attached to each other and shewed a very marked generous and kind mutual affection.

"As the child's blindness was of recent origin I had some hope of curing him. I had him taken into one of our hospitals, as much to remove him from amongst the other sick as to be better able to treat him. I made him first take a bath with soap and then prescribed bitter diaphoretics and applied the moxa[4] along the course of the facial nerve, where it emerges from the cranium behind the angle of the jaw. His head was rubbed with an alkaline camphorated linament and covered with a woollen cap, and his eyes treated with lotions of hot camphorated wine.

[3] I can find no record of the 12th Regiment of the Line being at Corunna. The regiments present at the retreat and entitled Light Infantry were the 43rd, 51st, and 71st.
[4] See note on the moxa, p. 244.

"At the second application of the moxa the boy became able to see light, at the fourth he could distinguish objects and colours and finally, at the seventh application, the sight was completely restored. I had taken care to prevent inflammation and suppuration in the moxa burns by immediately applying ammonia to them. To make this extraordinary success the more certain I also cauterized his arm. I obtained a small Spanish cloak for the young prisoner so that he was warmly clad, and finally I had the happiness of seeing him leave for France perfectly cured, in company with his father who was overcome by joy.

*   *   *   *   *

"I had come to the end of a trying and difficult task. Worn out and weakened by a catarrhal affection I had contracted during the Benevente campaign, and which I attributed to wading through numerous rivers and constant exposure to snow, rain and cold, I became susceptible to disease and contracted typhus fever from the English. However, I had sufficient courage on the third day of the disease to set out for Burgos, where I was hoping to rejoin the Guard which had left two days before. But delirium overtook me on the road, and I should probably have died had it not been for the constant and vigilant care of my pupil, my cousin Alexis Larrey, an intelligent young man already shewing great promise. On my arrival at Burgos I had lost almost all my strength and the use of my senses: the disease continued to progress for nine or ten days and for a short time I was in the greatest danger. I shall always carry in my memory the attentive care which the Surgeon-in-Chief, M. Beaumarchef, and Dr. Maisonade, a physician of Burgos, lavished upon me at this time.

"I used the first moments of my convalescence to have myself moved to Paris to the bosom of my family, which I only reached with the greatest difficulty."

*   *   *   *   *

Chapter 16

Second Austrian Campaign. Eckmühl and Ratisbon.
Essling. Lannes' death. Wagram. Casualties.
Return to Paris.

Larrey arrived in Paris on April 4th, 1809, a sick man, to find that a restless spirit was abroad in France which the reconciliation between Talleyrand and Fouché had done nothing to abate, and that the possible fate of the *régime*, should an accident of war or an assassin's dagger put an end to Napoleon was being widely discussed. These speculations were swiftly silenced, or at least driven underground, by the return of the Great Man and his vigorous treatment of the potential traitors. But meanwhile a second and different threat had become imminent and urgent. Smarting under the humiliation of Austerlitz and its consequences, Austria had been covertly making preparations for another trial of strength, and in this she drew encouragement and stimulus from the Spanish imbroglio. Not merely was she rearming and training her troops but in the diplomatic field she was sounding the Germanic states, furious at the restoration of the Duchy of Warsaw to the Poles and the imposition of a Bonaparte nonentity on the throne of Westphalia. Tentative soundings were even being made in St. Petersberg.

This visible and growing threat convinced Napoleon that he had no alternatives but to impose prompt and effective disarmament, or resort to war. But already Austria had gone too far to draw back and it seemed to her that with the support of England and probably of Germany the opportunity had arrived, and could not be let slip, to try conclusions again in favourable conditions with the tyrant whose best soldiers had so recently been defeated by mere bands of irregulars and guerillas in Spain, and whose cadres were filled with second class conscripts. Moreover the French forces were scattered from Magdeberg to Ulm, and a swift blow before they had time to concentrate might be decisive. Hence it was that early in April, 1809, the troops of the Archduke Charles crossed the Inn. Napoleon responded with unforeseen energy, and whilst the Austrian commander was dispersing his forces between Munich and Ratisbon he struck, and dividing them by a swift thrust at Landshut, he defeated the Archduke Charles at Eckmühl and threw him back upon Ratisbon, which he captured on the 23rd, when Marbot and Labédoyère gained immortal glory. The Archduke retreated into Bohemia with heavy losses in both men and material and the road to Vienna lay open.

*   *   *   *   *

"At the time of the opening of the Austrian campaign I was in Paris, convalescent from the disease I had contracted in Spain. Without waiting until my health was fully re-established, I set out on the 22nd of April, 1809, to rejoin the Imperial Guard which was already in Bavaria.

"On reaching Strasbourg we heard the news of the victory gained by the French and their allies over the Austrians at Ratisbon, and a few days later we met with a crowd of prisoners being conducted to France under the escort of our soldiers and those of our allies. We quickly passed through the first fertile and smiling fields of the German lands and reached Munich, where I stopped to spend a short time with Dr. Soemmering, who for a third time shewed me his superb museum of pathological anatomy.

"At Ebersberg we saw the results of the bloody combat which had taken place between our advance guard and the enemy, who had defended this difficult passage with the greatest obstinacy. After a few days very hard marching we caught up with the Guard before it reached Vienna. H.M. the Emperor, whom I had the happiness to see at his entry to the palace of Schönbrunn, received me kindly and gave me orders to prepare my ambulances for a second campaign.

"The enemy army had closed the gates on evacuating the capital to force the inhabitants to defend themselves, and after having crossed the Danube destroyed the bridges. But the sight of our siege preparations and a few hours bombardment decided the Viennese and the besieged troops to propose a capitulation, which was accepted and the next day we took possession of the town."

*   *   *   *   *

The battle of Essling which was fought on May 21st–22nd, 1809, ended in a decisive defeat for the French. The Archduke Charles advanced from a general northerly direction against Aspern, Essling and Enzersdorf, which lie in a semi-circle about a mile beyond the French bridgehead, on the far side of the last branch of the Danube. Most of the fighting was between Aspern and Essling, the fiercest being in the churchyard at the west end of Aspern, where the Austrians subsequently erected a noble monument (Fig. 20). To cross a river like the Danube in the presence of a hostile army of some 90,000 men was a prodigious undertaking. Its success depended on the seizure of the island of Lobau, which lies in a broad stretch of the river, but nearer to the left bank where the stream is relatively narrow, the main and most formidable part being on the French side. Since the island is about two to three miles broad and well wooded the work of building the main bridge was screened from the Austrians, and of course out of cannon shot. The defenders made a capital mistake in holding the island only as a weak outpost, and in any case were slow to realize the direction from which the attack was to come. The French had captured much bridging material in the earlier battles but they experienced great difficulty in anchoring their boats in the strong current, which was increased by the rising of the river during the action by as

FIG. 16. Surrender of Ulm.

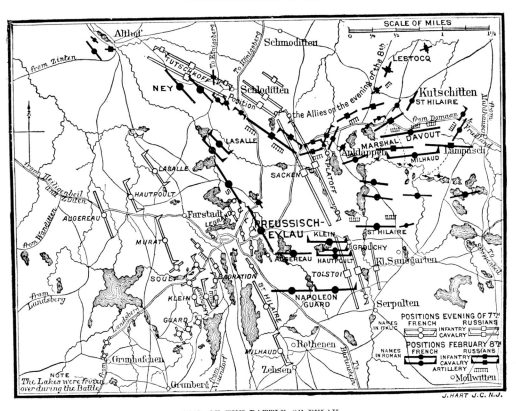

MAP OF THE BATTLE OF EYLAU.

FIG. 17. Plan of Eylau.

[To face p. 110

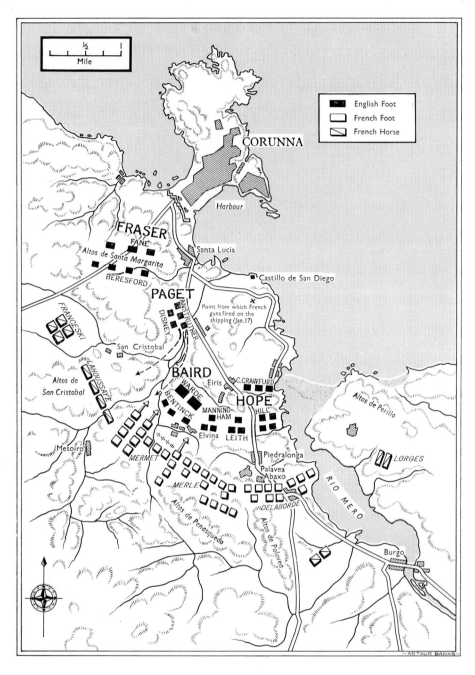

Labels within image: English Foot, French Foot, French Horse, CORUNNA, Harbour, FRASER, FANE, Altos de Santa Margarita, BERESFORD, Santa Lucia, Castillo de San Diego, PAGET, ANTRUTHER, DISNEY, Point from which French guns fired on the shipping (Jan.17), FRANCCESKI, San Cristobal, AHOUSSAYE, Altos de San Cristobal, BAIRD, WARDE, Eiris, C.CRAWFURD, BENTINCK, HOPE, MANNING HAM, HILL, Altos de Perillo, Mesoiro, MERMET, Elvina, LEITH, Piedralonga, Palavea Abaxo, LORGES, MERLE, DELABORDE, RIO MERO, Altos de Penasquedo, Altos de Palavea, Burgo, ARTHUR BANKS

FIG. 18. Moore's retreat in Spain. (Reproduced with permission from *Corunna*, by C. Hibbert, published by B. T. Batsford, London.)

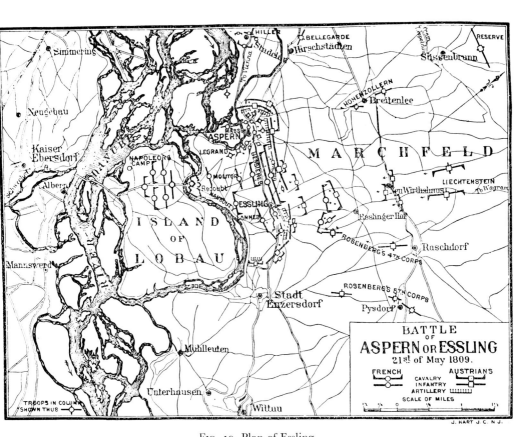

Fig. 19. Plan of Essling.

Fig. 20. Austrian Monument to commemorate the battle of Essling. The Church is in the background.

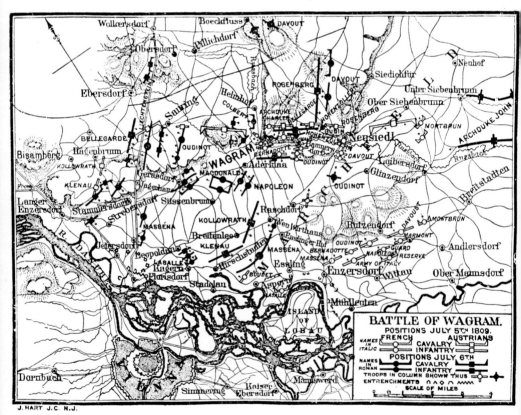

Fig. 21. Plan of Wagram.

much, it is stated, as sixteen feet. The breaking of the bridges not having been foreseen, the medical arrangements were concentrated at Vienna and to some extent in the small town of Ebersdorf on the right bank. The direction of these services was the responsibility of Desgenettes and Heurteloup. Larrey crossed with the Guard to the left bank where he set up an ambulance within the bridgehead, but he was handicapped by a lack of supplies and of means of evacuating his wounded. His account of the battle is as follows.

"Fresh preparations were immediately made for another campaign, and the construction of bridges for crossing the river and attacking the enemy's positions on the left bank was pushed forward. The points for crossing were where the Danube divides into a number of branches and forms several islands, one of which, Lobau, is of considerable size. During the 20th and 21st of May the Imperial Guard and a number of army corps seized this island and followed this up by quickly throwing bridges across the last arm of the Danube and at once attacking the enemy's advanced positions (Fig. 21). The result was indecisive. Our divisions maintained their footing on the mainland, and during the morning of the 22nd covered the passage of the Guard and the other corps which had reached the island, but the greater part of the army was halted on the near bank from the unexpected breaking of the first bridges. Nevertheless a general attack took place, this being the terrible battle of Essling, in which the major part was played by the infantry of the Guard where it shewed so much valour and intrepidity. This battle was equally indecisive, and during the night of the 23rd–25th we withdrew to Lobau. The passage was difficult because of the frailty and small number of the bridges which had been thrown across this last arm of the river. I had set up my most advanced ambulance at the entrance to the small forest which is on the left bank, and there we operated on all the seriously wounded of the Guard or the army. Those whose wounds were light, and those who could be transported easily, were moved as fast as was possible onto the island where other ambulances were established.

"It was at a very short distance from this extremely dangerous position that H.E. Marshal the Duke of Montebello (Lannes) was mortally wounded. He was on foot and returning from the battlefields to Imperial Headquarters when a ricocheting ball of large calibre in full flight struck and passed through his left knee and, without loss of force changed its direction and lacerated his right thigh, dividing the integuments and the most prominent part of the vastus internus muscle very near to the knee joint, which fortunately escaped damage. The duke was thrown down by the impact and suffered a violent cerebral concussion and severe shock to all his organs.

"The news being quickly brought to me I made all haste to the spot where the marshal had been wounded and had him moved to my ambulance. His face was colourless, his lips pale, his eyes sad and watering, his voice weak and his pulse hardly detectable. His mind was disturbed so that he did not realize his danger. How unhappy was my own situation! It was impossible for me to place any real hope in such succour as my Art offered; yet at the same time I could not, in so serious a case in so important a situation, leave the patient to nature's resources alone. How should I confront the acute and painful fact that the state of this great captain was already most desperate—he who had especially honoured me by his friendship and whom I had had the happiness of treating successfully for other wounds in Syria and in Egypt? I vow that this was one of the most difficult situations of my whole life. But I summoned up all my energies and called for the assistance of a number of experienced surgeons. We examined the two wounds with the utmost care. That of the right thigh was dressed first and in a very simple manner, as it had no especially serious features. That of the left knee was alarming on account of the splintering of the bone, the tearing of the ligaments, and the rupture of the tendons and the popliteal artery. All my colleagues realized that it was necessary to amputate the limb at once but none dared to undertake it on account of the small prospect it offered of success in the patient's state of stupor and extreme shock. However, encouraged by numerous examples of success in like cases, and heartened by a ray of hope and sustained by the desire which the patient manifested to have the operation performed, I determined to do it. It was over in less than two minutes and the marshal shewed very few signs of pain.[1]

"I applied the usual dressings and after having accompanied the Duke as far as the island of Lobau, where the Emperor saw him, I confided him to the care of the surgeon, M. Paulet. I regretted leaving the side of this illustrious warrior, but I was the only one of the Inspectors-General of ambulances on the battlefield, and a very large number of wounded men were awaiting attention on the island to which they had been transported.

[1] Marbot, who was Lannes' aide-de-camp, gives the following account of his fatal wound. Lannes had been very upset by the death of General Pouzet, who was killed at his side as they were walking together. He had sat down at the edge of a ditch in gloomy meditation, his hand over his eyes, his knees crossed: "a small three-pound shot fired from a gun at Enzersdorf ricochetted and struck him just where his legs crossed. The knee-pan of one was smashed, and the back sinews of the other torn. I instantly rushed towards the marshal who said: 'I am wounded. It's nothing much. Give me your hand to help me up.' He tried to rise, but could not. . . . We carried him to the *tête de pont*, where the chief surgeons proceeded to dress his wound, first holding a private consultation in which they could not agree as to what should be done. Dr. Larrey was in favour of amputating the leg of which the knee-pan was broken; another, whose name I forget, wanted to cut off both; while Dr. Yvan, from whom I heard these details, was against any amputation. This surgeon, who had long known the marshal, asserted that his firmness of character gave some chance of a cure, while an operation performed in such hot weather would inevitably bring him to the grave. Larrey was the senior surgeon of the army and his opinion prevailed. One of the marshal's legs was amputated. He bore the operation with great courage. It was hardly over when the Emperor came up. The interview was most touching. The Emperor, kneeling beside the stretcher, wept as he embraced the marshal, whose blood soon stained his white kerseymere waistcoat. . . . I should have liked to carry the marshal to Ebersdorf, on the right bank, but the broken bridge prevented this and we did not dare put him on board a frail boat. He was therefore compelled to pass the night on the island, where for want of a mattress I borrowed a dozen cavalry cloaks to make him a bed. We were short of everything and had not even good water to give the marshal, who was parched with thirst." Marbot was himself at the time suffering from a grape-shot wound in the thigh, which had been roughly dressed with tow and which kept him out of action for five weeks.

As far as possible I separated those of the Imperial Guard from those of the Line, but we gave the same care to all without distinction. I brought the surgeons of the different corps of the Guard to assist the medical officers of the ambulance and we did not rest until all the wounded on the island had been operated upon and dressed. Happily we had all the instruments necessary and a sufficiency of dressings, which I had taken care to have brought up by the ambulance orderlies who were commanded by M. Pelchet of whom I have already spoken. I owe great praise to all my collaborators but above all to MM. Rayfer, Cothenet, Mouton, Jourda and Maugras, who gave me the greatest assistance on this occasion.

"In spite of the promptitude and efficacy of our measures the wounded were in an ill plight, stretched out on the earth and either collected in groups on the river banks or dispersed in the interior of the island, where the soil at this time was dry and arid. The heat was very great in the daytime and the nights damp and frosty. The winds, which are frequent in these regions, constantly covered the wounded with clouds of dust, and the branches of a few trees or the leaves of the reeds gave only a poor shelter from the sun.

"The breaking of the bridges and the lack of boats for transport of provisions added to these vicissitudes and caused an extreme scarcity of the good food and comforting drinks which our wounded needed so badly. I was forced to have broth made from horse flesh which we seasoned, in default of salt, with gunpowder. The broth was none the worse for this and those who had been able to save some biscuit made an excellent soup: (it is not to be thought that this broth retained the black colour of the powder: cooking clarified it). On the third day we fortunately obtained provisions of all kinds and were able to distribute regular rations."

*   *   *   *   *

The island of Lobau is today largely covered by a jungle of low copse and undergrowth, filled in summer with masses of golden rod. The soil is river gravel, white and dusty, and except for the river and canals it has no water. The lack of cooking vessels for the crude soup Larrey provided for his men was overcome by using cavalry cuirasses, and to obtain the necessary flesh he ordered some horses picketed nearby to be shot. At this moment General Boudet, to whose command they belonged, arrived on the scene and roundly abused Larrey, swearing that he would report him to the Emperor. "You will do as you please," the surgeon replied; "but I doubt if the Emperor, who gave his own horses to the plague patients in Egypt and marched across the sand on foot, will congratulate you. For my part, as long as I am surgeon to this army I shall not allow the brave fellows who have been wounded under your command to die of hunger and thirst. Since you refuse these horses let them take mine." The general went off grumbling and did in fact complain to Napoleon, who meeting Larrey two days later at Ebersdorf taxed him with this: "So you feed your wounded on my general's horses?" "Yes, Sire, and would do so again should the needs of Your Majesty's army require it." Napoleon laughed and pinching the surgeon's ear with his familiar gesture promised that his services should not be forgotten.

"On the fourth day, the bridges being rebuilt, the wounded were removed to the hospitals which the Inspector-General, M. Heurteloup, had prepared at Ebersdorf and Vienna. I arranged for those from the Guard to be accommodated in the superb barracks of Reneveck, which was formerly used by the Imperial Artillery School, and kept them in this magnificent hospital until they were cured.

"After having organized my service there, I hastened to visit H.E. the Duke of Montebello who had been taken to the house of a brewer at Ebersdorf: he was lodged in a very small room, on one side of which was the brewery and on the other a dank and unhealthy courtyard. The weather at the time was changeable and very stormy.

"I found the Duke very weak, profoundly depressed, and with the pallor of death upon him. His mind was confused, his voice faltering, and he complained of heaviness in his head. He was restless, oppressed, sighed frequently, and could not tolerate the weight of the coverings on his bed although these were very light. Up to now he had been taking iced acidulated drinks. My presence seemed to calm him.

"The temperature had fallen rapidly from a sudden change of wind from the south to north and the rainstorms of the night before. I therefore suggested to the doctors (who were in charge of him during my absence) that he should be covered with flannel and given some good broth and wine at frequent intervals, and that the iced drinks should be stopped. His strength rallied a little and his sleep was more peaceful. The next day his wounds were thoroughly dressed for the first time: the dressings were soaked with sero-purulent fluid; the wound in the stump looked well and that of the right thigh gave no reason to apprehend any complication, in fact parts of its edges had already united. We covered the first light dressings with a simple digestive and soaked the compresses in hot sweetened wine. The next twenty-four hours passed off well. I treasured an illusion and began to hope, contrary to the opinions of my colleagues, which unfortunately were only too well founded, that I might see him recover. But during the sixth night after his wound an attack of pernicious fever occurred, which was first recognized by Dr. Lanfranc, physician to H.M., Doctors Yvan, Lanfranc, Paulet and I again met in consultation and it was agreed that we should give strong doses of quinine together with sulphuric ether. This treatment was begun and modified as the circumstances required. A second attack, although less alarming than the first, occurred twelve hours later and a third during the day, in which he was delirious, was followed by an almost complete prostration of the vital forces. The danger became more and more imminent, but as yet the wounds shewed no symptoms of gangrene, but the suppuration diminished sensibly.

"His Majesty, being informed of the danger of his brave Lieutenant-General, came to visit him on his bed of suffering. Dr. Franck, a famous physician of Vienna, was called in consultation: he approved of our treatment and desired to remain with us beside the patient, whose strength was gradually failing. Finally the Marshal fell into a state of complete delirium which was of short duration and died peacefully a few hours later. This was at the end of the ninth day after the battle and his being wounded.

"We were all very upset by his death, and I in particular was greatly affected. I was losing, in this honourable companion of Egypt, a powerful protector who had more than once shewn me marks of a real attachment. I was given the duty of embalming his body which was moved during the night to the Castle of Schonbrünn. We commenced the work at daybreak, eighteen hours after death when putrefaction was already advanced. I had the greatest difficulty in injecting the vessels and in emptying the cavities. I was forced to remove all the fatty cellular tissue from the whole body and the interstices of the muscles. The heart contained hardly any blood and the brain was separated from the dura mater by a distance of about twelve millimetres. The vessels communicating between the pia mater and the brain were ruptured; a small amount of dark blood was effused into the convolutions and the ventricles were filled with a reddish serous fluid.

"After I had completed this difficult and dangerous task, I returned to the Guard's hospital where I resumed the general direction of the health service, giving my especial personal attention to the care of the wounded."

*   *   *   *   *

After the bloody repulse of his first attempt to cross the Danube Napoleon withdrew the bulk of his forces to the right bank, but maintained and improved his communications with Lobau, upon which he gradually assembled a mass of 150,000 men. The bridges across the larger branch of the river were renewed and strengthened to deceive the Archduke Charles and ostentatious preparations made for a further attempt to cross the small arm at the same site as was used for the attacks on Aspern and Essling, which by now the Austrians had strongly fortified. The decisive crossing was made near the lower end of the island, opposite Enzersdorf, at the extreme left of the Archduke's defensive position. Here his flank should have received support from the army of the Archduke John, but this prince failed to carry out his orders in time, and in consequence the attack was launched against a vulnerable flank which in falling would imperil the whole line.

The crossing was made on the night of July 5th, amidst a violent thunderstorm and covered by a vigorous bombardment of the Aspern-Essling position by heavy guns, many of them captured in Vienna, which helped to mislead the enemy. Under the brave Sainte-Croix, a detachment of 2,500 French grenadiers landed and captured the village of Enzersdorf, enabling the marines of the Guard, commanded by Captain Baste, to throw eight bridges swiftly across the small arm of the river and the corps of Massena, Oudinot, Bernadotte, Davout, Marmont, and Eugène's Army of Italy to cross and overwhelm the Austrian left. The Archduke was forced to execute a vast retrograde movement to the high ground on the line Wagram-Neuseidel behind the Ruisbach stream and to abandon Aspern and Essling. The day closed with the Austrians holding this new position, which is one of some natural strength, the vigorous frontal attacks made by the French towards the evening having been for the most part repulsed.

The ground below Wagram slopes gradually to the open plain of Marchfield, and though the Ruisbach was a more formidable obstacle than it is today, and was edged with marshy ground, it was not impassable. There was little cover for the attackers and little possibility for unobserved manoeuvre, so that much of the fighting which followed was a matter of hard slogging and direct attack.

The partial stalemate of the 5th, was broken on the morning of the next day by the Archduke counter-attacking with both his wings, hoping to hold the French on his right and to roll up their left wing, which rested upon the Danube, after which he proposed to fall upon their right in an enveloping movement. But his manoeuvres were slow and ill-coordinated, and although Massena on the French left along the river was very hard pressed, he had the support of the heavy artillery on Lobau and the attack was held. The depleted Austrian centre was now energetic-ally attacked by the Emperor, and on the far right Davout steadily advanced until he captured Neuseidel, putting the whole line in jeopardy. Finally, largely by the vigorous use of their superior artillery, the French drove the Austrians from the heights of Wagram and became masters of the field.

It was a defeat but not a rout, the Austrians retiring along the roads to Bohemia in good order with losses not greatly in excess of those of the French, whose casualties included the dashing light cavalry leader Lasalle. The weather had been high summer, and in spite of the storm of the evening of the 5th much standing corn was set on fire by shells and gun-wadding and burned fiercely, obscuring the movements of troops and causing considerable confusion, as well as the death of many of the wounded. Macdonald, Oudinot and Marmont received marshal's batons for their part in the battle.

Larrey's account is as follows:

"New preparations were quickly made to recross the Danube and attack the enemy's positions on the left bank. We evacuated to France all the wounded in our hospital whose infirmities made it impossible that they would ever serve again. Eventually the order to march was given, and on July 1st the army and the Imperial Guard advanced to force the passage of the (main branch of the) river at the same place as at the battle of Essling. By the evening of the 4th the whole force had concen-trated on the large island of Lobau. A flotilla carrying a landing party of three thousand men, commanded by Count Baste, a ship's captain,[2] had the task of protecting the crossing of the last arm of the river and of capturing the advanced posts of the enemy who were entrenched on its

[2] Today Rear-Admiral.

banks. These operations were designed to be executed simultaneously. Just as the signal to attack is given a storm bursts with the greatest violence, the terrible claps of thunder being accompanied by sleet and torrents of rain. In the deep and gloomy darkness around us we can only see during the flashes of lightning. In spite of formidable obstacles our soldiers gain the opposite bank, capture the defending batteries and rapidly deploy in the plain. A number of bridges are quickly thrown across the river and the whole army effects its passage in a few hours.

"The enemy, surprised by the rapidity of these operations, withdraws precipitately to take up a fresh position on the line of Wagram, where battle is joined the same evening and becomes general without a decision being reached, so that for the rest of the night the two armies remained face to face. At daybreak we made a new attack which at first is stoutly resisted; but before long the enemy's left wing is rolled up, although his right, resting solidly on the Danube, manages to resist our efforts. His centre, consisting of the Imperial and Royal Guard, is threatened by our reserve and sees its ranks continuously thinned by their light artillery, whose fire seems to grow in volume until it covers the whole front.[3] Finally, the Austrian lines are captured, their divisions broken or destroyed by our terrible artillery, and victory is complete."

* * * * *

"I followed the movements of the Guard with the mobile ambulance up to the decisive moment, and we dressed all the wounded on the field, as they came to us case by case, but in the end their number became so great that I had to form a general ambulance depôt in the nearest village, and to this I brought all the wounded from the Imperial Guard, whose number was soon swelled by many of the officers of the Line who had been wounded by artillery fire. No more accurate idea of the events of this ever memorable battle can be given than by its faithful portrayal in the magnificent panoramic picture which was exhibited some time afterwards in Paris.

"Before nightfall some five hundred casualties had been brought to my ambulance, mostly men grievously wounded by cannon fire or having serious injuries which required extensive operations. . . . The account I am about to give of the patients upon whom I operated at the battles of Essling and Wagram strongly supports the principle I have laid down: that amputations should be performed on the battlefield, and not after the first symptoms have subsided—that is to say by the time the wounded have reached the hospitals. The latter is the view of Faure and his supporters, who maintain that we spread alarm amongst the troops by operating upon their comrades before their eyes, and that we disturb the bodily functions of the wounded and hasten their death. I believe that I have replied to this last objection. The first is refuted by the aid which the wounded men give to one another during the operations, and the con-

[3] Napoleon deployed 550 guns on this occasion. A larger artillery than any commander had previously put into the field.

fidence inspired in all by the sight of succour being given under the enemy's fire. Only the inexperienced or chicken-hearted can find a refuge in objections of this sort. 'The surgical amputation of a limb is the most philosophical work of all the human sciences,' the celebrated Dufouard declared.

"Nevertheless, surgeons with great names, amongst them our own contemporaries, designate the operation as *cruel* and *barbarous*, though any truly sensitive, courageous, and experienced man should be able to recognize and appreciate the wonderful results of amputation. I would call to witness the great number of wounded men, otherwise condemned to death, whose lives have clearly been saved by this operation.

"After the battle we pursued the retreating enemy to Snaïm, cutting him off from Moravia and confining him to this town and the surrounding country. Both of our wings came into action but during the night negotiations resulted in a suspension of hostilities, each side retiring to cantonments whilst these continued. General Headquarters returned to Schonbrün and Vienna, where they remained until peace was concluded a few weeks later."[4]

*   *   *   *   *

"A report of my work during this Campaign, to which I subjoined a list of guardsmen who had become incapable of serving on account of mutilations or other severe infirmities, was submitted to H.M. the Emperor, who was so good as to confer on me the title of Baron together with an annual income of 5,000 francs, a conspicuous proof of his munificence and sincere desire to reward every kind of service rendered to the State.[5]

"The time being come for the French to leave Vienna for their own country I completed the evacuation of the sick and wounded, and having arranged for their transport I set out for Paris, arriving there in December 1809. On January 1st, 1810, I resumed the direction of my service at the Guard's Hospital."

[4] The armistice of Snaïm was concluded on July 12th and the Peace of Vienna on October 14th, 1809.
[5] By the same decree H. M. confered a like honour and sum of money upon my colleagues M. M. Desguenettes, Percy and Heurteloup.

Chapter 17

*The Surgery of amputations. Importance of early
operation. The shoulder joint. The tibial condyles.
The hip. Aseptic healing. Importance of immobilization.
Larrey's "appareil inamovible."*

In the era in which Larrey lived and worked the amputation was the
most important major surgical operation. The surgery of the abdomen
was a closed book, on account of the probability of fatal peritonitis, and
that of the thorax a *terra incognita* into which no one ventured—indeed it
is only in our own century that this field has been opened to surgery.

There remained the limbs. All wounds became infected and suppuration
was looked upon as a *normal stage* in its progress, at which in favourable
circumstances "laudable pus" appeared as a prelude to the healing that
followed. The most dreaded wounds were compound fractures of bone—
that is to say fractures with a wound open to the exterior. In them the
customary septic process involved the broken ends of the bones, and the
inflammation that followed in the solid and partly inorganic structure of
the bone became long drawn out and involved the unfortunate patient in
prolonged suffering, hectic fever and haemorrhages, and too often ended
in loss of life. Injuries of this sort were especially dangerous when produced
by firearms, since the bones were apt to be shattered, the local tissues badly
traumatized, and fragments of clothing carried into the wound; the whole
area being thus made an ideal breeding-ground for the microbic invasion
which constitutes sepsis, and sometimes it was the source of other fatal
complications such as tetanus. In addition the main arteries, veins and
nerves were often severed, since they generally lie close to the bones, so
that the chances of haemorrhage were considerable; and even if this did
not occur or was overcome there was the prospect of gangrene of the
extremity from the interruption of its blood supply, or of permanent
paralysis from the severance of its nerves. Gangrene of an infective nature,
which Larrey called *traumatic gangrene* (p. 91), might also supervene
from the rapid spread towards the trunk of the septic infection, which
would be favoured by any interference with the limb's blood supply.

These many and varied considerations made obvious the supreme
importance of amputation in the minds of military surgeons; a point of
view which held the field until the Listerian era brought antisepsis to
revolutionize surgical practice. Amputation had the plain advantage of
removing the damaged limb *in toto*, with all the multifarious complicating
factors arising from the brutal action of the bullet or cannon ball, and of
leaving the patient with a simple wound in place of an infinitely com-

plicated one. True, this wound also generally became infected and suppuration followed, but the amputation incision had been made through healthy tissues which might be expected to offer the best chances of recovery.

This much was common ground amongst different surgeons and in the practice of the various nations, but there was no agreement as to *when* the operation should be performed or on the technical details of its performance. These problems are spoken of by Larrey in the preface to his *Memoir on Amputations*:

"After the battle of Fontenoy the Royal Academy of Surgery was desirous of reaching a decision as to which wounds caused by firearms required immediate amputation and in which this should be deferred. Such a question could only be solved satisfactorily by surgeons who had had experience both on the battlefield and in the military hospitals, and this was fully recognized by the Academy when it refused the laureate-ship to Le Comte because his doctrines had not the support of practical experience. The prize was bestowed on Faure, but his principles have not been universally adopted. Today, after twenty years of ceaseless war which have brought our Art to a high state of perfection, there should be no two opinions on the subject. It is only after having continuously directed the health service as Surgeon-in-Chief and Inspector-General of the Armies for so long that I am come to discuss the various opinions put before the Academy, and venture to give a definite answer to this large question, which I look upon as one of the most important of all in military surgery.[1]

"If it should be said that the amputation of a limb is a cruel and dangerous operation, and one always fraught with grave consequences for the patient who is left in a mutilated condition, and that for these reasons there is more honour to be gained by preserving the limb than by amputating it, however skilfully and successfully done, the reply which admits of no denial is that amputation is an operation of necessity which offers a chance of recovery to an unfortunate individual, whose death appears certain by any other method of treatment; and that should there be any doubt that amputation is absolutely necessary for the patient's safety we defer it until nature has pronounced her verdict and given the most positive indications. We are entitled to add that this chance of recovery is much greater today than it was at the time of the enquiry by the Academy. Faure, in fact, tells us that out of some three hundred amputations after the battle of Fontenoy only about thirty succeeded, whereas we have succeeded in saving three-quarters of our patients, amongst them a number who had two limbs amputated. We attribute this success: (1) to a better appreciation of the indications for the operation and of the time at which it should be performed; (2) to the more methodical treatment of the wound; and (3) to a simpler and more dextrous operation, which is less painful and quicker than the older procedure.

*　　*　　*　　*　　*

[1] The material of this Memoir was based upon a thesis I sustained for my doctorate at the *École Spéciale de Médecine* of Paris in 1803. (See No. 1 of the collection of theses.)

"When a limb is so injured by gunshot that its preservation is impossible it should be amputated at once. The first four hours are an isolated period of calm which nature is able to maintain, and advantage should be taken of this to administer the appropriate remedy, as in any other dangerous malady.

"Amongst armies there are certain factors which make early amputation advisable: (1) The difficulties of transport on badly sprung vehicles of the wounded from the battlefield to the military hospitals, are such that much damage may be done to the wound and to the whole body by their jolting, that many die during the journey, especially in very hot or very cold weather. (2) The danger inherent in a long stay in hospital: a danger which amputation diminishes by changing a lacerated gunshot wound into one ready for immediate healing, thereby reducing the likelihood of fever and hospital gangrene. (3) There are cases when the wounded have to be abandoned. Here it is of importance that the amputation should have been performed; because once done the wound can be left for several days without dressing and the subsequent ones are easily carried out. Moreover the unfortunate men may fall into the hands of surgeons who have not a similar skill in operating; a fact which we have noted amongst a number of other nations whose ambulances are not organized as well as ours."

Larrey's insistence on early amputation, when amputation was necessary, was a major factor in his undoubted success, and the conditions in which he considered it the only reasonable treatment he illustrated with a wealth of detail and the histories of many cases—some of them scattered through the pages we have already quoted—which make fascinating reading. Although he lacked our comprehension of the pathological basis of much of his teaching, clinical experience brought him to the practical conclusion that operation should be carried out on war wounds within the first four hours—which is the teaching of our modern writers.

When we consider the conditions of the operation we may well conclude that they were actually a good deal more favourable than might appear at first sight. There was, of course, no sterilization of knife or saw, but where a series of amputations was performed in quick succession the mere mechanical cleansing of the instrument by wiping, coupled with the bactericidal property of the blood, probably gave a rough degree of asepsis. Further, the conditions in a temporary shelter or field ambulance were far more favourable for avoiding sepsis than were those in the infected wards of any hospital building. This Larrey knew well, and in all his teaching he also urged the desirability of the rapid evacuation of the wounded as an important factor in their recovery. Though all his theories may not have been correct there is no doubt that the practice was of great benefit to his patients.

His operative technique is thus described: "The amputation should be circular and in most cases in the continuity of the limb. The skin and subcutaneous tissue being divided they are retracted by an assistant, and this is made easier by severing any bands which attach them to the outside of the muscles. (It is extremely important to avoid the very painful procedure, used by many practitioners, of seizing the skin with the fingers or dissecting forceps and pulling on it forcibly whilst dissecting it off with a bistoury.) The flesh is cut through to the bone by a circular sweep at the level of the retracted integument. It is sometimes necessary to make a third, or fourth, or even more sweeps to divide the adhering muscles completely and as high as possible, so as to prevent the bone from protruding. The operation is completed by cutting through the bone and the immediate ligation of the vessels, care being taken to cut the threads at the level of the stump.

"The resulting stump is a hollow cone which unites readily. To keep the edges in apposition all that is required is to hold them in place by a loose circular bandage and a fine perforated linen dressing which covers the wound. Immediately on top of this we place a pad of lint, which is kept in position by two rather long compresses placed so that they cross each other, and finish the dressing by a large bandage of suitable length, which should not pass over the end of the stump; this helps to control the action of the muscles and prevents their retraction.

"Bandages which cause tight union, such as the capelline and others of this nature, should be avoided. They obstruct and exhaust the parts by opposing the engorgement which is necessary for the production of a good suppuration. The subsequent dressings should be made with mild and simple measures, such as balsamic digestives to which tonic substances may be added according to the circumstances. Care should be taken to keep the vicinity of the wound extremely clean and to aid cutaneous transpiration.

"The method I have described can be used in all cases, including those for which amputation by flaps is commonly employed; which in my experience involves many inconveniences. I have tried both methods side by side, and the uniform success I have had with the circular one has convinced me of its advantages over the flap method, which is still recommended by a number of practitioners.

"Amputations through joints, or more precisely the extirpation of limbs, should be by flaps. These soon unite with each other and adhere over the articular surfaces, which should not become exfoliated since they have not been altered by contact with air or touched by the knife.

"Finally, the operation having been performed by one method or another, we have to supervise the after-treatment. It is not enough to have carried out an operation skilfully: it is just as important to foresee and to prevent the complications which may follow it."

*   *   *   *   *

It was sometimes imputed to Larrey that he was unduly fond of amputating. It is easy to see how such a prejudice might have grown up, and he relates many examples of differences of opinion between himself and his colleagues over this question—not unnaturally the decision in the outcome generally supported his view! His deep conviction of the life-saving effect of the operation and a fear of losing the opportunity of the fleeting hour may well have decided him in cases of doubt. At the same time it would be unjust to suggest that he was not prepared to temporize where the state of the patient and the wound seemed to him to warrant it.

"In particular we should try to preserve the upper limbs, which can be of greatest use to the patient even if considerably mutilated. This general rule does not apply to the lower extremities. When these are the seat of chronic ulcerating lesions with caries affecting the joints they are more harmful than useful; walking is painful and difficult, and there is an accumulation and stagnation of fluid in the limb due to chronic persistent inflammation. The engorgement aggravates the ulcers and often inflammatory changes and gangrene appear, making the unfortunate patients envy others whom they see walking with artificial limbs. . . ."

"Amputation in any case must be the last resort: but once the necessity for it is realized there should be no delay and it should be performed before the onset of early complications. If these are already present by the time the surgeon has been called to the wounded man he should wait until they have subsided. Only through the exercise of experience and skill can the precepts of good surgery profit the patient."

Although an untiring advocate of early amputation in military practice, which was largely made possible through the work of his mobile ambulances, Larrey fully accepted the alternative of delayed or *secondary amputation* in certain cases. This he considered appropriate in traumatic gangrene, in tetanic spasm—some of his cases were genuine tetanus, others may not have been—in the gross suppuration of compound fractures accompanied by hectic fever and diarrhoea, and where an unhealthy conical stump with necrosis of the bone had developed.

Amputation of the arm at the shoulder joint

Larrey was an innovator of this operation which he had employed as early as the Egyptian campaign, and according to Guthrie, the British authority on gunshot wounds at the beginning of the nineteenth century, he performed it more frequently than any other man. It had long been looked upon as a most dangerous procedure: prejudicial to the life of the victim and to the reputation of the surgeon. The falsity of these ideas was proved by Larrey, who operated by a method of his own devising.

Writing of the casualties at Wagram he says: "I amputated the arm at the shoulder in two soldiers of the Imperial Guard and three of the Line by my own method (p. 119); their wounds had no special features apart from being of a kind which necessitated disarticulation. I likewise operated on three others at Essling, bringing the total to fourteen, of whom twelve recovered completely. The thirteenth, a *fusilier-grenadier*, Grave by name, became depressed by the thought that he could no longer provide for himself and after telling his comrades that he wished to kill himself suddenly threw himself out of a window on the first floor and was killed. The fourteenth, who was very weak and very seriously wounded, died within twenty-four hours.

"My experience has long taught me that, other things being equal, amputation through a joint in a case of a recent wound is more successful than one in the continuity of a limb. The success obtained in disarticulation of the arm at the shoulder in the cases I have just described has confirmed me in this opinion.

"This difference of outcome from amputations in continuity appears to me to depend on the facts that in amputation in continuity: (1) The part of the bone cut through by the saw must become exfoliated, either in an obvious or an insensible way which nature at once attempts to effect; a process which involves the development and cicatrization of the vessels of the bone. This is a more or less long and difficult process depending upon the age of the patient, which makes the success of the operation uncertain, or else delays it. (2) The severance of a number of muscles the contraction and irritation of which is often accompanied by mishaps and, moreover, nature has so many parts to heal separately. (3) The extent of the damage to the different parts of the wounded limb; for should this reach to the joint such an amputation is futile.

"When we amputate at the joint we are more certain of success: (1) Because the section is made beyond the limits of the disease. (2) Because the adjacent bone remains intact and undergoes no alterations as a consequence of the operation. (3) Because there are no muscles to divide, if we except in certain instances parts of some muscles which are divided in the direction of their fibres rather than cut transversely.

"The division of tendons is no drawback, they are insensitive and unless they are exposed to the air for a considerable time they do not slough and they readily become incorporated in the scar of the flaps. A single difficulty present in this operation, which doubtless can cause it to fail, is the risk of including nerve trunks in the arterial ligatures; but it is easy to avoid this by carefully following the instructions.

"In conclusion, I can state that out of ten casualties requiring amputation, disarticulation will be successful in nine, whereas it is rare for two-thirds to be saved when the amputation is practised in continuity. This difference is still more marked in chronic diseases of bone, such as deep seated scrofulous caries, spina ventosa, or necrosis; and though the bony changes may appear to reach only for a short distance beyond the focus of obvious disease they usually extend to the joint above or very near to it A large number of examples have shewn me the truth of this.

"I think that the foregoing summary of the advantages to be gained from amputation at the shoulder joint should be an encouragement to practitioners of surgery to direct their attention to the site at which limbs should be amputated in both recent and chronic diseases."

"These views, which I communicated to the Institute on our return from Russia, confirm and extend the principles laid down in the Memoir relative to this operation to be found in my surgical account of the Army of Egypt. But as their chief object is to give the details of the operative procedure which I have adopted exclusively, and which experience has shewn me to be the best, I shall describe it as carefully as possible.

"We shall begin by assuming that the operation is unavoidable and that all preparations have been made for its performance.[2] The patient being seated at a convenient height, I commence by a longitudinal incision which begins at the edge of the acromion process and continues down to about an inch below the

[2] One is apt to forget that these operations were done without anaesthesia.

neck of the humerus: by this incision I cut through the skin and divide the fibres of the deltoid muscle into two equal parts. Next, I cause an assistant to retract the skin of the arm towards the shoulder, and I form the anterior and posterior flaps by two oblique cuts, from within outwards and downwards in such a way that the tendons of the pectoralis major and latissimus dorsi muscles are included in either section (Fig. 22). There is no fear of touching the axillary vessels as they are beyond the reach of the point of the knife. I then separate these flaps from their attachments: an assistant retracts them and at the same time compresses the two cut circumflex arteries, so that the whole shoulder joint is exposed. By a third circular sweep of the knife around the head of the humerus, the capsule and articular tendons are divided; the head of the bone is then pulled a little outwards and the knife is slipped round to the posterior aspect to divide the ligaments and tendons on this side. The assistant immediately places the index fingers of his two hands on the brachial plexus, to compress the artery and control the bleeding, and finally the cutting edge of the knife is turned backwards and the whole bundle of axillary vessels is cut through at the level of the lower angles of the two flaps and beyond the assistant's fingers. The patient does not lose a drop of blood. The end of the axillary artery is easily found without the pressure being relaxed and is seized with dissecting forceps and ligatured immediately: it only remains to tie the circumflex arteries and the operation is over.

"The wound is wiped and the flaps brought together and fixed in loose contact by two or three adhesive bandages and some fine linen steeped in a tonic liquid, such as hot wine, and the whole stump covered with a similar linen dressing. A pad of lint or fine tow is applied over this, and simple square compresses and a special bandage of my own contriving complete the dressing.

"The inflammatory swelling sets in soon afterwards and passes through its stages without incident; the suppuration is readily established between the fifth and sixth days; the depths of the wound become clean and the ligatures usually come away before the tenth day. Cicatrization begins from the circumference between the seventeenth to the twentieth days and advances rapidly towards the centre; it usually is complete between the thirty-fifth to the fortieth day. The scar forms a line parallel to the anterior edge of the scapula.

"This procedure is applicable to almost all military cases:

1st. Because, in general, all gunshot wounds which disorganize or mutilate the arm so extensively as to require amputation, destroy almost the whole or a portion of the point of the shoulder—it being the most prominent part—and usually there is sufficient of the soft parts left at the sides to form the flaps.

2nd. Because in the very rare instances of the destruction of the lateral parts and the preservation of the middle area, nothing is to be gained by forming a flap according to Lafaye's method or those who follow him; such a flap is bound to break down on account of its isolation and distance from the parts with which it should become adherent, and from the small number of blood vessels nourishing it. In such a case I divide this part down the middle and give these two flaps the shape which they would have had if they had been entire. I have found that the disarticulation of the arm without flaps heals better than when an attempt is made to preserve flaps formed in a way which is not natural. Thus, for example, in cases where there has been total destruction of the flesh of the point of the shoulder, I have seen some army surgeons cover the head of the scapula with a flap formed from the soft parts of the axillary region of the arm, in the confident belief that it would unite with the underlying tissues and take the place of superior or lateral flaps. The fate of such a flap could be foretold: it breaks down, secondary haemorrhages occur, the gangrenous affection extends by contagion to the whole wound and brings about the patient's death. This was the fate of two men operated on in this way in the last campaigns and for whom I could do nothing at the time I was called in.

"I would cite, as remarkable examples of the success of the operation without flaps, the cases of Generals Fugières (see p. 42), d'Aboville, and of many other officers and soldiers who are mentioned in my Campaigns. . . ."

"What is the explanation of the success we have obtained in disarticulation by the method just described? A success so great that in over a hundred such operations, performed in the armies or in Paris, more than ninety have given a most fortunate result, as can easily be proved from the registers of the Pensions Office at the Ministry of War. I shall try to indicate this, without presuming to pronounce too positively on the question.

1st. The vertical incision in the centre of the point of the shoulder really determines the rest of the operation and facilitates its performance: further, it is made in the twinkling of an eye. The two flaps are formed exactly and precisely to the desired size immediately afterwards, so that this incision has the effect of a circular amputation. The head of the humerus is always easily disarticulated. By having the vessels held before I cut through the fold of the axilla I obviate all haemorrhage, and there is no risk to the patient's life: this is an inestimable advantage and on it depends the success of the operation.

2nd. It is natural for the flaps to heal readily, since their union is in the vertical line of the glenoid cavity of the scapula, and most of the muscles of the stump have been divided in the long axis of their fibres or cut across at their tendinous insertions, which favours the union of the wound and a linear scar.

3rd. Finally, we believe that there are very few nerves in the shoulder joint concerned with internal life, whereas there are many of these around the hip-joint: this may explain in a general way the frequent success of the one operation and the failure of the other.

"From what has been said it will be easy to make a comparison between my method of disarticulation and the other known procedures: a matter on which I myself shall not presume to judge."

*   *   *   *   *

Amputation through the Tibial Condyles

"During our campaign in Egypt I twice had occasion to amputate the leg very close to the knee joint, at about the level of the head of the fibula, which I found it necessary to remove. The success I was fortunate enough to obtain dispersed my early fears about operating through the substance of the tibial condyles. Would not one expect the advent of necrosis—very easily set up in the spongy substance of bones—and its rapid spread; leading to involvement of the knee joint and its ultimate ankylosis? No such complication occurred in these patients and the healing of the stump was as quick, to within a matter of a few days, as in amputations of the leg at the seat of election, that is to say three or four fingers' breadth below the tibial tubercle.

"Since that memorable expedition I have used this new method a number of times for wounds which did not allow of amputation at the latter site, and I have had at least as much success as by the other procedure. Army-Surgeon Garrigues, having on many occasions performed this operation above the level favoured by authors, expounded its advantages in his inaugural thesis printed

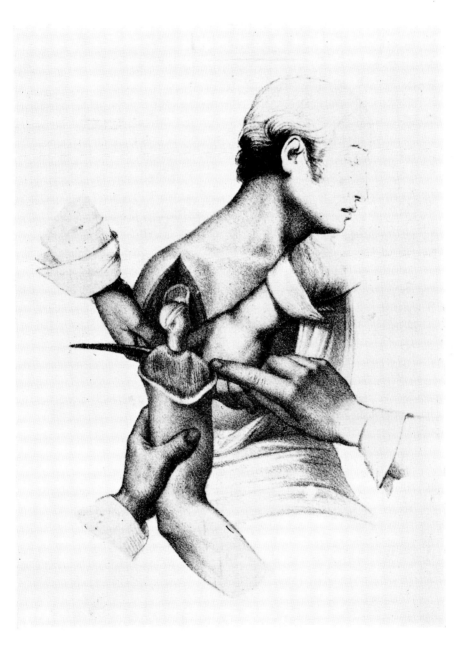

FIG. 22. Amputation at the shoulder.

[*To face p.* 126

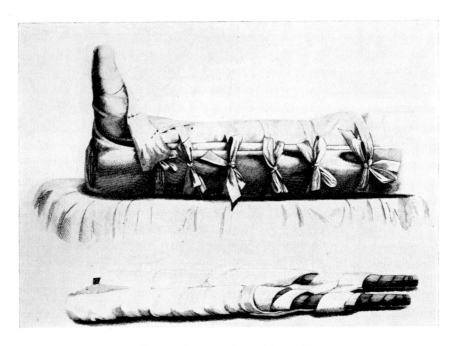

FIG. 23. Larrey's *Appareil inamovible*.

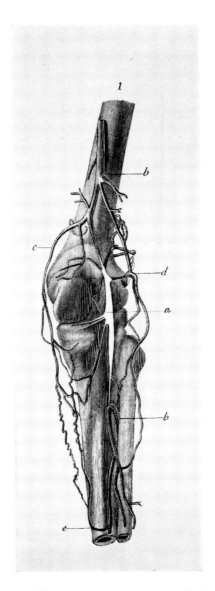

FIG. 24. Collateral anastomoses around the knee.

MÉMOIRES

DE

CHIRURGIE MILITAIRE,

ET

CAMPAGNES

DU BARON D. J. LARREY,

Chirurgien en chef de l'Hôpital de la Garde royale, ex-Inspecteur général du service de santé militaire; ex-premier Chirurgien de la grande armée en Russie, Saxe, etc.; Commandeur de l'Ordre Royal de la Légion-d'Honneur, Chevalier de l'Ordre de la Couronne de Fer; ancien Professeur de l'Hôpital militaire d'instruction du Val-de-Grâce; Docteur en Chirurgie et en Médecine. Membre de l'Institut d'Egypte, des Sociétés de la Faculté de Médecine de Paris, d'Émulation, Philomatique; Associé correspondant de celles de Toulouse, de Montpellier, de Lyon, de l'Académie Impériale Josephine de Vienne; des Académies de Berlin, d'Jéna, de Munich, de Bruxelles, de Madrid, de Rome, de Naples, de Turin.

Eò adductus sum ut multis meorum æqualium hinc
indè errantibus viam monstrarem et aliquantulùm
munirem.   BAGL. PRAX. MED., *lib. I, cap. I.*

TOME IV.

~~~~~~~~~~~~

PARIS,

Chez J. SMITH, Imprimeur-Libraire, rue de Montmorency.

=======

1817.

FIG. 25. Title page to Larrey's Mémoires. Vol IV.

in 1806. In praising the work of this estimable surgeon, whose principles we have partially adopted, it behoves us to say that in his enthusiasm he has gone a little beyond the limits marked out by experience and anatomy.

"I shall not analyse this dissertation but shall limit myself to a description of the procedure which I use in place of that generally employed up to the present, and I shall indicate the upper limits which should not be passed if the patient is to be preserved from complications of a most serious kind. The reader will be able to judge for himself the difference between my teaching and that of M. Garrigues.

"Although I had performed this operation at my new seat of choice on many of those wounded in the battles of Austerlitz and Eylau, I was never able to follow the results for a sufficient length of time until the battles in the last Austrian campaign, where cases of amputation were as numerous as they were varied.

"At Wagram and Essling we amputated the legs of nine guardsmen at the level I shall describe. The serious wounds they had received from artillery fire reached almost as high as the knee, so that my colleagues who saw them were all of the opinion that they required amputation through the thigh. I dissipated their fears about amputating below the knee joint and I declare, with the conviction which comes from experience, that it is no more dangerous an operation than the more usual one at the seat of election: but it is important, contrary to the opinion of M. Garrigues, not to go above the level of the tibial tuberosity, which may be divided through its thickest part or, at the very most, at the insertion of the patella tendon. An imaginary horizontal line at this point usually passes below the articulation of the fibula and the base of the expansion of the tibial condyles, but the relation of the tuberosity to the head of the fibula varies in different subjects and for this reason the tuberosity should be taken as the extreme limit. By making the section too high the patella tendon is severed from its attachments and the synovial bursa behind it opened, and often the lateral insertions of the articular ligaments are cut; resulting in retraction of the patella, effusion of synovial fluid, profound alterations in the joint, and other grave complications which may endanger the life of the patient or necessitate amputation through the thigh at a later date.

"By dividing the bone at the level of the tibial tuberosity the insertion of the patella ligament is preserved, as well as those of the flexor tendons of the leg which are necessary for the movements of the stump: the synovial capsule is not interfered with, and the condyles are cut through low enough for us not to fear caries. If we compare amputation of the leg by this new method with that through the thigh, which is advocated by authorities for the cases for which I propose it, we are bound to be convinced that the advantages of the former to the patient are inestimable. To begin with, life is much less imperilled, since we attack the lesser appendage. The operation is equally easy in both cases. The healing of the scar in the stump is as quick in leg as in thigh. I have never seen bone necrosis develop in the spongy part of the tibia: on the other hand this tissue rapidly diminishes in bulk, on account of the vascular changes which occur there; it quickly becomes covered, its healing is rapid and there is no obvious exfoliation. When the part of the fibula which remains is short, as is usually the case, it should be removed. I have done this many times; it is functionless and interferes with the use of an artificial leg. It is important to preserve as much skin as possible, since it comes together during healing and in the end covers the stump; in addition it is necessary to divide the part of this integument opposite to the tibia vertically, to prevent its perforation.

"Such is the operative procedure we have used in the cases in which we believed it to be required. The stump, which includes the knee and one or two fingers' breadths of the leg, provides the patient, when he becomes convalescent, with a solid point of support. The *sustentation* of his body is sure, and he carries out all the movements of walking with the greatest ease and without the aid of a stick. He can readily use an artificial leg of natural shape since his knee is kept flexed. The stump, of course, is not so long that it projects beyond the calf of the mechanical leg, and the patient can manage this as well as if it were entered into the socket, as it is in those in whom amputation has been performed above the malleoli. The latter operation is not favoured by experienced surgeons, not only because not all who have undergone such an amputation—soldiers for example—can afford the sort of mechanical leg necessary, but also for the important reason that it is almost always associated with serious complications, since the small amount of subcutaneous tissue and muscle in this part of the leg and the density of the bones make healing difficult: furthermore, nervous irritation is more apt to develop at this site than at the seat of election and the suppuration, which is always blood stained, is only established with difficulty.

"I have seen many amputations performed through this part and almost all the patients have died of either nervous fever or tetanus. General * * * * , who was operated upon in this way at the battle of Wagram, is a striking example. It is therefore better whenever possible to amputate the leg high rather than too low, and only to go as high as the thigh when the knee joint is really damaged.

"We shall add some observations on a number of wounded men operated upon by this method after my return to Paris.[3]

"The first, Louis by name, a corporal of dragoons of the Guard, was brought to hospital for a kick from a horse in his left leg. There was a contused wound of some centimetres in extent in the front of the upper part of the leg, with comminution of the tibia and fracture of the fibula. The flat surface of the horseshoe had struck him in such a way as to cause an injury similar to that produced by a spent cannon ball. At first sight the wound did not appear particularly serious so that, contrary to my own opinion, most of my colleagues thought the limb could be saved. I regretfully concurred in this decision and contented myself with cleaning the laceration, removing bone fragments, and putting the limb in a loosely-fitting fracture dressing, soaked in camphorated Goulard water. During the early stages there were no serious complications, but between the ninth and thirteenth days these appeared, in the shape of acute stabbing pains, gangrenous inflammation in the wound, fever, insomnia, etc. We used all the appropriate means of treatment, but the symptoms continued to worsen; the limb was threatened with total gangrene and the patient was in imminent danger.

"A number of purulent sinuses developed and before long there was a haemorrhage from the anterior tibial artery, which caused the patient's collapse and made amputation necessary. An unusual occurrence during his treatment was a convulsive hiccough, brought on by the lightest pressure on the leg or on its dressing.

"The same persons who earlier were opposed to amputation now wished that it should be done through the thigh; but as the knee was so far unaffected I performed it through the leg, at the risk of a second operation higher up being required should the tibial condyles prove to be fractured or subject to caries;

[3] I prefer to report cases upon which I have operated in Paris, as I have been able to follow the results of the operation at greater leisure and with more care.

and I thought that in this state of uncertainty it was better to expose the patient to the chance of a double operation than to deprive him of his knee, the advantages of which from all accounts are inestimable. The amputation was therefore done through the condyles, a little above the tibial tuberosity. We had great difficulty in dealing with the adynamic condition which supervened after the first stages had been passed. However, his strength was regained, the wound became clean and thanks to care and attention we had the happiness of saving the man and preserving his knee: the scar of the stump was firmly consolidated at the end of four months. Today the soldier walks with a wooden leg without stick or crutch. . . ."

* * * * *

"If amputation be urgent to save the life of a wounded man, in cases such as we have been discussing, it is no less so when two of the limbs are mutilated by a ball. I have noticed that when there is a delay of only a few hours such patients almost invariably die. Before the invention of the mobile field ambulance which makes it possible to attend to casualties on the battlefield, pensioners who had lost two legs or two arms were never seen—even today they are rare—which means that the operation is usually done too late. The double nervous irritation from two disorganized limbs causes so great a disturbance in both the interior life and that of external relation, that the wounded man succumbs in a short time from the effects of his severe pain and suffering. Once this state of perturbation is established amputation will not stay its progress. I have seen many soldiers die although operated on within twenty-four hours, because even so the operation had been too late. Out of three in whom I amputated two limbs at Wagram, the one who was operated on first, within a few instants of being wounded, was the only one to live: the two others died in spite of all the care we could give them. The case of the first is interesting by reason of the similarity in the healing of the two stumps and their symmetry, which was very convenient when it came to the patient's walking, which he was able to do on two wooden legs. The necessity to obtain this symmetry is one of the precepts of my teaching which I was able to put into practice here. Many cases of this sort, on whom I operated in Egypt and Poland, have been gratified by the ease with which they can walk without crutches, and with hardly the need of a stick."

Amputation through the hip joint

This formidable undertaking was rarely attempted in the era we are dealing with, and was often taught to be quite unjustified. But occasionally there were men bold enough to submit their patients to it, sometimes, as in military practice, because the limb had already been practically disarticulated by shell or cannon ball, or, less frequently, in civil practice because it offered the sole, if slender, chance of saving the victim from certain death. Guthrie, in the first edition of his book,[4] remarks that it is

[4] G. J. Guthrie *On gunshot wounds of the extremities, requiring the different operations of amputation, with their after treatment.* 1815.

seldom performed and widely condemned, as "an unnecessary cruelty unworthy of the character of a surgeon". Percival Pott (1714–1788) said that he had seen it done, "and am now very sure I shall never do it, unless it be on a dead body". Brodie (1783–1826) performed it unsuccessfully at St. George's Hospital. A British army surgeon, Brownrigg, had one success in four or five attempts in Spain, the man reaching England alive and well, but no details of his cases are forthcoming.

Larrey, to whose views on early amputation Guthrie pays generous tribute, performed the operation seven times. Once, as a young officer with the Army of the Rhine; twice at St. Jean d'Acre, on an officer who survived for seven days and succumbed to plague, and on a soldier who died during the retreat. At Wagram he operated on two guardsmen, admittedly hopeless cases, in order to relieve their sufferings; both died shortly afterwards from shock. In Russia he performed the operation on a prisoner who survived for twenty-nine days and died—it was believed— from the combined effects of dysentery, starvation and bad food. Finally, at Mozaisk, he operated on a French soldier who reached the hospital at Witebsk three months later, and was seen there by the surgeon in charge who wrote to Larrey that the man was cured. Although he hoped one day to find this patient at the Invalides, Larrey never saw him again and was thus deprived of the satisfaction of personally confirming his success. However, it seems reasonable to credit him with this. His conviction that the operation was practicable and in suitable cases justifiable remained, and there is evidence that his faith in this influenced its successful performance at a later date by Guthrie upon a French prisoner, François Gay, whom he saw in a British hospital in Brussels, after Waterloo (p. 242). This must have changed Guthrie's outlook, for in the second edition of his book (1827) he says that he saved one out of two cases he operated upon.

Larrey's own account of the operation, written after the Egyptian Campaign, is as follows:

"I shall now report the results I obtained from amputation of the thigh at the hip joint. I have had occasion to perform this operation three times; once in the Army of the Rhine, when I directed the mobile field ambulance, and twice in Egypt. The first of these operations was performed without mishap and the patient lived for several hours in so tranquil a condition that the outlook seemed favourable, but a forced march of a night and a day in the rigours of winter with the fatigue and disturbances of transport were probably the causes of his death.

"Before I give the details of the other two cases I wish to shew the practicability of this operation and its necessity in certain circumstances. I shall also describe my technique.

"However cruel an operation may be it is an act of humanity in the hands of a surgeon, since it may save the life of a wounded man when this is in danger; and the greater and more urgent the danger the more prompt and energetic should be the succour. '*Ad extremos morbos, extrema remedia equisite optima*' (Hippocrates). In this situation the surgeon does his duty without thought for his reputation.[5]

[5] Larrey constantly uses the charming expression *l'homme de l'Art*, which I can only

"The successes I had obtained, albeit rarely, in the double amputation through the thighs, or in that of the arm at the shoulder joint, greatly encouraged me to undertake the disarticulation at the hip. Towards the middle of the last century the Academy of Paris drew the attention of all the surgeons in Europe to this by offering a prize in so important a surgical problem. Most of the memoirs of this learned company spoke in favour of the operation, though there was not a single example of success in acute conditions, such as wounds caused by firearms. The accounts given by authors and the successes obtained concerned chronic diseases, such as caries of the head of the femur, *spina ventosa* and gangrene of the limb.

"The alarming aspect of the wound, the difficulty of disarticulating the thigh bone from its cavity in the *os innominatum*, the danger of the retraction of the flexor muscles, of haemorrhage, and from the damming-back of the blood, are no doubt the reasons which have prevented army surgeons from performing the operation, for cases which required it must surely have occurred more than once in their practice.

"To these objections it may be replied:

1st. The size of the wound is more alarming than dangerous. The caesarean operation on the living woman is successfully performed, and is recommended today by many practitioners. The chief surgeon of the Rouen hospital (l'Aumonier) has successfully removed a large scirrhus of the ovary. We have examples of the arm and scapula being torn off in serious accidents, and yet the subjects have recovered. Moreover, by the operation the surgeon will reduce the size of the wound by more than a half. The example of M. Pelletan enlarged my views. This illustrious surgeon, having unsuccessfully performed an operation for aneurysm of the axillary artery, far from being discouraged desired that drawings should be made of the tumour, the anatomical relationships, and his operative procedure. These drawings are on view in the museum of the School of Medicine to evoke the genius of the practitioner of the surgical Art, to illuminate his actions, and to shew to all and sundry that the disease is more terrible than the operation.

2nd. The manual difficulties, and in particular the disarticulation of the head of the femur, are diminished by the method I have devised. I submit this to the judgement of my colleagues.

3rd. The retraction of the muscles has been exaggerated. In the operations I have performed it has been negligible, or in any case has stopped far short of the pelvic openings. Again, my method has the advantage of obviating this inconvenience.

4th. The dangerous effects of haemorrhage can be prevented by the temporary compression of the orifices of the cut vessels by intelligent assistants, and their immediate and systematic ligation. These ligatures stop the flow of blood more easily and more certainly than those which include in their grasp the flesh and cellular tissues around the arteries. As to the damming-back of blood, which practitioners have regarded as a fatal effect, it is of no consequence. I believe that I have given proof of the lack of foundation for this fear in my memoir on amputations, which will be found at the end of my account of the campaign of Austerlitz.

I shall further adduce, in support of my opinion on the practicability of amputation of the thigh at its origin, the account recorded in the *Opuscules* of M. Mouraud, p. 183. This author relates the case of a soldier who had both of

lamely translate as *the surgeon*. He also refers to *l'Art* for the surgical art, but usage hardly permits of a literal translation, however we may regret this.

his legs amputated high up as well as his two arms, the latter so close to the shoulder that he could not hold anything in his axillae. Despite this state of immobilization he enjoyed good health. I recall also the case of Samuel Wood, whose shoulder was torn off. In the course of the present work, and more particularly in my memoir on amputations, examples have been given of cures obtained without any internal disturbance in cases of amputations of a whole limb, and also of a part of both upper and lower limbs in the same patient.

"I believe that the extirpation of the thigh is indicated in three principal conditions arising from wounds caused by firearms.

"*The first* is where the limb is shattered or shot away by a cannon ball, or the explosion of a shell or bomb, so close to the joint that an amputation in continuity is impossible.

"*The second* is where a cannister shot or large bullet shatters the upper end of the femur near the trochanters, and ruptures the femoral artery or the sciatic nerve.

"*The third* is when gangrene develops or threatens in the leg and thigh as high as the hip joint, as a result of a wound causing violent disintegration of the soft parts. I have seen a number of such cases.

"Those who have recommended the operation of disarticulation are not agreed as to how it should be done. Almost all, fearing haemorrhage from the femoral artery, begin by the ligation of this vessel, and then having formed a flap from the buttock muscles they expose the posterior part of the joint, open its capsule, cut the round ligament, and finish the operation by forming an internal flap.

"This method is extremely painful, difficult and dangerous. The bleeding from the gluteal, sciatic, and circumflex arteries is very difficult to arrest with the limb still in place. The bone is disarticulated with the greatest difficulty, and from the different positions in which the patient has to be placed there is a risk of tearing the ligature from the femoral artery, or that in passing the knife from the cotyloid cavity to divide the attachments of the triceps adductor muscles this vessel may be wounded above the ligature however much care has been taken to apply this close to the crural arch. There are other drawbacks which it is not necessary to give in detail.

"In my method of operating I place the patient at the foot of his bed in a nearly horizontal position and stand on the inner side of the thigh I am operating on. A strong and intelligent assistant compresses the femoral artery at the point where it passes over the bony channel of the same name. I then make an incision in the integument of the groin along the course of the femoral vessels, which I expose. I dissect them carefully, and having isolated the nerve which lies on the outer side, I pass a curved blunt needle between it and the artery, so as to include both artery and vein, and tie them.[6] I am careful to place this ligature immediately below the crural arch, so as to be above the origin of the profunda femoris, which would give rise to a fatal haemorrhage should it be cut during the operation without this precaution being taken. Having tied this ligature and placed a reserve one in position, I thrust my knife perpendicularly between the tendons of the muscles attached to the small trochanter and the base of the femoral neck, in such a way that the point comes out behind and diametrically opposite, and by directing the knife in an oblique direction inwards and downwards I sever with a single cut all the parts which

[6] It is possible to dispense with the preliminary ligation of the femoral artery if one has very intelligent assistants. There are many advantages in tying the ligature later, at the extremity of each vessel.

will form the inner flap, which should not be too bulky. An assistant retracts this flap towards the genitals and the joint comes into view. The obdurator and some branches of the pudic arteries have been cut and must now be ligatured. A single incision with a bistoury suffices to lay open the whole joint capsule, and by abducting the thigh the head of the bone is almost dislocated. The round ligament is seen and, as may well be imagined, is easy to sever with the same bistoury. I then take a small straight knife to form the external and posterior flap, which is done by passing its cutting edge between the bony margin of the cotyloid cavity and the great trochanter, and I finish the flap by dividing the parts in an outward and downward direction, keeping fairly near to this prominence and giving the flap a rounded shape. The assistant who supports the flaps closes the mouths of the severed arteries which are now ligatured in turn. It is necessary to tie them all, down to the smallest, to prevent consecutive haemorrhage and to enable the flaps to be united. If the parts are healthy a number of interrupted sutures may be inserted by means of the needles I have described, but the muscle must not be touched; it suffices for the sutures to include the skin and fat. The flaps are kept in contact by graduated compresses steeped in red wine and by a suitably applied retaining bandage.

"This method is quick and I have always found it easy. I thought of it before I joined the armies, and the trials I made upon the dead and on animals made me hopeful of its success.

"In the period which follows, the surgeon should watch over the general state of his patient: bleeding if there is the least sign of plethora, refreshing medicines, antispasmodics, rest and diet ought not to be neglected. By the aid of these measures it is possible to prevent the complications which often accompany such large operations as amputations. The adhesion of the flaps takes place promptly, and suppuration only occurs in tissues which have been bruised or seriously injured by the damaging agent and are left behind.

"The cases which follow appear to me to clarify the problem which has occupied the academies without a decision being reached; and the success which I have obtained, although not complete, leads me to believe that my efforts will not be fruitless for the development of our Art. Those who practise surgery should see in the operation which I suggest a means of snatching from death victims who up to now have been abandoned to it.

"The second wounded man on whom I had reason to perform this operation was an officer of the 18th demi-brigade, Bonhomme by name, who was brought to me from the trench of St. Jean d'Acre with an enormous wound of the right thigh, the result of a bomb explosion.

"The muscles were lacerated or destroyed over a large part of the circumference of the thigh; the femoral artery had been torn five or six fingers' breadth below the crural arch, and the femur comminuted up to the level of the great trochanter. The officer had lost a large amount of blood and was in a weak state; in fact I thought that without the amputation of his thigh, which was called for there and then, he had only a few minutes to live. I went to work at once as I shall describe.

"I exposed the common femoral artery. I passed two ligatures, with the precautions I have mentioned, and tied the artery and femoral vein. The formation of the inner flap and the division of the joint capsule were easily accomplished; the bone was promptly disarticulated and I finished my operation with the formation of the external flap.

"Because of the regular shape of the flaps I was able to obtain an exact apposition, and it was easy to fix them in relationship to each other by the aid of adhesive plasters and a retaining bandage. The wounded man passed the remainder of the day and the following night in as tranquil a state as could be desired. I administered some antispasmodic potions and prescribed refreshing drinks and light broth with a little wine. On the second day the dressing was soaked with blood-stained effusion, but there were no engorgement, pain or tension in the stump. The second night was passable and the patient had three hours good sleep. On the third day I removed the outer parts of the dressing in order to renew them. This day was an excellent one. His excretions were easily made and the officer declared that he was hungry. I allowed him rice soup at night and morning.

"On the third night and following day he was slightly heated, with throbbing in the stump and general feverishness; this was followed by profuse sweating, calm and sleep. On my visiting him the next morning I found the dressing soaked with a purulent exudate. The flaps had already united over the greater part of their surface leaving at their anterior and posterior junctions a gap of about five centimetres where I had left the ligatures of the vessels. I dressed the wound methodically and renewed the bandage. On the fifth day everything was in the best possible state: the suppuration in the two small wounds which remained was already established and laudable. On the sixth day his condition was yet better and everything promised me a cure; but the overcrowded state of the ambulances and the impossibility of isolating the wounded, even those most severely hurt, in the circumstances in which we found ourselves, were the causes of an unfortunate event during the following night, which our difficult position had not allowed me to foresee.

"A soldier, who had been developing plague in his tent for several days, was hit in the leg by a cannon ball, just as he was being brought to hospital. Although very ill with plague he was taken by my orders to the ward for the wounded, where he was laid on the same straw paliasse as the officer of whom I have been speaking and infected him with plague which shewed itself on the sixth night. Two days later the wound in the stump became gangrenous, and its progress was so rapid that death came quickly to destroy the hopes that his favourable condition had roused in me two days earlier.

"My last case was a young man of about twenty, a drummer in the 2nd Light Demi-Brigade. His right thigh was blown off at about the middle by the explosion of a bomb at the last assault on Acre; the fracture extended into the joint and the flesh was lost and disorganized. Although very weak from loss of blood he was in great pain which he expressed by the most terrible cries.[7] I at once proceeded to extirpate the thigh by the

---

[7] I have found that these large wounds are followed very quickly by fearful pain and violent muscle spasms, which soon lead to convulsions and death. For this reason it is advisable to resect the broken bones and torn flesh with all speed so as to render the wound as simple as possible; once the operation has been done the wounded man's sufferings are calmed and he blesses the hand which has aided him.

same method as in the preceding case. As this young man was rather stout I thought that I would insert a number of sutures to keep the flaps in place and prevent their separation.

"Some long compresses were arranged in cruciform fashion on the stump and the whole kept in place by a suitable bandage. The operation was carried out without delay and with a minimum loss of blood. Shortly afterwards he became calm and had several hours of good sleep. The movements of the army, which almost immediately began to prepare for its retreat to Egypt, obliged me to send him away with the other wounded and I learnt later that he had died on the march."

*   *   *   *   *

Larrey recognized that in favourable circumstances the wound resulting from an immediate amputation might heal if left untouched under its original dressings; and that divorce from the hospital ward and freedom from interference were important contributory factors to such a happy outcome. We have already remarked that in conditions in the field, with the knife being plentifully exposed to the antibacterial action of the blood and mechanically cleansed by repeated use, and with the full *débridement* which Larrey favoured a wound could result which was not highly infected and was also devoid of *débris* of all sorts and of dead tissue. Such a wound, if kept away from the infected atmosphere of a surgical ward, was not ill-placed for uncomplicated healing. As his experience grew Larrey's references to cases of this sort became more frequent, until in his later campaigns we find him plainly advocating such a line of treatment. He gives a number of examples of its success, amongst these one particularly interesting to us—that of Colonel Lawless. Lawless was Professor of Physiology at the Royal College of Surgeons in Dublin. He joined the United Irishmen, fled to France to escape arrest, and there became commander of the 3rd Foreign Regiment which was composed almost exclusively of Irishmen. At the crossing of the Bober (Battle of Dresden) his left leg was shattered by a cannon ball. Larrey wrote:

"As I was with my light ambulance at this advanced post during the engagement, where I was in great danger, I was able to attend to him at once and amputated the leg through the tibial condyles. Since the army and the Guard were retiring on Dresden I advised this honourable patient to mount a horse again and make his way to his home in France, without stopping and without touching the dressing. I advised him simply to sponge the exterior daily, and to keep the stump wrapped in a piece of cloth or sheepskin. By such measures dressings were unnecessary, especially during the season of approaching winter. My advice was followed exactly, and the general covered the long journey from the battlefield to his home at Tours on horseback, with his stump carried in a stirrup bandage passed over his shoulders and without having it dressed on a single occasion. On his arrival his health was generally satisfactory, and on the dressing being removed the wound was healed with a linear scar."

Lawless lived for many years, attaining the rank of major-general, and died in Paris.

It is to be added that this teaching does not revoke his condemnation of the closure of amputation wounds by "first intention". By this was then understood the tight suturing of the whole of the opposing surfaces, as practised by the Prussians and Russians, and also by the British (although Guthrie (1815), whilst admitting that it was "almost a law in surgery," frankly criticized it).

But Larrey also discovered another great principle in the treatment of wounds—*the value of immobilization*. This seems to have been to some extent forgotten until its importance was again emphasized in the Spanish Civil War and Second Great War. It is not easy to say at what stage he arrived at this conclusion, although he mentioned in 1841 that his method had been published for more than a quarter of a century.[8]

He advocated that wounds, whether with or without fractures, should be infrequently dressed and immobilized by his *appareil inamovible* (Fig. 23) which I shall translate as "fixed appliance". He insists that the benefits of immobilization are: the prevention of pain, the promotion of healing, and the prevention of hospital and other "gangrenous affections" by obviating the exposure of the wound to air. His apparatus was simple, light, solid and afforded continuous compression. Larrey was no lover of elaborate materials. It was his doctrine that the Army Surgeon should be able to improvise whatever he needed from the materials at hand, and obtain these from the resources of the country. Had he not at Smolensk dressed wounds with paper from the town's archives and made splints with the parchments; and on the Island of Lobau made his men's soup from horseflesh and salted it with gunpowder? He fashioned his appliance from the simplest materials. It consisted of two long, stiff, cushions made from new straw, rolled in a sheet and fixed one on each side of the limb and padded where necessary with small flattened bags filled with chaff. This is surely the prototype of the "Edinburgh box-splint" of my student days. With the appliance in position the patient was able to walk on crutches, the foot carried in a stirrup-like sling suspended from the neck. The appliance was to be worn for about seven weeks. It seems to me that we have here the application of both the principles of ambulant treatment, and the closed plaster method so recently made popular.

[8] The first description I have been able to find of it is in Larrey's *Réceuil de Mémoires de Chirurgie* (1821) p. 314 *et seq.*

Chapter 18

*The Surgery of arteries. Pathology of aneurysms.
Arrest of haemorrhage. Collateral circulation and
arterial canalization.*

The cause of spontaneous aneurysms was a much debated matter in the
eighteenth and nineteenth centuries and, indeed, it was not until the
specific lesions of syphilis were recognized in the coats of the arteries in
the twentieth that the real nature of the lesion became known. The earlier
debate largely centred upon whether the disease was due to mechanical
causes or to some spontaneous disease, the latter view being held by
Scarpa and by Larrey's medical colleague, the Emperor's favourite
physician, Corvisart, who spoke of an *acre délétère*. Larrey gave much
thought to the question, and pointed out how excellently the arterial
system is adapted to withstand shocks, and how difficult it was to imagine
external violence rupturing the walls of these vessels in such a way as to
cause dilatation without leading to gross haemorrhage. Further, he also
found it difficult, on any mechanical theory, to understand the relative
absence of the disease amongst porters and those accustomed to carry
heavy loads, and its incidence amongst soldiers who are exposed to great
physical fatigue and sudden exhausting marches. The frequence of the
malady amongst the athletes of the amphitheatre, mentioned by Bichat,
he associated with their notorious intemperance, depraved moral character, and "infection with various viruses". He then goes on to make the
striking statement: "If it were possible to go back to the original causes
of the internal aneurysms of persons who have died of them, we should be
convinced that these reside in a special virus which becomes localized in
some or other part of the living body, according to the affinity this has to
attract it. Above all the syphilitic virus, which no doubt circulates with
our body fluids and is fully capable of being nourished during its constant
circulation by fresh absorption without there being any external symptoms at the time; this virus, I say, at the encounter with the slightest
obstacle can fix itself upon those parts with which it comes into contact
and for which it has a marked affinity.

"Thus it is easy to conceive that the coats of the arteries are early and
readily attacked by such a virus, since it is by these conduits that it is
carried. It begins by irritating some point on the inner wall. The re-
activity of this area is at once altered; a kind of latent inflammation is
set up, the elasticity of the arterial coats is weakened, their connective
tissue becomes congested and, as a result of a change in their texture,

their walls give way before the impulse which the blood receives from the heart."

This is a remarkable analysis of the aetiology of arterial aneurysm and of the changes produced in the wall of the vessel by syphilis. He goes on to say, in describing the formation of an aneurysm: "When the erosion has reached the last layers of the internal tunica (media) the blood presses against the external tunica, distends it and forces it to dilate; which occurs all the more readily since its fibres are flexible and extensible and do not seem as easily acted on by the virus as are the inner coats."

When we come to the surgery of arterial wounds Larrey's views on the arrest of haemorrhage are worth quoting:

"When the arterial tube is cut or destroyed in its entirety by some wounding agency a haemorrhage occurs which is governed by the vessel's size or other special circumstances, after which the two ends undergo a form of retraction and the walls come into contact and adhere to each other with more or less promptitude, depending upon whether this retraction is assisted by the direct compression or constriction of the vessel by some external mechanical cause, or by the contraction of adjacent muscle fibres. Direct compression is more prompt and more efficacious, because the internal coat of the artery puckers and becomes inflamed almost at once. It has frequently happened to us that after an amputation on the battlefield the ligatures have become detached within a few hours of operation, as a result of the hurried transport of the patient or from some other accident, and that this has not produced haemorrhage: nevertheless, to prevent such an accident, which may occur very early, especially if the ligatures are pulled upon, I cut them off at the level of the wound in the stump so that they are not exposed to traction. The rupture of arteries with total destruction of a segment of the tube is followed by a constriction of the two ends, which is proportionate to the amount of stretching the vessel has received from the wounding agent: for example, whether the wound has been caused by a projectile propelled by gunpowder, such as a bullet, grape shot, shell fragments, etc. In such cases there is but little primary haemorrhage and in the absence of some cause for asthenia, which may prevent the adhesive inflammation, the obliteration of the two ends of the vessel is complete and there is no haemorrhage: if, however, the arteries run in rigid tissues there is no retraction, and the haemorrhage continues and is very difficult to arrest—a fact I have noted many times in the arteries of the scalp. In any case an artery retracts only a little in length, but it contracts strongly and elongates a little, coiling upon itself with a corkscrew movement, which can visibly be increased by pulling on its extremity. When the artery has become detached or isolated from the tissue round about, and forcibly stretched before being cut or ruptured, it is possible to see the end nearest to the heart undergo the torsion and elongation I have mentioned. I have several times seen this phenomenon in wounds due to firearms, or where a limb has been torn off. It proves: (1) That the main wall of an artery consists, as we have said elsewhere, of spiral motor fibres, made up of equal numbers of small arterioles and of elementary fibres similar to those of the muscle coats of the intestines or the radial fibres of the iris (the researches and beautiful injections of Prochaska lend support to this); (2) That it is not the clot which arrests haemorrhage, for there is none within these retracted vessels at least in the early stages, and the cessation is due to this special form of contraction.

"If only a part of the circumference of an artery is laid open or wounded the haemorrhage becomes arrested with difficulty or is not arrested at all, and the patient is always in danger; but even so nature attempts to bring about the retraction of the arterial tube and the approximation of its walls. Certainly the torsion would be prompter and more complete if the vessel were totally divided; but in spite of the obstacle opposed by the undivided part of the vessel, the opening or wound is capable of closing so as not to allow the passage of blood (as we see in veins after the operation of bleeding); its edges come together from the effect of the contraction and torsion of the vessel, and finally they adhere to the membranes or cellular tissue round about, especially if the opening is small (as for example in a puncture) in which the vessel's channel is preserved and the blood continues to pass: this is a very rare event for I have only seen it three times. In what follows I shall briefly report my observations on the subjects in whom this occurred; but, and I repeat it, the clot does not arrest the haemorrhage and the facts described are relevant to this.

"To begin with the whole extent of the wound should be cautiously explored, and if nothing is found which appears likely to destroy the adhesive inflammation which has begun in such a vessel we should content ourselves with debriding the angles of the wound and with applying an ordinary dressing and keeping the patient absolutely at rest.

"Should on the other hand the haemorrhage recommence spontaneously, it is not sufficient merely to ligature the upper end of the artery; the lower end must also be tied, especially if the vessel be a large one. This precaution is not so necessary for the small arteries in which the blood flows backwards less readily.

"If only a part of the artery is wounded it is necessary to expose it and apply ligatures above and below the opening, and then to divide the vessel between them, according to the teaching of Aetius.[1] Should the artery be quite isolated and well exposed we may begin by dividing it and follow this by tying the ends. This method is the quicker and more certain, at any rate where the circumstances do not give any hope of preserving the calibre of the vessel; but should the latter be the case ligation should be suspended and the healing work of nature assisted by all the measures which the Art and the skill of the surgeon can devise. In cases where a wound is complicated by injury to an artery *débridement* is always necessary, since the mass of blood clot which fills it, however large this may be, is incapable of arresting the haemorrhage, in spite of what may be said by those who believe in this: not only does the blood seep through these clots, but the presence of such carbonized fluid in the interstices of the muscles or other cavities causes dangerous complications of which I have often spoken. In such a case the clot should be removed at once, the artery exposed if necessary, and a direct ligature applied. . . ."

"When the arteries are small and deeply hidden in the depths of fleshy parts it is often difficult, not to say impossible—at least without a good deal of sacrifice—to expose the injured vessel for ligature. In these cases I have had much success even in most desperate ones from the use of a narrow tent of lint steeped in a balsamic substance impregnated with a few drops of sulphuric acid, which can be guided deeply in by the finger until the end of the severed vessel is reached and recognized by its pulsation. The haemorrhage ceases at once and rarely recurs. A rather tight retaining bandage completes the dressing.

[1] See the *History of Surgery*, by Peyrilhe, Vol. II, p. 643. (Aetius of Amida was a Greek physician born at the beginning of the 6th Century A.D. A latin translation of his works was published at Bâle in 1542. He described treatment of brachial aneurysm by ligation of the artery above the sac.)

"To stop haemorrhage from the very small vessels contact with cold air, bathing with oxycrat or cold water, or moderate pressure are usually successful; these methods are always inadequate for larger vessels and I therefore entirely disapprove of the practice of not applying ligatures to the arteries in the amputation of a limb, and of attempting to obliterate them by means of the forcible union of the flaps of the stump as I saw done in Saxony, Poland and Russia.

"*First case.* During the Saxony campaign in 1813, a young ex-guardsman, François Fourmy, was brought to the hospital in Dresden suffering from a bullet wound of the left thigh which he had received in the battle beneath the walls of that town. The ball had passed obliquely through the lower third of the limb, from within outwards, destroying the femoral artery a few lines above its passage through the aponeurosis of the long portion of the triceps adductor (*adductor magnus*). There had been severe haemorrhage at first which was followed by general weakness, coldness of the extremities, and loss of pulsation in the popliteal artery. After debriding the anterior wound and removing the blood clots from the space between the two wounds it was possible to feel a gap made by the missile in the inner edge of the femur at the site the artery should occupy. At the bottom of the wound, a little above this defect, a small pulsating conical eminence was felt, which was the retracted end of the ruptured artery. As there was no fresh haemorrhage I confined myself to a simple dressing and awaited developments. I prescribed a sedative regimen, insisted upon the most complete rest, and took care to do the dressings myself for the first few days. The haemorrhage did not recur, the wound healed, and the patient left hospital perfectly well sixty-one days after being wounded.

"The circulation and the functions of the limb returned gradually and several months later the soldier was able to walk without crutches. Pulsation in the popliteal artery had not returned, and it is probable that between the site of the wound and the bifurcation of the artery into the tibial and peroneal branches the vessel has been converted into a fibrous cord.

"*Second case.* On passing through Brussels I had the opportunity of seeing a young English soldier who had a wound similar to that of the aide-de-camp Arrighi, with the sole difference that in the Englishman the wound was on the left side of the face, and the external carotid artery was not entirely severed as in the other, moreover the haemorrhage had recurred at the time of removal of the first dressing. The English surgeon had been careful to expose the common carotid and surround it with two very tightly tied direct ligatures: when these came away the edges of the wound were brought together, healing occurred promptly and the patient was well very shortly afterwards. Pulsation was absent from the temporal artery, and as the trunk of the facial nerve had been destroyed by the bullet the movements of the facial muscles and sensation were lost on this side, as they were with Arrighi. This is the second example I have encountered of a wound of the carotid in man being cured by the aid of our Art."

Collateral Circulation and Arterial Canalization

Amongst other problems in the field of vascular surgery, Larrey encountered several cases of aneurysmal varix, one being occasioned by a communication between the subclavian artery and vein due to a sabre thrust received in a duel. In spite of the passage of arterial blood into the brachial and jugular veins the patient survived. His treatment was mainly symptomatic together with bleeding from the arm and jugular vein. Larrey's detailed analysis of the various vascular phenomena in this case gave him a very marked insight into the phenomena of a collateral circulation, which he discusses at length and records the following further case, "upon which I have founded these views".

"Pierre L . . ., forty-six years old, of fair complexion, average height and robust constitution, a veteran of the Paris battalion, had suffered in the early years of his military life from a number of syphilitic conditions which, according to his story, were treated with every possible care. In 1794 he was wounded in the right thigh, by a bullet which passed from the inguinal region to the buttock on the same side without however injuring either the femur or the principal vessels, although the wound was long in healing. He habitually kept the leg semi-flexed and was unable to get about without crutches. One day, having suddenly and unwisely extended the affected leg, he felt severe pain in the popliteal region which obliged him to take to his bed and to keep the leg bent and immobile. For a long time he was deprived of any kind of exercise. He tried walking on a wooden leg, but before long the knee, leg and foot became so swollen that he was forced to give this up and to apply to the Invalides for the assistance his condition demanded."

The following is the picture of the patient as depicted at the time by Dr. Ribes, then assistant surgeon at the Invalides.

"The patient was pale, weak and extremely thin; his leg was partly flexed and he could not extend it completely, even by great efforts. It was swollen and the superficial veins of the knee and lower leg were a little dilated. An aneurysmal tumour, which could be both seen and felt to pulsate, occupied almost the whole of the popliteal space. During the night he was often awakened with a start by an acute burning pain which reached from the affected part to the sole of the foot on this side; in the day this particular pain was absent and he was left merely with a very unpleasant sensation of formication in the whole limb.

"M. Sabatier, having decided to treat the condition by refrigerants, first resorted to general blood letting to diminish the sanguine plethora, he also prescribed acidulated mucilaginous drinks with nitrous spirit, and applied ice to the tumour.

"After some fifteen days of this treatment the pains had diminished and the aneurysmal sac had become less fluctuant and its pulsations less obvious. At the end of a month its size was considerably reduced and all the other symptoms improved.

"By the second month everything indicated a considerable thickening of the walls of the sac with a great diminution in its size. After this improvement the patient himself continued to apply ice by night and day with a rare perseverance.

"At the end of the third month the tumour had shrunk to the size of a pigeon's egg and no longer pulsated, and at the end of the fourth M. Sabatier allowed him to walk with crutches. The limb at this time was cold and considerably wasted and its movements were almost nil: nevertheless, by degrees, both the nutrition and circulation became re-established.

"At about the eighth month, M. Ribes shewed this soldier to M. Caillot, professor at the Medical School of Strasbourg, and they both agreed that there was only a very small, hard, non-pulsating and insensitive tumour in the popliteal region: the limb however was not yet capable of complete extension and the patient could not support himself without crutches.

"A year had scarcely passed when, having had a stumble, the soldier noticed for the first time the presence of arterial pulsation at the sides of the knee; this alarmed him and caused him to hurry to his doctor to consult him about the

142

new development. Dr. Ribes, to his great surprise, found that these pulsations came from the small articular vessels which were considerably dilated. From this moment the patient's cure was considered complete, and in a short time the man resumed his ordinary duties and was lost sight of.

"In 1811, thirteen years after being thus cured, the patient developed melancholia[2] which was followed by all the symptoms of organic disease of the heart. The condition progressed and on the 21st December of the same year death put an end to his unfortunate career. His body was buried without anyone thinking of an autopsy. M. Ribes, although he was not informed of the event until some fifteen days later, obtained permission to exhume the body in order to use it for his researches, but before concentrating his attention on the limb which had been the site of the aneurysm he examined the state of the principal organs.

"The whole body was very emaciated. On opening the chest the ventricles and root of the aorta were found to be considerably dilated and aneurysmal. The abdominal aorta was exposed and injected, but the passage of most of the injection mass was arrested at the centre of the popliteal artery (the site of the aneurysmal tumour). M. Ribes then endeavoured to make the injection *via* the posterior tibial artery but without success, and was obliged to inject each of the new large arterial branches separately; a procedure as tedious as it was difficult on account of the state of putrefaction of the corpse. Nevertheless the dissection and demonstration of these interesting vessels was accomplished by this expert anatomist with an unexpected success, and the result has been the remarkable specimen which he shewed in 1812 at the Society of the Faculty of Medicine. With the author's permission I have had this drawn and an engraving made (Fig. 24).

"I shall not give a detailed description of the specimen; the drawing and the accompanying legend suffice for this. I shall only observe, in agreement with my friend, that the trunk of the popliteal artery having been obliterated, nature has employed all her resources to preserve and re-establish the circulation in the limb. . . ."

Larrey goes on to say that the resources of nature, in developing a collateral circulation, when a main trunk is occluded, explain the success obtained by Abernethy, and subsequently by Astley Cooper, in the ligature of the external iliac artery. He also observed and described several examples of the *re-canalization* of arteries occluded by thrombus, of which the following is the briefest:

"A young guardsman provided us with a third example of this phenomenon. He was sent to hospital some time last July to be treated for chronic head-ache, the result of a fall. I employed a number of different treatments, and amongst them ordered a small blood-letting by lancing the left temporal artery: a few days after this minor operation a swelling the size of a pea appeared at the site of the incision, which gave all the signs of an aneurysm, and continued to grow. I had graduated compresses applied to the little tumour, and by these means M. Gimelle, one of our assistant surgeons, was able to cause its disappearance in a few days, and with this the pulsations of the arterial branch beyond also disappeared. For some time we believed that the whole of the injured artery was obliterated and converted into a cord;

[2] Possibly General Paralysis of the Insane although this condition is not often associated with tertiary manifestations.

but later it was noticed that the pulsations had reappeared and were present from below the scar to the full extremity of the vessel, so that it could be truly affirmed that the blood was once more passing through the same arteries; just as happens in a vein of the arm when a thrombus forms as a result of the small opening made by a lancet in blood-letting. Pressure on such a varicose swelling causes it to disappear, along with the branch of the vein which lies above; but the lumen becomes re-established soon afterwards and the circulation in the vein continues just as before the bleeding. It, therefore, seems to me that the spontaneous occurrences I have described are analogous."[3]

*   *   *   *   *

[3] The author believes that he was the first to describe fully the distinction between "organization" and "canalization" of vessels. *Journal of Pathology and Bacteriology* 1958. vol. LXXV. pp. 1–7.

Chapter 19

*The Russian Campaign (1). Preamble. The Vistula.
The Moscow Campaign. Wilna. Witebsk. Casualties.
Smolensk. Valutina. Dorogobouje.*

The campaign, which culminated in Wagram and the further defeat oⁱ
the retreating Austrians at Znaïm, ended with the signing of the Treaty
of Vienna on October 14th, 1809. In less than three years time the Imperial armies were to cross the Niemen to open the disastrous Russian
campaign. The events of these years are amongst the most interesting in
Napoleon's career, for in them we see the beginning of the great decline
and the struggle of the Colossus, harassed by ever growing irritation and
frustration despite his enormous power, against the accumulation of
events which were to defeat him.

The crushing of Austria, and the seeming apogee of the Emperor's
career in his marriage with the daughter of her defeated ruler, the Russian
alliance, the humiliation and subservience of the German states—these
were great assets to put into the balance against the obstinate hostility of
England, the failure to complete the conquest of Spain, and the obduracy
of Pius VII. And yet, despite the puny potential of his remaining enemies,
the scales slowly tilted against Napoleon. The continental blockade,
which was to bring commercial England to ruin and force her to sue for
peace, proved a two-edged weapon, and his exasperation at its ineffective-
ness drove him to extend his territorial annexations and France's
dominion far beyond her natural boundaries: to the incorporation of
Holland and the mouths of the Rhine, the overlordship of the greater part
of Poland and Italy, and dominion over certain Swiss cantons and the
Hanse towns. To the people of these subjugated countries the consequences of French rule seemed to be the destruction of their commerce,
ruinous imposts, and the conscription of their sons to maintain the
Emperor's relations on thrones for which they had no hereditary title,
special aptitude, or legitimate claim. Resistance was countered by
extreme severity; disobedience by occupation; and gradually the vicious
circle enlarged, leading to the ever wider dissipation of French military
strength and the progressive accession of more and more imperial responsibilities, bringing in their train increasing dividends in resistance and
hatred. And over all lay the shadow of Spain. Spain, the graveyard of the
marshals' reputations! Dupont, Messina, Ney, Soult, Jourdan, Marmont,
Suchet, either singly or together all learned in her arid soil and burning
heat the bitter lesson of defeat and failure, and sometimes disgrace. To
pacify this inhospitable land, to drive the English into the sea and bring

back the much needed legions to France was the perennial plan—a plan baulked by the pertinacity of Wellington and the unquenchable hostility of the peoples of the Peninsula.

And all the time the drama drove on towards the campaign in the north. Its inevitability is a matter on which historians may yet speculate and from which we today may try to find guidance against the greater cataclysm which with a horrible sameness threatens the later world.— "You arm. . . . And you also. . . . But you began it first. . . . Nay, that is not truth, it was you. . . . We have no wish for war. . . . And we are equally averse from it. . . ."

Yet the fact seems incontestable; that Napoleon planned the invasion of Russia with perfect deliberation in spite of the frankest warnings from Caulaincourt. His thoroughness even went to the length of having the copper plates of the great map of the Russian Empire stolen from St. Petersburg and in spite of their bulk and every risk carried to Paris, where French characters were substituted for Russian before the copies were issued to his generals. He anticipated that by the middle of 1812 the reinforcements sent to Spain would have settled that affair, and in this expectation he recalled the Young Guard and a considerable body of cavalry to France. But the Spanish campaign miscarried, and by April the two key fortresses of Ciudad Rodrigo and Badajoz had fallen to Wellington. Alexander of Russia on his side seems to have gone to great lengths to avoid any stigma of aggression, even to the extent of refusing defensive alliances. But in the face of an obvious threat he slowly assembled his main armies on the Dwina and Dnieper, and decided with his advisers that if war came they should imitate the tactics of the English in Portugal and withdraw before the enemy, leaving nothing to the invader but desolation: a form of warfare well suited to the vast and sparsely inhabited empire of the Czars with its docile population. On the 24th of June Napoleon crossed the Niemen with 400,000 men, closely followed by 200,000 others.

*   *   *   *   *

On the resumption of his work at the Guard's Hospital in 1810, Larrey gave weekly lessons on clinical surgery, drawing freely on his experiences in the late campaign. The third volume of his *Mémoires* closed with Wagram and was published in 1812. He wrote no more until 1817 when his world was profoundly changed. Waterloo had been fought, Napoleon had fallen and was a prisoner in exile, and Louis XVIII had returned for the second time. It was in this setting that he produced his fourth volume. In the years that had passed his fortunes had fluctuated much, but these are matters we shall pass over for the moment to maintain the sequence of his historical narrative and take up the story where he left it.

Larrey now describes himself as *"Surgeon-in-Chief to the Hospital of the Royal Guard, and ex-chief Surgeon to the Grande Armée in Russia, Saxony, etc. Formerly Professor at the Military Hospital of Val-de-Grâce."* This gives a hint of the extent to which he had been stripped of his appointments and emoluments. He no longer speaks of the Emperor: he is the Head of the Army, the Commander-in-Chief, or, more rarely, simply Napoleon.

The narrative commences with the campaign in Russia. He writes factually, and though always loyal to Napoleon he occasionally permits himself to be a little more critical of events than he was before.

*　　　*　　　*　　　*　　　*

"Flattering myself with the prospect of a period of repose, which it seemed might well be expected after twenty years of extremely active service, I conceived the idea of bringing together and having printed the notes of my war diary, so that young medical officers might profit by them.

"This difficult task had barely been completed at the end of the year 1811, with the publication of three volumes of my Memoirs, when we learnt that the government was once again making enormous preparations for war and taking measures which denoted a distant expedition. My apprehensions were quickly confirmed by an unexpected order to report for duty, which I received together with the decree (of the 12th of February, 1812) nominating me Surgeon-in-Chief to the *Grande Armée*, so that I no longer had any doubts about the imminence of a new campaign.

"The rendezvous for General Headquarters was Mayence, but before setting out I had to arrange for the service of the Guard's Hospital, which was my responsibility, and the personnel of its ambulances, which on my advice was confided to M. Paulet, deputy Surgeon-in-Chief.

"I left Paris on the 24th of the month and reached Mayence on the 1st March. That day was taken up in calling on the military authorities. The next day I received from the temporary Intendant-General, M. l'Ordonnateur Joinville, instructions for the organization of my service. The greater part of the troops had already crossed the Rhine and were moving towards Prussia by forced marches. We were ignorant of our destination, the general opinion being that we were to embark on the Baltic for England, or other more distant lands. General Headquarters left Mayence in the rear of the troops on the 8th March, and was at Fulde on the 12th. After a short stay we left for Erfurt, which we reached on the 18th.

"We were soon ordered to move to Magdeburg. The bad weather and the damage to the roads by the passage of the artillery made this short march exceedingly arduous. Whilst we were in Magdeburg, Baron Desgenettes, Physician-in-Chief to the army, and I took steps for the improvement of its hospitals. The town, which is commercially one of the most important in Germany, had become under French domination an almost impregnable military centre; it was a considerable *entrepôt* of arms and an immense magazine for the armies of the Confederation of the Rhine. Consequently it should have been one of the principal citadels of the Elbe and one of the strongest keys to Saxony, and great activity was going on in fortifying it and making preparations against a siege. The town is noteworthy for its cathedral and arsenal. Othon Guerricke[1] the celebrated inventor of the pneumatic machine was born here.

"From Magdeburg, General Headquarters was ordered to Berlin by way of Brandenburg. As soon as we arrived there I called together all the surgeons of the army, to classify them and post them to the ambulances. I also began a course of instruction in military surgery and in the practice of operations. The zeal of the young medical officers of the Berlin Academy rivalled that of our own: they regularly attended my lectures and participated in our work in the operating theatre,[2] in which they were encouraged by M. le Chevalier Goercke, Surgeon-General to the Prussian armies. This renowned practitioner is most solicitous for his pupils, devoting his care and his nights to them as if he were their father. We were overwhelmed with kindness and attention by our worthy colleagues, and we shall always recall with pleasure the marks of interest we received from MM. Hufeland, first physician to the King; Grœffe, Professor of Surgery; Wibel, Physician-in-Chief to the Prussian armies; Rudolphi, Professor of Anatomy and Director of the Anatomical Museum, etc.

"Before leaving the capital I organized six divisions of mobile field ambulances, each with eight medical officers. Every surgeon daily exercised his division under my instruction in the practice of operations and bandaging. There was the keenest competition and the most perfect discipline amongst all the surgeons.

"We left Berlin on the 30th of April, and arrived at Frankfort-sur-Oder on May 2nd. During the time we spent there I worked hard to perfect our ambulances and to improve the local hospitals, which we found in a very sorry condition.

"Two remarkable monuments in this town are much admired by foreigners: one is the tomb of General Kleist; the other, on the right bank of the river and very near to the bridge, is a mausoleum erected to the glory of Prince Leopold of Brunswick, governor of the town, to perpetuate the memory of the heroic act of devotion to which he fell a victim in April, 1795.[3] Magnificent allegorical statues record the virtues of the prince and the grief of the citizens.

"On May 10th we reached Posen. We were still ignorant of the object of our campaign, although the number of corps continued to increase and a formidable artillery park and innumerable wagons arrived from all directions. I used the few days we had here to perfect the organization of the field ambulances and to continue to practise my colleagues in operations.

"The Grand Army was soon assembled on the left bank of the Vistula. An enumeration at the time of the crossing gave us a strength of 400,000

[1] Othon Guerricke, the inventor of the air-pump.

[2] This may have been the occasion on which Larrey became known to the Prussian surgeon who intervened in the order to shoot him after Waterloo.

[3] Duke Leopold of Brunswick was drowned in the Oder in trying to save life on the 27th of April, 1795.

FIG. 26. Map of the Russian Campaign. (Reproduced from *Napoleon's Russian Cam*

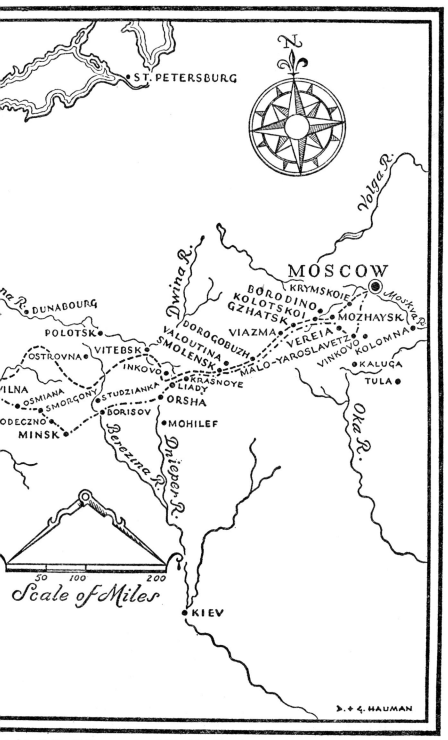

N

ST. PETERSBURG

Volga R.

MOSCOW

na R. DUNABOURG

Dwina R.

KRYMSKOIE
BORODINO
KOLOTSKOI
GZHATSK
VIAZMA
DOROGOBUZH
VALOUTINA
SMOLENSK
MALO-YAROSLAVETZ
VEREIA
MOZHAYSK
Moskva R.
VINKOVO
KOLOMNA
KALUGA
TULA

POLOTSK

VITEBSK
OSTROVNA
INKOVO
KRASNOYE
LIADY
ILNA
OSMIANA
SMORGONY
STUDZIANKA
ORSHA
ODECZNO
BORISOV
MINSK
MOHILEF

Berezina R.

Dnieper R.

Oka R.

50   100   200
Scale of Miles

KIEV

D. + G. HAUMAN

ated by J. David Townsend, published by Houghton Mifflin & Co., Boston, U.S.A.).

men: Frenchmen, Spaniards, Neapolitans, Italians, Austrians, Prussians, Bavarians, Wurtembergers, Westphalians and Saxons; in all ten army corps including the Guard and the Cavalry Corps. Able generals were at their head under Napoleon's command. General Headquarters, which was in the rear, advanced to Thorn on the morning of June 2nd, and on the following day all the commanders were called together for the constitution of a number of special councils. I was made a member of the Grand Council for Hospitals. After receiving the recommendations and observations of each of these councils on the branches of the service with which they were concerned, the Commander-in-Chief issued an order of the day in which the route of the troops was laid down, together with the measures to be taken for the rapid crossing of the barren countries we were about to traverse to enter Russia."

The Moscow Campaign

In following the advance of the *Grande Armée* across Russia, and its subsequent retreat from Moscow, we shall be concerned in the main with the route of Napoleon's Headquarters, to which Larrey was attached. This is apt to give the reader the erroneous impression of an army marching in column along a single road. In fact the invasion was on a broad front, stretching from the Austrian border to the Baltic, its flanks being adequately guarded although most of its strength was in the centre. As the campaign developed the centre of the army became more and more detached from its wings, and ultimately left these far behind. From Dorogobouje onwards the advance was in fact almost in a broad single column, with the Poles on the right and Eugène on their left.

At the time Napoleon occupied Wilna, Macdonald was posted at the extreme left, on the lower Dwina, with Gouvion St. Cyr on his right. The Emperor was in the centre opposite Kowno, with the corps of Oudinot, Ney and Davout, together with the cavalry under Murat and the Guard, 200,000 men in all. The right wing consisted of Schwartzenberg's Austrians and Reynier's corps, with Jerome to their left between Bielstock and Grodno (Fig. 26).

It was not long before things began to go badly on the flanks of this vast front. There were many reasons for this; amongst them the cosmopolitan nature of Napoleon's army and the presence of unwilling allies, such as the Prussians in the north and the Austrians in the south. Other factors seem to have been a lack of enthusiasm of the Poles for the war, the inordinate length of communications, and the jealousies between the marshals and senior generals, who on many occasions failed to co-operate with each other. After early successes St. Cyr was unable to withstand the pressure of his opponent Wittgenstein and was gradually forced back from the Dwina, losing contact with Macdonald. On being wounded, he was replaced by Oudinot, himself in ill health, who conducted a prolonged fluctuating campaign around Poltsk on the St. Petersburg road. Eventually the whole of the Dwina line was lost, and Wittgenstein was able to march up the river and in the end join hands with Admiral

Tchichakoff's army, thrusting up from the south after its release from the campaign in Turkey.

On the right wing Schwartzenberg and Reynier had impressive successes at the outset, so much so that Napoleon demanded a marshal's baton for the former from the Emperor of Austria, but as time passed and the features of the campaign began to become clear, the Marshal's ardour cooled and he remained quietly in Volhynia, a party to Metternich's understanding with the Russians, by which each party engaged "to do each other the least possible harm."

By the time Smolensk was captured the wings of the army were no longer in line, and with Schwartzenberg remaining passive Tchichakoff was able to capture Minsk and eventually to reach the Beresnia at Borrisow, and make himself master of the vital bridge which Oudinot had been warned to occupy, but arrived too late and failed in his attempts to dislodge the Russians.

Thus the *Grande Armée* in its retreat had Tchichakoff before them on the Beresnia, Wittgenstein outflanking them on the north and Kutusoff in the rear. Except for the Guard, Victor's corps which had been ordered up from Smolensk, and Oudinot's 6,000 men, the Grand Army was by this time disintegrating. Furthermore the month Victor's men had spent in Smolensk had helped to empty its depôts of their stores, which was a disastrous matter for the retreating army.

Napoleon's success, such as it was, in crossing the Beresnia at Studianka was made possible by his feint at Borrisow, which deceived Tchichakoff into concentrating at the latter point and left the precious ford, as well as the crossing of the Zemlin marshes with their twenty-two wooden bridges, undefended.

To continue with Larrey's narrative:

"After a general review we resumed our march and reached Heilsberg on the 10th of June, the anniversary of the battle fought by the French before this town in the Polish campaign of 1807. Headquarters did not halt and was directed along the Tilsit road, but before long we turned back again and took the road for Kowno, which we entered on June 24th. A number of detachments of the Russian advance guard which were in the town had just time to retreat and destroy the bridge, but our scouts crossed the Niemen on boats and came up with part of their rear-guard with which they had several skirmishes, that gave us about a hundred wounded whom I took into the Kowno hospitals. This town is well situated on the right bank of the Niemen, at the end of some high land which stretches in serpiginous fashion to the outskirts of Wilna. The road skirts the edge of an exceedingly deep gorge and is so isolated that once entered upon there is no possibility of turning back.

"Between Kowno and Wilna our advance was made difficult by the bad roads, constant rain and lack of shelter. These, and the immoderate use of *chenaps* (the brandy of the country), proved fatal to a large number of conscripts of the Young Guard. This liquor is truly pernicious to those unaccustomed to it, especially when drunk too strong. It is made from fermented corn, with the addition of stimulating and narcotic plants which give it a stupefying effect all too easily seen in these young soldiers. Those who died from drinking it shewed a loss of muscular power, giddiness and collapse; their eyes half-open, lustreless and watery, with injected conjunctivae. In the end the victims fell into the ditches or even on the road, where they succumbed almost immediately: many of them had gangrenous spots on their feet and legs.

"Our advance guard entered Wilna almost without resistance. On the previous day the Emperor Alexander was still in the town and little thought that the French were so close. Minor engagements at its gates and in the neighbourhood brought us 150 wounded, whom I had moved into the hospitals of Saint-Jacques and the Charité. I cannot sufficiently praise the Grey Sisters of these hospitals for the care they gave to our patients.

"Amongst those upon whom I myself operated, or whose dressings I supervised, were several cases with unusual features. The first was a Polish officer who had been wounded twenty-four hours earlier. His body was blown up with general emphysema to the greatest possible degree; his skin so distended that his limbs were made stiff and rigid, the folds about the joints obliterated and his eyes quite hidden by the inflated eyelids. His lips were of a prodigious thickness and interfered with the taking of liquids. His pulse and respirations had almost ceased; his anxiety was extreme and his voice weak and broken: in fact it was clear that he was in imminent danger.

"A thrust from a Cossack's lance had caught him obliquely beneath the angle of the scapula and penetrated his chest and lung. Although the wound of the integuments did not correspond with that in the intercostal muscles, its edges had been brought into close apposition by adhesive plasters. The wounded man had been put at once onto a cart and brought to Wilna, which he reached during the night. Air, which was continuously escaping from the lung, made its way through the opening in the chest into the subcutaneous tissue, from whence it infiltrated all over the body producing this enormous emphysema.

"My first care was to take off the adhesive strapping and open up and clean the skin wound, and bring it opposite to the opening in the chest. Dry (*sic*) cups were at once applied to the wound and these rapidly became filled with gas and blood. I then brought the lips of the wound together and maintained them in position by means of a piece of perforated linen steeped in hot camphorated wine. Other cups were successively applied to scarified areas over the whole of the body and especially to the thorax and the extremities.

"I had him treated several times a day with camphorated and ammoniated wine embrocations. I repeated the cupping as often as was necessary, and in addition made simple scarifications on parts where the cups could not be applied. I prescribed infusion of *arnica montana* as a drink, with some good broth and wine.

"After his wound had been attended to the patient felt relieved; the danger disappeared and he improved continuously. At the time we left, his body had lost two-thirds of its inflation and everything pointed to his speedy recovery. On our return from Moscow I met this officer; he was in such good health that I should not have recognized him had he not made himself known to me. This recovery greatly astonished me.

"A peasant from one of the farms near Wilna, who was dangerously wounded in the left shoulder by a firearm at point blank range, was brought to the hospital shortly after the Polish officer. The Mother Superior begged me to see him and to help him. At the first glance I realized what great disorganization his wound had occasioned, but before examining him I sent for the surgeon to the hospital, Professor Becu. The ball had passed through the arm from before backwards, very close to the shoulder joint. The muscles, brachial nerves and axillary artery had been ruptured or torn, and the humerus and a large part of the shaft of the bone had been smashed to fragments below its head. The limb was cold, insensitive, incapable of movement and threatened with total gangrene and the shoulder and the whole of the side of the chest were covered with a deep ecchymosis. The wounds of entrance and exit were of no great size, and as they gave no hint of the derangement I had recognized the consultants at first thought that the extirpation of the limb, which I had suggested, was unnecessary and that the patient's arm might be preserved; but in the end they agreed to my observations and concluded that the operation should be done at once. In spite of the disordered state of the parts I was able to employ my own method. The operation was painful and difficult, since one fragment of the fractured head of the humerus was entangled amongst the cords of the brachial plexus below the subscapular muscle, and moreover the artery had been torn very high up and I was forced to look for it beneath the pectoral muscle in order to ligate it. Several months afterwards, by which time the patient had recovered completely, he succumbed to an internal malady the cause of which is unknown to me. I had obtained for him a provisional indemnity of 600 francs. . . ."

"One of the Wilna professors shewed us an anatomical museum which had recently been begun and contained a number of interesting specimens, amongst them a large collection of skulls of malefactors. For executions they employ a kind of guillotine which has been in use in Lithuania from time immemorial. One of the skulls was that of a man famed both for his crimes and his bravery who, after having escaped from prison on many occasions, fell into the hands of justice and was about to suffer the capital punishment to which he had been condemned, when he tried to kill himself by cutting off his principal genital organs. He attempted this with a small blunt knife which he had skilfully hidden. In spite of numerous efforts he barely succeeded in opening his scrotum and exposing one of the organs. In his impatience, time being short, he seized it with his fingers and abruptly tore it out. The spermatic cord ruptured within the abdomen some distance away. The extreme pain was quickly followed by syncope and other serious symptoms which caused the execution to be postponed. He was removed to hospital, from which he shortly afterwards succeeded in escaping and returned to his occupation of poacher. The avulsed testicle had been found in his hand and was preserved in spirit of wine: the cord is about three inches long. After committing a number of other murders the wretch was once again taken, condemned to death and decapitated forthwith.

"At Wilna we made arrangements for the reception and care of six thousand patients.

"The marching orders of the Grand Army and General Headquarters were announced in an order of the day of July 9th and at the same time the subordinate headquarters of the army corps were warned to be ready to march at the close of a review to be held on the 10th. I was officially invited to a *levée* of the supreme head of the army and there received a direct command to attend the review with our mobile field ambulances. This was ordered for four o'clock but only took place at six. The weather was calm and hot, but thick clouds covered the horizon and threatened a storm which burst upon us a few minutes later. The fanfare announcing the arrival of the Commander-in-Chief blent with continuous claps of thunder, whilst a frightful storm descended upon the earth. The sky was obscured to a point at which we could only recognize each other at a short distance and during the flashes of lightning. A violent hailstorm, whipped up by the strong winds, caused the lines to break and most of the cavalrymen to dismount to avoid being thrown. The terrified horses attempted to break away and crowded against each other. In another instant we were inundated by torrents of rain and hail. Finally Napoleon and his staff were forced to return to the town and to abandon the review. Never have I seen so violent and terrifying a storm! Was this an omen of the disasters awaiting us?

"We did not, however, delay our march and moved on Mentianoni and Benchenkowiski, where our advance guard engaged the Russian rearguards in an encounter which was the more severe as the enemy was extremely well posted. Nevertheless our troops attacked resolutely and broke his lines, forcing a precipitate retreat. This combat gave us about six hundred French and five hundred Russian wounded, the latter being abandoned on the battlefield. I had them all moved into the Jewish temples in the town, where they received the succour they had the right to expect from us. I shall mention some of those on whom I operated.

"A Russian colonel, who was one of the first to be brought to the hospital, had received a sabre blow from one of our cavalrymen which had cut through the whole of the base of the nose. The weapon struck him obliquely, causing a wound which extended from both canine regions and the corners of the upper lip into the maxillary bones at the level of the nasal fossae. This produced a flap, bounded by the vault of the palate, which fell down onto the chin and was only attached to the living part of the face by two small strips of the upper lip, one at each corner of the mouth. On one side of this flap could be seen the whole extent of the nasal fossae and the cavity of the mouth, minus the alveolar arch; the other part included the whole nose, the upper lip and the palatal vault, all of which were turned down onto the chin. When I arrived on the scene one of my pupils, finding that the severed part was cold and only adherent at the two points mentioned, was about to cut it away altogether and dress the wound as best he could. I took the scissors from him and after examining the wound proceeded to suture it. I had some difficulty in removing the clots of blood from the nasal fossae, where the dust had hardened them like plaster. I detached the portion of the palatal vault which adhered to the flap constituted by the anterior half of the upper alveolar arch, which on one side had been separated from the rest of the jaw between the canine and the first molar teeth and on the other between first two molars, and I also removed a number of pieces of the nasal bones and of the frontal processes of the maxillary bones. I then brought the lip and nose into their proper relation and sutured them in position by interrupted stitches, beginning at the root of the nose and working down on the two sides, so as to unite the edges by ten parallel sutures. A dressing of fine perforated linen soaked in saline was applied over the whole of the triangular wound. I inserted a piece of a large gum-elastic catheter into each nostril to preserve their form and diameter, and fastened them externally by a loop of thread through their ends. Graduated compresses were placed at the sides of the nose, and a retaining bandage completed the dressing. I had the satisfaction of learning on my return from Moscow that this superior officer was completely cured and without any deformity. His case is remarkable for the severity of the wound and the small number of blood vessels which remained between the flap and the skin of the face. The nose regained its life, and its union with the edges of the wound was exact and perfect.

"On the same day we carried out a number of amputations of the foot, and of the leg through the substance of the condyles with extirpation of the fibula, as well as of the arm at the shoulder-joint: in general these were completely successful. The more interesting cases will be described in my notes relative to such operations.

"From Benchenkowiski we marched to Witebsk. We reached its outskirts on the evening of the 26th July and the next day were confronted by the enemy who had taken up a position before it. We attacked almost at once and a fierce but indecisive engagement followed, for the Russians were very advantageously posted on the edge of a semicircular hill and protected by a river over which they had destroyed the bridges. The town is built on a fairly lofty plateau at the extremity of the hill. During the night we deployed our troops to turn this position and bridge the river at suitable points, but at daybreak we found that the Russians had retired. We quickly entered Witebsk in pursuit but did not know the direction they had taken, which was no doubt the reason for the Commander-in-Chief's giving the order to retire. He himself returned to the town with his headquarters staff and the whole of his guard, whilst definite information was obtained as to the Russian army's manoeuvres, and some rest given to the troops who up to now had made continuous forced marches. We were already feeling the lack of the necessaries of life and the soldiers had not received regular rations for several days."

* * * * *

Napoleon, at this phase of his campaign, was endeavouring to drive a wedge between the two Russian armies confronting him. The army of Barclay de Tolly to the north of the watershed between the Dnieper and Dwina, was covering the road to Moscow through Witebsk; and that of Bagratian was a considerable distance to the south. Barclay retreated the more quickly of the two and a gap opened, which became wider as Bagratian failed to conform to Barclay's movement. Had Napoleon's manoeuvre succeeded there seems every likelihood that he might have defeated both armies in detail, but though Davout quickly hurled his force into the gap, and drove Bagratian pell-mell back to the Dnieper, the other part of the southern pincer, Jerome's corps, was unable to overtake the Russians in spite of the most exhausting marches. Bagratian escaped, and Napoleon bitterly castigated Jerome for his failure. He wrote from Wilna on July 4th: "I can only express my dissatisfaction at the small amount of information I have from you. I know neither the number of Bagratian's divisions, nor their names, nor what you are doing. I have five or six columns in motion, to intercept Bagratian's march. I cannot think you have so neglected your duty as not to have pursued him the very next morning. . . . My operations are stopped for want of information from Grodno. I have had none since the 30th. The Chief of your Staff does not write; Prince Poniatowski does not write. . . . You are jeopardizing the whole success of the campaign on the right; it is not possible to carry on the war in this way." Finally he deprived the culprit of his command and placed him under Davout's orders. Jerome, who was King of Westphalia, was equally bitter in his resentment of this slight to his royal dignity, and retorted by resigning his command. Thus Napoleon's first great combination, which might have brought the campaign to a brilliant conclusion, failed. The decision to halt at Witebsk was not altogether due to a lack of information about the situation of the Russian armies. The rapid movement of so large a force of so heterogeneous a character as Napoleon's, composed to a considerable extent of unseasoned troops, had involved serious losses from desertion, disease, especially dysentery, and exhaustion. The heat at this time was excessive with the temperature as high as 92–95°F., and almost as trying as the cold was to be later. A detailed inspection of every corps at Witebsk shewed that on an average 40 per cent of the effectives with which the Emperor had crossed the Niemen a month earlier were no longer with him. The cavalry, it is said, had lost a third of their horses. Larrey certainly glossed over the condition of the army at Witebsk. Caulaincourt, Napoleon's Master of Horse and a former ambassador to Russia, who was sent by the Emperor to visit the wounded, wrote: "It is impossible to give any idea of the utter want experienced at first. The lack of order, the indiscipline of the troops and even of the Guard, robbed us of the very few means that remained at our disposal. Never was there a situation more deplorable, or a spectacle more heart-rending for those who could think and had not been dazzled by the false glamour of glory and ambition. With the exception of the chiefs the indifference of the administration was complete. The innumerable wagons, the enormous quantities of supplies of all sorts that had been collected at such expense during the course of two years, had vanished through theft and loss, or through lack of means of bringing them up. They were scattered along the roads. The rapidity of the forced marches, the shortage of harness and spare parts, the dearth of provisions, the want of care, had all helped to kill the horses. This campaign at express speed from the Niemen to Wilna, and from Wilna to Witebsk, had already cost the army two lost battles and deprived it of absolutely essential provisions and supplies without any real result. . . . From a spirit of inexplicable and unpardonable meanness the provisioning of the ambulances had been inadequate. . . . We had got only as far as Witebsk, we had not fought a battle, and there was not even any surgical lint."

*   *   *   *   *

Larrey continues:

"On our initial advance to Witebsk we had found a number of places suitable for use as hospitals, of which we were in great need. These were quickly organized for the reception of the casualties from the engagements of July 27th, 28th and 29th, of which there were seven hundred and fifty French and almost as many Russians. I took great pains to see that the first dressings were all done on the battlefield; but for this we had to use the soldiers' under-linen and even our own shirts. Three hundred and fifty of the most seriously wounded Russians had been forgotten or deliberately abandoned in houses from which the inhabitants had fled. In spite of the searches I organized we only discovered them four days later. It would be difficult to paint the heart-rending picture presented by these unfortunate men, most of them mutilated by artillery fire, who had been unable to leave their place of asylum to beg for help. We found them lying on filthy straw, covered with ordure and wallowing as it were in infection. In most of them necrosis or hospital gangrene had caused mortification in limbs which had been shattered by bullet or shell, and all were perishing of hunger. I hastened at once to ensure their nourishment and then had them all dressed, and performed the more difficult operations myself. Finally, I had them taken with our own wounded into the hospitals we had prepared, where they received the same help and succour as the French.

"Forty-five amputations of the arm, forearm, thighs and legs were performed in my presence by the surgeons of our light ambulances. All the operations done within the first twenty-four hours were generally speaking successful; on the other hand in those only performed on the third, fourth or fifth day the outcome was not good. This difference was seen and appreciated by all the surgeons in the armies and left no doubt of the necessity for immediate amputation when amputation is required.

"I superintended the satisfactory organization of the service of the four hospitals we had set up at Witebsk in all matters within my province, and held myself in readiness to leave with the light ambulances. We pursued the enemy in the direction of Smolensk, a fortified town advantageously placed on a high plateau, and guarded on the Russian side by the Dnieper and on our front by lakes and marshes. This was the key to the ancient kingdom of Poland; its defence was easy, especially against attack from the Russian side. About thirty thousand Russians were entrenched in the fortress and on the neighbouring heights.

"In passing through the Krasnoë ravine our advance guard came up with the Russian rear-guards who were unable to withstand our vigorous attack. Fourteen cannon and several colours were left in our possession,[4] and we also captured a large number of prisoners many of whom were wounded: these I had taken to the synagogues and attended to at once. On our side we had five hundred wounded, almost all by cold steel. I left a number of medical officers in the town in charge of a hospital we established there.

"The army soon reached a position below the Smolensk heights, which it was necessary to attack and carry in detail with the bayonet. This operation, although very difficult on account of the nature of the ground and the number of tortuous defiles which had to be traversed, was effected within twenty-four hours. I arrived with our ambulances in time to attend to the wounded: the next day, the 18th August, the town was attacked and taken by assault. Everywhere the enemy offered the most vigorous resistance, but of what avail could this be against the valour and intrepidity of the French, proved in so many combats? The capture of Smolensk will be regarded as one of the most famous feats of arms in the whole campaign. Fire had broken out in many parts of the town and its suburbs during the attack, and this resulted in a terrible conflagration since most of the houses are built of wood. This occurrence favoured both the Russian retreat and the French occupation.

"The assault on Smolensk was one of the bloodiest I have ever seen. The gates of the town, the breaches, and the principal streets were full of corpses and the dying, almost all of them Russians. Their losses were immense: it would have been difficult to count the number of dead we found in the ditches of the town, in the hill ravines, along the edge of the river, and on the crossings of the bridges. On our side we had about six thousand wounded and twelve hundred killed; most of the former were given immediate first aid on the battlefield.[5] I performed a large number of operations in the ambulances of the advance guard, from whence we evacuated our casualties as rapidly as possible to fifteen large buildings which we had converted into hospitals, most of them in the town but some close to important points on the battlefield and others in the suburbs.

"Here, as at Witebsk, we were without every kind of material necessary for the treatment of the wounded. As happened so often I had to improvise means to make up for what we lacked; thus, in place of linen for dressings,

---

[4] These guns were the first trophies to be taken from the Russians.

[5] Bagratian in falling back to Smolensk was engaged by Davout at Saltor-Nowka. Of this battle the victor wrote that the enemy, "left on the field some 1,000 dead and more than 4,000 wounded, of whom seven or eight hundred are in our hands, as well as one hundred and fifty to two hundred prisoners." Presumably the rest were slaughtered!

which we had exhausted in the first few days, as well as that belonging to the wounded themselves, I employed paper which we found in the Archives building which we used as a hospital. The parchments also served us as splints. Tow and birch cotton (*betula alba*) took the place of lint, and we also used paper as bedding for the patients.[6] But what difficulties we had to overcome! What toil and labour did we not endure in this crisis!

"Almost all the townsfolk had deserted their houses and most of those which might have supplied our requirements had suffered from fire or pillage. I was ably assisted in all my efforts by the surgeons belonging to the Headquarters Ambulances and the Guard. We were fully occupied, night and day, in dressing the soldiers who had been wounded by fire or steel; and in spite of the dearth of every necessity all the requisite operations were performed within the first twenty-four hours, in which I myself performed eleven amputations of the arm at the shoulder-joint amongst others. Nine of these were completely healed before our return from Moscow; the other two succumbed to dysentery. This extraordinary success confirms the favourable opinion I had formed of this operation. I also carried out a number of amputations of the thigh in its upper quarter, by the method of forming two flaps.

"It was extremely difficult to obtain provisions for the hospitals and for the large number of sick and wounded, both French and Russian. The Russians were treated side by side with our own men and received the same care and succour. We did however manage to save from fire and pillage a considerable quantity of the most urgently required medicaments and some wine and brandy. The nearby country was scoured for cattle and foodstuffs, and we received from the reserve ambulances linen for dressings and lint. These different reliefs and the indefatigable zeal of our surgeons quickly ensured the recovery of all the lightly wounded. Most of those with serious wounds were in good general condition by a month later, when a sudden scarcity of everything necessary for subsistence arose, with the exception of flour of which we had received several convoys from the interior. All save those with wounds in the lower limbs managed to avoid the worst effects of this dearth; the rest suffered badly.

"The imperative necessity of caring for some ten thousand Russian and French wounded in the Smolensk hospitals, and my personal conviction that after so great a success and with the approach of autumn rains the army would be unlikely to advance further to the north, was the reason for my leaving five of our light ambulance divisions in this town and all the reserve medical officers. I myself, with the sixth division and my two special pupils, left for Valutina, which is five or six leagues from Smolensk on the Moscow road, where our advance guard under General Gudin had fought a very severe engagement with the enemy rearguards who were well posted on a chain of hills which lie along the right bank of the Dnieper and stretch upstream, parallel to the town of Smolensk and the

[6] Wounded Austrian prisoners, captured at the Piave battle in 1919, had had their wounds dressed with paper, so effective was the allied blockade against the importation of cotton.

adjacent mountains.[7] I dealt with all the wounded from this engagement, amongst them the general himself, but I arrived too late to perform the operation which his wound required. One of his legs had been shot off by a cannon ball and the calf of the other destroyed down to the bones. A very intense inflammation occurred in both limbs: erythrism and gangrene quickly developed, and death on the third day ended the sufferings of this brave and worthy general who had captured at the point of the bayonet the almost impregnable position of the Valutina mountain, although it was defended by the grenadiers of the Russian Imperial Guard. No doubt this fresh success, or the anticipation of a final and decisive battle at an early moment, encouraged Napoleon to pursue the enemy who was retreating on Moscow. In order to overtake him I hurried on the dressing of the six or seven hundred wounded men we received and was constrained to leave behind my sixth light ambulance division which returned to Smolensk with them. My two assistants were now all who remained to me when we at last succeeded in overtaking General Headquarters at Dorogobouje. After passing through this town, and the chain of hills in front of it, the Dnieper is crossed for the last time and the immense plains which constitute the greater part of Russia proper came into view. On entering them one encounters a number of earth hillocks, like pyramids, on the river bank, which the people of a nearby village told us were the tombs of the victims of a bloody battle fought here in former days between the Russians and the Poles. Baron Percy, in a very erudite memoir read at the Institute, has described similar monuments which he observed in different parts of Germany. The sight of these tombs produced a painful impression on me. Were they not also bound to inspire gloomy thoughts in our men who found themselves so far away from their own country at a season when the rains, the first stage of winter in this climate, were about to begin, and when we could not fail to realize that the bad state of the roads would expose the advancing army to great dangers of the kind we had already experienced at Pultusk in the first Polish campaign? Although the Russian roads are of great width they are neither metalled nor kept in good repair. These plains, which stretch as far as Moscow and beyond, are covered with abundant crops in summer and in winter more or less thickly overlaid with snow.

"Hardly had we crossed the Dnieper at Dorogobouje than I suddenly began to feel all the symptoms of sea-sickness, such as frequent nausea, yawning, giddiness or vertigo, and vomiting. I seemed to see a scintillation or quivering of the earth at the immeasurably distant horizon, which

[7] The engagement at Valutina was between the Russian army retreating from Smolensk, and Ney's corps which was in pursuit, together with Gudin's division and some of Murat's cavalry. Ney overtook the Russians with all their baggage whilst they were passing through a defile; they strongly reinforced this detachment and what commenced as a rearguard action developed into a real battle, which might have been fatal for the Russians if Junot, who had crossed the Dnieper two leagues above Smolensk, had marched to the sound of Ney's guns and generally shewn more vigour. Instead he awaited orders, although warned by Ney and Murat to be ready to act: this failure had serious consequences for the French. The engagement cost the Russians six or seven thousand men and the French about as many.

affected my senses like the scending of a vessel at sea. The illusion or sensation was more marked when I was on foot than on horseback and almost nil when I lay down; a horizontal position being the most comfortable. This indisposition troubled me until I returned to Smolensk. What could have been the cause? Was it an optical error, or an excessive sensibility of my organs, which had been upset by the impression caused by the constant movement of the large masses of men and the other objects which were always around us on these immense plains?

"On passing through Dorogobouje we found that all the houses which could have been of use to us were on fire and the rapid spread of the flames forced us to bivouac. The town had been fired by the Russian soldiers and all the inhabitants had fled. This was the beginning of every kind of privation. So grave an experience should have warned us of the misfortunes which awaited us along the rest of the road we had yet to cover to reach Moscow. Swept along by an invisible power, lulled by vain hopes of peace, we continued to advance. Soon we reached Viasma (Aug. 28th), a town of considerable size and an important centre of commerce for the two Russias, with immense stores of oil, brandy, soap, sugar, coffee and furs. We found it almost wholly encircled in flames. The army had great difficulty in passing through, and as the wind was strong it was impossible to prevent the spread of the fire. Here, too, the inhabitants had left the town and it may well be imagined what we suffered amidst such desolation. The soldiers, however, managed to find some corn, oil, brandy, sugar and a little coffee in some of the houses which had escaped the flames, and even in the cellars of some of those which were on fire.

"From Viasma we moved quickly on Giad (Ghjat), a less important town with a very long single street and most of its houses built of wood. We marched through it, as through the other towns, in the midst of flames. However, the heavy rain which came down as we were entering put out the fires and allowed Headquarters and the Guard to lodge in such houses as had not been destroyed. The fields round about were covered with large white cabbages, which with some bacon and biscuit we found in a shop were a great sustenance to us, and our soldiers for once were able to satisfy themselves.

"The rains, though they had not lasted long, had made the use of the roads impracticable for artillery, so that the army was forced to halt in the neighbourhood of Ghjat to wait for the fine weather which none of us dared count upon. However, to our great pleasure and surprise, the wind suddenly changed to north north-east and brought dry weather. During this halt we learnt that the Russian army had definitely taken up positions on the heights of Mosaisk (Mojaisk) near to the Moskova, where it was strongly entrenched. Orders were issued to prepare for a great battle and I was told by the Commander-in-Chief to make all the necessary preparations.

"This news greatly perturbed me, since all my surgeons had been left behind at Smolensk and the ambulance wagons had not yet come up. To supply my deficiency in medical officers I asked for a general order putting all the regimental surgeons at my disposal, except for the senior surgeon and assistant and sub-assistants of the infantry and the senior and sub-assistant surgeon of the cavalry. This gave me forty-five surgeons, assistants or sub-assistants, whom I attached to General Headquarters.[8] An extension of our stay at Ghjat for another twenty-four hours gave time for a number of our ambulance wagons to come up, and I was extremely glad, despite the distance which separated us from our reserve, to be practically ready to give whatever assistance might be required on the day for which we were preparing."

[8] It would seem that a lack of information of the Emperor's intentions was the root cause of this failure. Larrey, as he has told us, left five of his ambulance divisions behind at Smolensk to attend to the large number of French and Russian wounded, and his sixth and last at Valutina to deal with the further considerable casualties there and to evacuate them to Smolensk. He was uncertain how far the forward movement would continue—as indeed at this point was Napoleon himself—and hardly envisaged a further advance of some two hundred and fifty miles to Borodino, to be followed within twenty-four hours by the great battle for Moscow.

In this campaign Larrey found himself for the first time the responsible head of the medical service in place of Percy, who was twelve years his senior and at the time in ill-health. Although he does not seem to have been personally responsible for the general insufficiency of the medical arrangements, such as Caulaincourt described, it is possible that this seeming error of judgement in the distribution of the ambulances may have influenced Napoleon in his decision to re-employ Percy in the Waterloo campaign, and to bring back Larrey to his old but subordinate position of Surgeon to the Guard, in which he had rendered such splendid service.

Chapter 20

The Russian Campaign (2). The Moskova battle.
Wounds near the knee. Casualties. Entry to Moscow.
The Moscow hospitals and other buildings. The
Kremlin. Burning of Moscow. Murat surprised by
Kutusoff.

"After thirty-six hours marching we found ourselves face to face with the Russian army. It held an entrenched position on the crest of a circular hill, stretching from the Calouga river and the great Moscow road, which were on our left, to some forests which we could see far away on our right. At the foot of the hill is a deep brook, not easily fordable, which made the position almost impregnable.

"The lack of food and forage, and especially oats, had produced a state near to exhaustion in both men and horses. Having at last reached the line of battle we were without every kind of necessity. Even water was extremely scarce and had to be got in the teeth of the enemy from the brook just mentioned. Ghjat and the abbey of Koloskoi, which was close to the battlefield, were almost without resources. The fires in Ghjat, which the inhabitants had entirely forsaken, broke out afresh at our departure and fanned by the high winds reduced the town to cinders in a few hours. Only the churches and three or four houses built of brick were spared: these we used as hospitals, and here I was obliged to leave yet another section of my medical officers.

"Nevertheless, on September 5th, at two o'clock in the afternoon, the columns of our advance guard deployed and attacked the first line of the enemy which they threw back upon the second. We captured a number of redoubts together with their cannon. The whole position tottered and everything promised a satisfactory outcome when night came down on the combatants and forced both sides to cease fighting and to retire to their respective positions.

"I dressed our wounded during the night and evacuated them at once to the abbey of Koloskoi, where I had set up a general ambulance of the rear.

"The day of the 6th was used to rest the troops and make an exact recognizance of the enemy's lines. I made the most of it to prepare dressings and to instruct the thirty-six surgeons whom I had managed to assemble in their duties and to arrange for the disposition of all the

ambulance materials. The positions to be occupied by General Headquarters and the headquarters of the Guard were designated by Napoleon
himself and a proclamation to the Army was made on the night of the 6th
of September. Before betaking myself to this bivouac I went down the
whole of the line to give my orders to the corps and divisional ambulances.

"Before daybreak I betook myself with my ambulance to the spot
designated. It was a space of about five hundred toises[1] in circumference
at the centre of the line, near to the General Headquarters tents. At
sunrise the battle began with a general attack: Prince Eugène commanded the left wing, Prince Poniatowski the right, and Prince Murat
the centre, where the Commander-in-Chief was with the Guard.

"More than two thousand pieces of artillery of the two armies fired at
the same time. Our battalions dashed through the enemy's cross-fire to
capture the foremost redoubts and break his lines. The left wing threw
back the column defending one of the strongest position on the Moscow
road and rapidly pushed forward in the direction of Mozaisk. Our centre,
under the direct orders of Marshal Ney, after being exposed to very
intense fire from the numerous batteries and redoubts which defended
this most important part in the enemy's line, mastered the formidable and
almost impregnable position.

"The leader of the attacking column, General Caulaincourt,[2] was killed
at the first redoubt, where Generals Morand and Lansnaberg who succeeded him in command, were both wounded. The latter died a few days
later, a bullet having passed through his stomach and injured the intestines.
The loss of these generals delayed this column, and it had great difficulty
in maintaining its position in the captured redoubts. Prince Poniatowski's
flank attack had a similar success and advanced equally firmly against
the opposing enemy masses. Their whole line was shaken, their advanced
position carried, and without doubt they would have been totally cut off
if our reserve had been able to support our centre,[3] and if the length of the
line of infantry and cavalry, both by now much fatigued, had not become
so greatly extended, and finally if the daylight had lasted. As it was
victory hung in the balance for some moments; but our batallions rallied:
animated by a fresh impulse and advancing rapidly they took possession
of the whole field of battle, vigorously driving the Russians before them.
The latter's strong resistance was fatal to many of them, the rest hurriedly
retreated on Moscow, where they did not halt but continued to march on
Calouga.

"This sanguinary battle lasted from six o'clock in the morning until
nine o'clock at night. On our side some forty generals were killed or
wounded and about twelve to thirteen thousand officers and men put

[1] An ancient measure of distance. The approximate equivalent of two metres.
[2] The brother of the Duke of Vicenza, Napoleon's Master of the Horse and celebrated
diplomat.
[3] Napoleon has been criticized, and this is implied in Larrey's words, for not employing
his last reserves—the Guard—at this critical stage in the battle, as Murat pressed him to
do. As he hesitated, Bessières, who commanded the Guard, remarked: "Let me remind
Your Majesty that you are now seven hundred leagues from France." The request was
refused, as were two later ones.

hors de combat. The number of the wounded reached as many as nine thousand five hundred. The enemy loss was estimated at more than twenty thousand. It would be difficult to depict all the frightful scenes of this terrible day, where more than five or six hundred thousand combatants were engaged in an area of about a square league of ground. Two-thirds of the wounded passed through our general ambulance, as its position was known to the whole army through the order of the day and by its closeness to the General Headquarters tents.

"I had hardly finished making the essential preparations when the wounded arrived in crowds, and there would have been great confusion had I not insisted on the rules for priority in dressing which I had used in the other battles, the principles of which are laid down in the account of my earlier campaigns. I owe the greatest praise and thanks to M. Laubert, Chief Pharmacist to the army, and to many of his young assistants for the zealous aid they gave me in these distressing circumstances. The paucity of assistants of higher rank forced me to do all the difficult operations myself, and at the same time I had to keep an active eye on both this ambulance and on those of the Line.

"About two or three hours after the commencement of the battle I was called to the aid of General Montbrun, the commander of one of the cavalry corps, who was mortally wounded. It was necessary to attend to him on the spot where he had been struck down, as a cannon ball had passed across his loins from one side to the other. There was little to be done as death was certain and that soon. I applied a dressing and had the general moved to a small village at no great distance, where he died a few hours later. I was in great danger whilst attending to him for a ball killed some horses behind us. I went back to my ambulance but was again called away on account of Generals Nausouty, Lansnaberg and Romeuf. The first had received a bullet through the inner side of his right knee which fortunately had not involved the joint. I debrided the wounds, applied a suitable dressing, and returned him to the hands of Chief Surgeon Bancel who looked after him until he had recovered. I have already mentioned the case of the second of these generals whose wound appeared to require only a simple dressing and suitable subsequent treatment; this was carried out with the utmost care but unfortunately unsuccessfully. I was unable to find the third officer and did not see him until the next day. He had been attended to on the battlefield and carried to the same village as General Montbrun. There had been a failure to recognize the great destruction in his right haunch and adjacent lumbar region caused by a nearly spent ball which had left no external mark. The parts were disorganized and distended by a large effusion of blood, and a long incision which I immediately made through the skin revealed the extent of the internal derangement. The muscles were lacerated and pulped, and the iliac bone and lumbar vertebrae fractured. It can well be imagined the amount of disturbance that had been transmitted to the abdominal viscera and the general died that night. No greater courage could possibly have been shewn than was exhibited by these honourable victims, whose names deserve to be inscribed in the annals of history.

"I returned at once to the general ambulance, where far into the next night I continued to perform difficult operations without intermission. Our work was the more arduous as the weather was very cold and often foggy, The northerly, north-easterly, and north-westerly winds had been continuous during the month and were now very strong owing to the nearness of the equinox. It was only with the greatest difficulty that we could keep an indispensable wax torch alight during the night for me to see to ligature arteries. All the surgeons gave the most signal proofs of courage and devotion throughout this day. The corps' ambulances and those of the regiments were at their posts and fulfilled their duties perfectly.

"Out of eleven subjects on whom I performed amputation of the arm at the shoulder on the first day of the battle, I learned later that only two perished during their evacuation; all the rest had reached Prussia and Germany with their wounds healed before we ourselves returned to these countries. The most remarkable of all was a major of one of the infantry regiments of the Line. As soon as his operation was over he mounted his horse, which he did not want to lose, and took the road; nothing prevented him from making his way directly back to France, where he arrived three and a half months later with his wound healed. . . ."

"Amongst the other wounded was an under-officer of dragoons, who required an extirpation of the thigh. A number five ball had passed through the limb from the outer side of the fold of the groin to the great trochanter. All the muscles in its track were destroyed and the bone broken into fragments as high as the hip-joint. The patient had nevertheless lost but little blood, and as he shewed no serious symptoms attributable to commotion of the internal organs he was, except for the local condition, in a favourable state for the operation, which I undertook with all the more confidence as he himself demanded it, although it was done on the battlefield. The internal flap had already been formed by the wound and was only a little smaller than if I had fashioned it from the parts myself. The pectineus muscle was separated from it, this I left in place without interference and cut beneath it to divide the round ligament which was holding a portion of the head of the bone to the glenoid cavity, and finished my operation in the usual way. Having tied all the ligatures I brought the two flaps into apposition and fixed them with adhesive bandages and a suitable dressing. The patient was moved to the abbey of Koloskoi, from whence he was evacuated in turn to Witebsk and Orcha. The surgeon who received him at the latter town wrote to me that he had seen him perfectly cured. I do not know what has happened to him since."

Wounds of the femur near to the knee

"Although gunshot wounds of the thigh, with fracture of the femur, generally speaking require amputation, there is another less known condition in which this is imperative, as otherwise the patient is condemned to die after suffering terrible pain and unprecedented torments.

Such a wound may appear most favourable for the preservation of the limb, since the danger is not obvious from the exterior.

"When a bullet in full flight pierces the thigh from front to back immediately above the patella it either passes right through or is arrested in the popliteal fossa, depending on the resistance offered by the bone. In either case the femur is fractured transversely above the condyles and these bony protuberances are separated from each other by a vertical fracture which opens into the joint. The individual is immediately thrown off his balance and falls to the ground, thus aggravating the internal derangement. It is easy to imagine the chain of severe complications and the end result of such a wound: on the other hand it may be difficult to appreciate its gravity. If the ball has passed through, without damaging the popliteal artery, the two wounds do not to a casual glance suggest its full gravity; there is little or no displacement of the fractured bones and the patient does not suffer much during the first few hours, but before long swelling sets in and an adequate examination can no longer be made. Thus on the one hand we are led to think that the wound is not serious enough to require amputation, and on the other we cannot ascertain the full extent of the lesion responsible for the symptoms which follow. This no doubt has frequently led practitioners into error, and has deceived me myself in certain wounds of this sort which I have hoped to cure without operation. Experience has brought me to a firm conclusion as to which gunshot wounds of the thigh with fracture demand amputation, and which permit of an attempt being made to preserve the limb by the ordinary methods of treatment. Whilst postponing the full discussion of this question we may give an account of our experience in the matter at the battle of the Moskova.

"The first case of the kind I saw, and fortunately discovered its full gravity, was that of the colonel of the cuirassiers of the Imperial Russian Guard, Count Sackoveninsk, a superb warrior of robust build and rather fat. This senior officer was brought to me at the general ambulance with a number of his comrades, he having received a bullet wound above the left knee. After fracturing the femur the bullet had come to rest beneath the skin over the popliteal space, from whence it was removed by the chief surgeon, M. Bancel, who was about to apply a splint. I was nevertheless called to examine the wound, which at first sight did not seem dangerous, but more detailed investigation shewed me that there was not only a complete fracture of the lower end of the bone, but that the condyles were split by a vertical fracture which appeared to communicate with the joint. I did not hesitate to propose amputation: the medical officers who were present did not approve of this and the wounded man himself was undecided, but after a few moments reflection he changed his mind and asked me to operate at once. I carried out a circular amputation above the wound, using the method laid down in a number of articles in my *Campaigns*, and the patient was removed to a nearby village, together with other prisoners. The objections which had been urged against the operation caused me to dissect the amputated limb as soon as this was possible. The bone was broken at its junction with the condyles by a transverse fracture and the condyles separated from each other by a further vertical fracture. The joint was full of black sticky blood, the popliteal artery lacerated and the leg muscles infiltrated with blood: certainly it would be difficult to find a case which demanded amputation more imperiously. I shall speak of this patient again after our return from Moscow. Three very similar cases were brought to us the same day; in all of them the amputated limbs were examined by one of my pupils and the same state of affairs found.

"Generally speaking the wounds received in this battle were severe, as most of them were caused by artillery fire and those from musketry were at point-blank range, or nearly so. Moreover the Russian bullets, as I have several times remarked, are much larger than ours. Many of the wounds from artillery required the amputation of one or more limbs. In the first twenty-four hours I performed about two hundred amputations, which should have had favourable results had there been some shelter for the victims, along with straw, covering and food. Unhappily we were without all these necessities and were far from places where they could be obtained.

"At first the lack of transport forced us to place our casualties in the nearby villages and the Koloskoi Abbey, which received the largest number. Our cavalry had previously occupied these scattered localities and had consumed every form of forage, so that during the first few days it was only with the greatest difficulty that we could get enough straw for the wounded to lie on. The small quantity of bread and flour which the army had with it were quickly consumed. The wounded were reduced to horse-flesh, potatoes and cabbage stumps, with which we made their soup. This food failed before long as the advance of our convoys was very difficult since the roads were infested with Cossacks.

"Linen and lint for dressings were also almost everywhere unobtainable, but we ought to have been supplied with some of the things we most needed, such as bread, flour, beer, medicines, and dressing lint, from the places where we had found stores of them. In response to my demands orders for this were given by superior authorities, but as the carrying out of such measures usually depends on a number of people it involves great difficulties: time passes and the wounded do not receive the succour they have the right to expect. The surgeons, the only consolers of these unfortunate men, were forced to wash linen which had already been in use for the dressings themselves, or else to see it done under their own eyes so that a daily change could be made. It is to the indefatigable zeal and industry of my colleagues that most of the wounded owed their recovery.

"On the day after the battle the army marched in pursuit of the Russians, who decided not to make a stand at Mozaisk where they had a very favourable position. I put off my own departure for three or four days to complete the treatment of our wounded, and of such Russians who were later brought from the battlefield to our ambulances.

"On entering Mozaisk we found many parts of the town on fire. All the inhabitants had fled and the chief houses were full of Russian wounded who had not been able to follow their army and had been left without any sort of assistance. Almost all these unfortunate men had mutilated limbs and were incapable of making any movement to procure themselves food. Their most pressing need, if we except the dressing of their wounds, was the raging thirst which tormented them and appeared to me to have caused the death of many of the poor fellows who lay mingled with the living. The Russian surgeons had performed amputation on about ten of them, including two in whom the arm had been removed at the shoulder joint. Two large flaps had been formed and united by sutures: an upper or scapular, and a lower or axillary. A number of ligatures had been passed through the latter to include the axillary artery. In one man an enormous swelling was present in the stump, in which erythrism and gangrene developed the same day and he died the following night in spite of my having taken the precaution of dividing the ligatures. The second patient was moribund from haemorrhage, which had come on shortly after the amputation. It appeared that all the arteries had not been tied, but regardless of this an exact union of the flaps had been made as in the first case, and the sutures were even more numerous. I was never able to find out his fate.

"With the help of a number of men of the Guard, whose humanity I had often proved, I immediately provided for these unfortunate men's more urgent needs. I gave them water and distributed some tubs of biscuit I had discovered in the basement of a shop. I had the dead removed and dressed those who had not so far been treated. The churches and Town Hall were made fit to receive the French wounded and the Russians were placed in the merchants' houses. Finally, I left a surgeon in charge, together with the few medical officers who remained to me, preferring to await the arrival in due course of those in our rear.

"After two days at Mozaisk, Headquarters moved towards Moscow in the rear of the army. Hardly were we a few miles beyond Mozaisk when despite our nearness to one of the greatest capitals of the world we found ourselves on an arid, sandy desert, the gloomy solitude of which was depressing to the soldiers and seemed to presage the utter desertion of Moscow and the misfortunes which awaited us in that city, the wealth of which should have offered us a very different lot.

"It was with difficulty that the army crossed this void. The horses were worn out and weakened by hunger and thirst, for water was as scarce as forage, and the men had much to put up with. We were overcome by fatigue and lacking in the very necessities for subsistence. There had been no distribution of rations for a long time and the scanty resources found at Mozaisk only sufficed for the young and old Guard. A large number of conscripts amongst the former fell victims to the abuse of *chenaps* (local brandy). They could be seen to stagger from the ranks, turn around, and fall to their knees or into a sitting posture. There they stayed motionless and died soon afterwards without uttering a sound. These young men were predisposed to the pernicious effects of this liquor by weariness, privation and extreme exertion.

"We reached one of the suburbs of Moscow on the evening of September 14th, and learnt that the Russian army in passing through the city had taken with it the populace and public functionaries. There only remained a few of the lower class people and servants, so that the next morning we met with hardly anybody in the principal streets and the houses were completely abandoned. What surprised us very much was to see fire breaking out in many of the distant quarters of the town which our soldiers had not yet reached, and particularly in the bazaar of the Kremlin, a vast colonnaded building somewhat like the Palais Royal at Paris.

"After what we had seen in our march across Little Russia we were amazed by the size of Moscow, the number of its churches and palaces, the splendid architecture and convenience of the principal houses, the richness of their furnishing and the many *objets de luxe* to be found in them. The streets are for the most part spacious, regular and wide, and nothing in the city is discordant. Everything spoke of its wealth and its immense commerce with all the quarters of the world.

"The different forms of architecture of the palaces, houses, and churches added greatly to the beauty of the city; some quarters advertised the nationality of their inhabitants by the character of their buildings; so that it was easy to distinguish the French quarter, the Indian, Chinese, and German. The Kremlin may be looked upon as the citadel of Moscow: it is in the middle of the town on a slight elevation and surrounded by an embrasured wall flanked at intervals by towers armed with cannon. The bazaar I have spoken of, which ordinarily is well stocked with Oriental merchandise and precious furs, had succumbed to the flames and the only articles we were able to use were those stored in the cellars which our soldiers were able to break open when the fire was over, almost the whole of the outside of this beautiful building being destroyed. The rest of the Kremlin consists of the palace of the Emperors, the Senate building, the archives, the arsenal, and two very ancient temples; all of them splendid edifices forming a majestic ensemble around the parade ground. One could imagine oneself transported to the public square of ancient Athens, where on the one side the Areopagus and the Temple of Minerva claimed one's admiration and on the other the Academy and the Arsenal. Between the two temples is the Tower of Ivan, which is rather like an Egyptian minaret and contains a number of bells of different sizes. At its foot is another enormous bell, which is mentioned by all historians. From the top of this tower the whole of the town and suburbs may be seen, laid out in the form of a star with four bifurcated arms. The coloured roofs of the houses, and the gold and silver covering of the domes and capitals of its many steeples give this city a most picturesque appearance. One of the chapels of the Kremlin, which was the burial place of the Emperors, is of un-surpassed richness, its walls covered with plaques of gold or silver-gilt five or six lines thick, on which the story of the Old and New Testaments is depicted in relief: the massive silver lustres and candelabra are quite remarkable.[4]

[4] Desiring to send the customary trophies of his conquests to Paris, Napoleon selected as the most imposing in Moscow, the great iron cross of Ivan Veliki from the dome of the Kremlin; an object of much pious veneration amongst the Russians which he proposed

"The hospitals, which particularly interested me, are worthy of the most civilized nation in the world. The great military hospital forms three sides of a parallelogram. The main part borders a large road and faces an immense barracks, comparable with the Royal Military School in Paris. Two lateral buildings at either end form the boundaries of the court, which gives onto a large and beautiful garden which serves as a promenade for the patients. A colonnade with columns of composite orders forms the facade of this building, which is on two floors. You enter a spacious vestibule, from which doors open to the ground-floor wards, and a magnificent staircase to the upper floor. The wards run the whole length of the building and have windows on both sides reaching almost from floor to ceiling; all have double panes of glass as is usual everywhere in Russia and are completely closed in winter: they are warmed by ornamented stoves placed at suitable intervals. Each ward has four rows of fifty beds, separated by sufficient space for health. The three principal buildings contain fourteen main wards of about the same size, so that the total number of beds may well reach to nearly three thousand. The workshops, pharmacy, kitchen and other accessories are separate and within convenient reach of the wards. This is one of the largest, best conducted, and finest hospitals I have ever seen. We found only a very few wounded there, whom we removed to a smaller hospital near to an establishment called the Institute, which is devoted to the education of children of soldiers killed in war.

"The civil hospitals, which I also visited to arrange accommodation for our wounded, were equally interesting. The four principal ones are the Cheremetow, Gallizin, Alexandra and the Foundling. We appropriated the first, which is noteworthy for its shape, construction and interior arrangement, for the sick and wounded of the Guard. It is built on three floors and shaped as a crescent, with the secondary buildings at the rear. A fine central doorway gives access to a domed chapel furnished with stucco columns and fine pictures, wherein lie the remains of its royal founder. The pharmacy is one of the finest and best provided I know of. The wards, which are reached by corridors, are of different sizes; the beds and other furniture were in good condition. Here we found about twenty old pensioners of the Prince's household, whom we isolated in one of the better quarters so that they should not mix with our patients, and we treated them in the same way.

"The Gallizin hospital at the opposite end of the city is the finest in Moscow. We used it for the wounded French officers and accorded the same care to some thirty severely wounded Russian officers who had been left there by their comrades when they evacuated Moscow. Two of these had undergone amputations of the leg and one of the thigh. The latter

to erect above the dome of the Invalides. To dismount it was a matter of great difficulty on account of the height and its enormous weight. The sappers of the Guard were given the task, but their clumsy efforts resulted in the cross falling to the ground and being broken into three pieces. The fragments were nevertheless taken away in the retreat with other of Napoleon's baggage, but were abandoned during a Cossack raid outside Krasnoë where so much transport was lost.

died during our stay from reabsorptive fever caused by a conical stump. The amputation wounds were already infected with hospital gangrene when I first saw them. One patient died of this infection which took on a very severe form; the other we were able to cure. The disease destroyed a flap which the Russian surgeon had formed from the calf, but once the wound became open and flat healing commenced, although its progress was very slow. Many of the other Russian officers were suffering from extensive fractures of the legs with disorganization of the soft parts; I had much difficulty in persuading them of the necessity for amputation, which two accepted: it was the means of saving them, and before long they were cured.

"Two French officers, attached to the Polish army corps of Prince Poniatowski, were brought to this hospital from the advance guard. Both of them had been severely wounded and had undergone amputation, the one through the thigh and the other the leg by the leading Polish surgeon, M. La Fontaine, the author of a work on *The Plica*. In each case the two flaps had been joined by first intention and their edges kept together by a large number of interrupted sutures. One of these officers had a severe haemorrhage when he reached hospital and his wound was already the seat of gangrene. I immediately cut the sutures and found the stump full of coagulated blood, but no sign of a ligature: however no fresh haemorrhage occurred and the patient was considerably relieved, but the gangrene continued to progress and a few hours later his life ended.

"The second, M. F. . . ., was in a state of violent erythrism which I could not relieve by any known means: here, too, the stump had been tightly stitched. We cut the sutures and applied emollients to the whole of the limb and for a short time were able to hope that all would be well; gangrene, however, appeared and advanced with terrible rapidity, it soon reached to the thigh and the patient died within twenty-four hours.

"The Foundlings Hospital, on the bank of the Moskowa beneath the cannon of the Kremlin, is without doubt the largest and best building of its kind in Europe. It consists of two parts; one which includes the entrance, accommodates the Governor who is chosen from amongst the old generals of the army, together with the administrative staff, the medical officers, and the various persons belonging to the service of the hospital; the second is in the form of a complete square. In the centre is a large courtyard, containing a fountain and a reservoir which distributes the river water throughout the hospital. Each side of the building has four large floors and a corridor, which though not very wide is sufficient to allow people and air to circulate freely: the wards occupy the rest of each wing. In every ward there are two rows of curtained beds of a size suited to the children. The boy's part is separated from the girl's and the utmost cleanliness and order are found everywhere.

"It is noteworthy that the first of these two buildings, and the larger part of the wards in the second, are vaulted and so solidly constructed as to be fire-proof. The workshops and the accessory establishments are generally speaking of the highest efficiency.

"At the time of their retreat the Russians took away all the children of both sexes over seven years of age and left behind only a few of the very young ones whom we placed in a separate part of the hospital. The remainder of the building we used for the reception of such of the French wounded who were incapable of transportation. We chose this place in the belief that it would be the one most respected by the Cossacks in the event of our army making a hurried retreat.

"Hardly had we obtained possession of the town, and put out the fire which the Russians had set going in the best quarters, than it broke out again with even greater intensity and rapidly spread from one part to the other so that it encompassed the whole city. The first of its two chief causes is correctly reported as the deliberate act of certain Russians, who are believed to have been convicts released from the prisons when the doors were thrown open at the retreat of their army. These wretches, urged by orders from above or on their own initiative, and no doubt with pillage as their object, went openly from one palace or house to the next setting them on fire, which the French patrols although numerous were unable to prevent. I saw a number of them caught in the act with lighted quick-matches and combustible materials in their hands. The penalty of death inflicted on those caught red-handed made no impression on the rest, and the fire continued for three days and three nights without intermission.[5] It was in vain that our soldiers pulled down houses to stop its progress: the flames quickly crossed the gaps and in the twinkling of an eye the buildings thus isolated became involved. The second cause was the strong equinoctial winds, always especially violent in these parts, which fanned the flames and caused the fires to spread with extraordinary rapidity.[6]

"It would be difficult in any circumstances to see a more horrible sight than that which now met our eyes. It was especially during the night of the 18th September, when the fire reached its greatest intensity, that its effects were most amazing; the weather being fine and dry and the winds

[5] One of these incendiaries made his way torch in hand into the palace occupied by General Grouchy and was about to set light to his bed-curtains, when the general's son (who related this to me) suddenly leaped upon him and with the help of his servants succeeded in throwing him out, where he was arrested by a French patrol and taken before a tribunal set up to deal with the fire-raisers.

[6] Thiers asserts, and Madelin says that it is undoubted, that the firing of Moscow was deliberately done by the orders and actions of the Governor, Rostopchin, who opened the prisons, provided the inmates with instructions and the means of spreading the conflagration, and had all the fire pumps removed. Marbot says that, on the night of the 15th September, French and German traders came to warn Napoleon that the town was about to be set on fire, and that this was confirmed by a Russian police-agent who was reluctant to execute the order. The Emperor at once prescribed the most severe measures and sent out patrols, some of whom caught the brigands in the act, but this was too late to be effective. Thiers adds a circumstantial account of the gales which blew first from the east and, when the whole of the western quarter was aflame, abruptly changed to the north-west, and some hours later with equal suddenness backed to the south-west. The Emperor speedily evacuated the Kremlin, where four hundred ammunition wagons were parked in the courtyard and four hundred thousand pounds of powder stored in the magazine. Only the Guard remained behind to endeavour to fight the flames.

blowing continually from east to north or from north to east. During this night, the fearful picture of which will remain for ever engraved on my memory, the whole city was engulfed; great sheets of multicoloured flame rose everywhere as high as the clouds, covering the entire horizon and spreading a brilliant light and burning heat to a great distance. These sheaves of fire, spouting out in every direction and carried by the strong winds, were accompanied in their ascent and rapid spread by a terrible hissing noise and by thundering explosions, the result of the firing of gunpowder, saltpetre, oils, resins and spirits, with which most of the houses and shops were stocked. Glazed iron sheets covering buildings were quickly detached by the heat and fell some way away; large portions of roofing or flaming pine beams were carried long distances and served to spread the fire to houses which might be thought far enough off to be safe. Horror and fear engulfed everyone. The Guard, General Head-quarters and the Commander-in-Chief left the Kremlin and the city and established a camp at Petroski, a castle of Peter-the-Great on the St. Petersburg road. I stayed behind with a number of my comrades in an isolated stone-built house at the top of the free quarter near the Kremlin, and from here I could easily see all the features of this terrible fire. We sent our wagons into the fields and for the whole time were on the *qui vive* to deal with developments or to forestall them.

"The people of the lower class who had remained in Moscow, driven from house to house by the fire, uttered the most lamentable cries. Trying to save whatever they had of value they loaded themselves with bundles which they could barely carry and which they might often be seen abandoning to save themselves from the flames. The women, impelled by their natural humanity, carried one or two children on their shoulders and dragged along others by the hand. To escape the death which menaced them on every side they ran with their skirts pulled up looking in every corner of the streets and squares for a refuge; but the fierceness of the fire quickly forced them to fly precipitately from such shelter and many of them unable to escape found an unfortunate end in this labyrinth. I saw old men with their long beards on fire being dragged along on small carts by their children in the struggle to get them away from this veritable inferno.

"As for our soldiers, tormented by hunger and thirst they braved every danger to get the foodstuffs, wines, liquors and other things they desired from the cellars and burning shops. We could see them running pell-mell through the streets by the side of the despairing inhabitants, carrying whatever they had been able to snatch from the ravages of this fearful fire. In the end, after eight or ten days, the immense and superb city was reduced to ashes, except for the Kremlin palace, the churches and a few large houses which were built of stone.

"This catastrophe spread alarm through the army and threatened grave misfortunes. We all began to wonder if we should be able to find much longer the food, clothing or other materials urgently needed by the troops. What more sinister thought could possess our imagination! Nevertheless General Headquarters returned to take up residence again

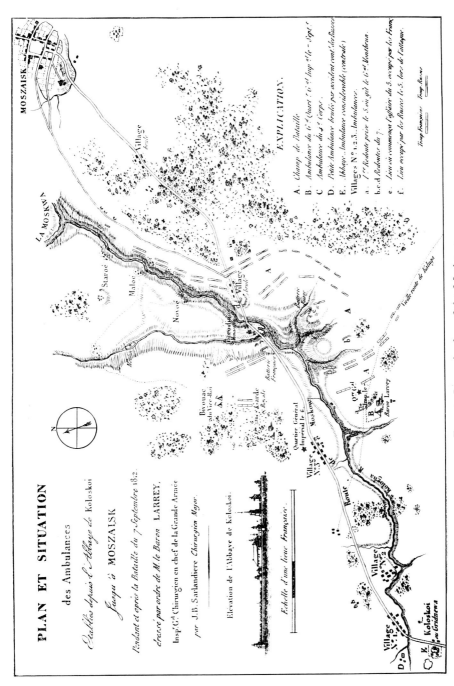

FIG. 27. Larrey's plan of the Moskowa.

in the Kremlin, the Guard occupied some houses in the free quarter which had escaped the fire, and each of us once more took up his duties.

"By dint of much searching we discovered some storehouses of flour, meat, salt fish, oil, brandy, wines and liqueurs. Several distributions were made to the soldiers but too much was kept back or stored. This excess of caution, which is sometimes no more than a pretext for inaction, resulted in the burning or abandoning in these warehouses of all sorts of supplies which would have been of the utmost value and could even have sufficed the army for more than six months had it remained in Moscow. Moreover every use should have been made of the furs and cloth stuffs to provide the troops with suitable garments to protect them as much as possible against the severe cold we had to expect. As for the soldiers, who never look to the future, far from worrying about this lack of foresight they were only concerned with looting wines, liqueurs, or gold and silver articles, and thought nothing of the rest.

"The unexpected plenty which resulted from their indefatigable explorations affected discipline and upset the health of the more intemperate men. This of itself should have been a reason to hasten our departure for Poland. Moscow became for us a new Capua. The enemy's leaders deceived ours with hopes of peace, the preliminaries being always on the point of signature from one day to the next. All the time clouds of Cossacks ranged over our cantonments and daily carried off many of our foraging parties. Meanwhile General Kutusoff gathered together the remnants of his army and was reinforced by recruits from all directions,[7] whilst under divers pretexts his advance guards insensibly drew nearer to ours. Finally the crux of the negotiations approached, and at the very moment when the general,[8] who was acting as our ambassador, should have obtained a definite decision the army corps of Prince Joachim (Murat) was surrounded. It was with difficulty that the general made his way through the obstacles barring his return to Moscow, and several detachments of our troops and a number of cannon were captured. However, though at first routed the different units rallied and broke through the enveloping Russian column, and after having gained a favourable position they counter-attacked and eventually repulsed the bulk of the enemy cavalry, retaking some guns and liberating a number of men who had been made prisoner in the first attack.[9] The arrival of General Lauriston and a

[7] Marbot says that some 15,000 Russian stragglers returned to the suburbs of Moscow: "These men . . . went about freely among our bivouacs, sitting at our soldiers' fires and eating with them, without it occurring to anyone to make them prisoners. This was a great mistake, for they gradually rejoined their own army whilst ours was growing weaker every day from sickness and the effects of the first cold weather."

[8] General Lauriston, who was used by Kutusoff and Alexander as a catspaw to delude Napoleon, whilst keeping the French static in Moscow.

[9] This was the battle of Woronovo (Winkovo) at which the Russians profited by Murat's complacency in believing that by his vain ostentation and friendly advances he had secured immunity from attack. His outposts were neglected and his surprise complete. This setback made Napoleon all the more anxious to defeat Kutusoff before retreating to avoid the appearance of being forced into this.

number of wounded at Headquarters finally confirmed the renewal of hostilities. Orders were at once given for the immediate departure of the army. The *générale* was beat and each unit prepared for instant movement. We hurriedly made our own arrangements and marched out on the 19th October."

Chapter 21

The Russian Campaign (3). The Retreat from Moscow.
Engagement at Malajaroslaw. Mozaisk. The Dnieper.
Ney's rearguard. Smolensk. Krasnoë. Cognats.
Mme. Bursay. The Beresina tragedy. Napoleon's
departure. Increase in cold. Wilna.
Kowno. Königsberg.

With the descent of winter and the failure of all his many attempts to
reach an understanding with the Russians, Napoleon was faced with the
alternatives of wintering in Moscow—even if practicable a risky undertaking with such uncertain allies as Austria and Prussia on the rear of the
wings of the Grand Army, and with Paris bereft of her master—or of
retreat. For a moment he toyed with the possibility of an audacious dash
towards St. Petersburg, to unite with Victor and Macdonald in Courland,
but in this he was opposed by the Marshals and, strongly urged by Davout
and Daru, he determined to retreat. The decision taken it remained to
decide the line of this. The Emperor was still hoping to inflict a really
crushing defeat upon Kutusoff, and by so doing to avoid giving to the
world the picture of a foiled enterprise ending in a forced retreat. His
first thought was to thrust south to Kalouga and bring the Russian army
to action whilst still retaining his base at Moscow, but suddenly he
changed his plans and decided to move through that province with
his whole force by a route through Malajaroslaw, and by crossing
Suvaroff's front to avoid a heavy and probably costly engagement. This
involved the final abandonment of Moscow, but offered a retreat through
undevastated and fertile country. But his encumbered and ill-disciplined
army moved too slowly and the Russians, although deceived for a time,
discovered his movements and by forced marches reached Malajaroslaw
almost at the same time as the French.

In the resulting desperate encounter, in which Larrey gives great
credit to Eugène, the town was taken and retaken six times and was
finally captured at the seventh attempt with the aid of an Italian division.
The Grand Army lost some four thousand killed, and the Russians six
thousand. This left Napoleon with the difficult decision whether to continue the attempt to force his way through to Kalouga, which would now
involve a full scale battle with Kutusoff, which the latter might again
decline, or to retreat upon Mozaisk. After three days consideration of the

position, and urged by his Council of War, he began his retreat through Mozaisk and Smolensk and along the devastated route across the battlefield of the Moskowa, which presented the harrowing picture of 50,000 corpses half-devoured by wolves. The army which had left Moscow on October 19th, retired from Malajaroslaw on the 27th and reached Mozaisk on the 30th. Thus after ten days of marching and fighting, and the consumption of most of the provisions they carried with them, the French found themselves a bare twelve leagues from Moscow, and this at a time when the weather had broken.

The hardships and horror of this retreat are to be read in what follows, but it is widely agreed that they might have been greatly mitigated had more thought gone to its preparation. Caulaincourt asserts in plainer language than Larrey's that much of the disaster was due to the lack of stores, of horses for the artillery and transport of the sick and wounded, of a failure to shoe the animals with frost nails, and the provision of winter clothing for the troops—of all of which he warned Napoleon. As to the horses, he asserts that they fell by the roadside chiefly because they were not properly shod for crossing the ice, and having once fallen were unable to rise and ended by lying where they fell to be cut up for food. In his own headquarters out of 715 animals with which the campaign started, and which he was at great pains to see properly shod in Moscow, only 80 had been lost by the time Wilna was reached on December 8th.

As far as the sick and wounded were concerned, although Larrey is eloquent enough about their sufferings he by no means over-emphasizes their dreadful lot. From the beginning the medical arrangements on this campaign had been deplorable. Napoleon, accustomed to campaigning in the more densely populated and well cultivated countries of Europe, seems to have made little allowance—if any—for the far more meagre resources of Russia; a dearth aggravated beyond calculation by the deliberate destruction of the towns and villages through which the army passed. Nor were his heavy transport wagons suited to her indifferent sandy roads. Innumerable wagons and enormous quantities of supplies vanished through theft and loss or lack of means for bringing them up. The medical supplies had been inadequate or abandoned in the initial mad rush across Russia and at Witebsk, as early as the month of July, the wounded lay on the ground, without even straw beneath them, in crowded churches and warehouses with their wounds undressed, in numbers far beyond the capacity of the few surgeons and doctors, who had neither linen nor medicines. The ambulances lacked even the cases of instruments, which had been left in the rear or lost with the wagons when the horses collapsed and died. This gave the transport drivers no regrets, since the breakdown of the service on which they were employed meant an end to their personal privations.

On the return to Mozaisk the army encountered the mass of severely wounded men from the Moskowa. Numbers of these were picked up and placed in or on wagons or forage carts, already loaded with wounded from Malajaroslaw. A few fortunate ones, whom the Emperor placed in his own carriages, were cared for by the medical men of his household, but most of the rest died from cold, exhaustion, or neglect, and since the vehicles became lost not a score of them reached Wilna.

From his position at Headquarters, in close association with the Guard who maintained some discipline of a sort throughout, Larrey can have had but inadequate knowledge of the conditions through the length of this long column of over 100,000 men, strung out over many miles of desolate and ravaged country, without organized sources of supply and dependent for themselves and their horses upon such plunder as they could find in their unorganized foraging parties, made in the face of death or capture from the bodies of Cossacks hanging on their flanks—themselves dependent on the same means of sustenance. The misery of the Line regiments was probably greater than that of the Guard, to say nothing of that of the mass of refugees from Moscow. Kutusoff's contemptuous reference to the French Commander "abandoning his wounded to the vengeance of the angry people" leaves us no doubt about the fate of the many who were left alive along the trail of the Grand Army.

"Before leaving Moscow we evacuated all the sick and wounded capable of being moved to Mozaisk, under the escort of a strong division of infantry commanded by General Claparède. Those whom it was not possible to send away we brought to the Foundling Hospital where I left them in the care of three divisions of medical officers. I placed some French surgeons, who had long been resident in Moscow and had asked for employment, in charge of the Russian wounded in the expectation that by caring for these men they would merit good treatment from the Russian government. The majority of the French civilians who had been living in Moscow followed the sick convoy which Napoleon confided to the charge of a divisional commander.

"The intention of our Army Chief was to attack the enemy's main body and to march directly to Kalouga, so as to reach Poland through the Ukraine. The general fear of scarcity of food and the memory of our earlier privations caused all our comrades to provision themselves. Some filled wagons, others loaded their horses, and the soldiers stuffed their knapsacks with food.[1] Never had the army been encumbered with so much transport as ours on its exit from Moscow! I doubt if Darius at his departure from Babylon carried with him such an amount of spoil and baggage. A moist penetrating fog on the following day made movement of this vast transport very difficult and led to early disorder, since each one wanted to save his own provisions. However we managed to catch up with the advance guard in the evening of the 23rd. The enemy promptly evacuated his position and fell back on Kalouga.

"Prince Eugène, who commanded the advance guard, was ordered to make his way by a cross-country road to Malajaroslaw, a small town in a defile in the mountains through which Kutusoff's army had to pass. But the treachery of the guides and the bad roads so slowed his march that the enemy reached the pass two hours ahead of him. Nevertheless our general crossed the rivers and mountains and attacked vigorously, and

---

[1] Thiers says that these provisions were exhausted before the army reached Mozaisk.

after a sanguinary battle took possession of the defile, albeit too late to prevent the larger part of the Russian troops from passing through. It was one of the battles which brought most honour to this commander. The Russians lost more than six thousand men and left a large number of prisoners and numerous cannon and artillery wagons in our hands. On our side we lost a number of distinguished soldiers, amongst them General Delzons, commanding the advance guard, one of my companions of Egypt and an officer of great merit and rare courage. We had nearly two thousand wounded, many of them officers of high rank, whom we dressed on the battlefield and carried along with us in the rear in private carriages brought from Moscow. I must especially praise MM. Assalini, first surgeon to the Prince; Pincon, chief surgeon to this army corps, and the other surgeons of the corps and of the Guard's ambulances for their assiduity and devotion to our wounded.

"General Headquarters and the Guard reached Malajaroslaw at the close of the action and witnessed Prince Eugène's victory. We spiked the guns and burnt the captured wagons, and after a number of reconnaissances pursued the enemy for several leagues along the Kalouga road beyond the pass. I had the Russian wounded brought to Malajaroslaw, and though I was unable to stay there to treat them, I left them in full confidence that they would be looked after by their compatriots.

"The Staff and the Guard retired the same evening to a large village two leagues from the battlefield, which they had occupied the day previously. I followed and arranged an ambulance for the reception of the isolated wounded from the battle. At daybreak the next morning, the 25th, as Napoleon and his escort were returning from Malajaroslaw, where the Prince had slept, they were suddenly surrounded by several thousand Cossacks who had been hidden by thick fog. A large number of our light cavalry were wounded, several cannon carried off, and Napoleon himself was in great danger. However the cavalry of the Guard having located the enemy, performed prodigies of valour and drove him off in spite of strenuous opposition and recaptured the artillery. There was now no alternative but a prompt retreat, which was begun the next day though we did not as yet know the direction we were to take. We marched through Borosck, or the 'nut-town' as our men nicknamed it, from the large quantities of nuts we found in the houses during our earlier advance, and through some pleasant, rich and well populated country. It had been hoped that we might have been able to continue our retreat through the Ukraine but Napoleon, no doubt wishing to save the sick and wounded, of whom there were a great number in the ambulances at Mozaisk, Koloskoi, Ghjat, Viasma, etc., and being aware that Tormasow had reached Borrisow and cut our communications, decided to return along the road by which we had advanced and which we reached a few days later. There was great discontent throughout the whole army over this decision, for all foresaw the frightful misery we should have to endure in crossing a vast country which was now a desert, ruined by the destruction of its towns and villages and the continuous passage of our troops and the Cossacks. We re-entered Mozaisk where there were many sick of both nations, and evacuated all who were able to walk or could be carried. The rest I gathered into one hospital and left them, together with the Russian wounded, in charge of some medical officers and with such necessaries as we were able to find. A large proportion of the transport had already vanished, and we were only able to make an inadequate distribution of some biscuit and flour which we found in the shops.

"However, the march continued and we reached Koloskoi. Between the engagement of the 24th and our arrival at Mozaisk the weather had been very fine, but as soon as we left that town the wind came from the north-east and the cold increased and became very severe, so that when we recrossed the battlefield of the Moskowa we found that the bodies of the dead were frozen.

"The ambulances which we had left behind in our advance were located in the villages along our route and at the Koloskoi Abbey. In one of them were the Russian officers whom I have already mentioned; they were cured of their wounds and many of them came to find me to express their gratitude. They asked if they might be allowed to remain behind, a permission which I obtained easily enough, and I even left them some money to buy urgent necessaries from the wandering Jews pending the arrival of their compatriots. At the same time I charged them to look after our own sick: I have reason to think that these officers will have protected them, remembering the aid they received from us.[2]

"At Koloskoi I took the same measures for our wounded as at Mozaisk. I spent part of the night in operating on a number who were in danger of succumbing to the effects of extensive fractures and deep ulceration of their limbs. They were placed on army wagons and followed the transport of General Headquarters; the medical officers of our ambulances who went with them being instructed to dress their wounds daily. Our lack of every necessary was already extreme: snow was falling abundantly and it became steadily colder.

"It was here that the disorganization of the army began which we could only partially arrest at Wiasma. The road had become difficult since the earth was covered with snow, and the soldiers suffered a great deal in their bivouacs.

"At Wiasma a few rations of flour were distributed and a very small amount of bread. General Headquarters and the Guard remained for twenty-four hours to allow the men some rest and to distribute the small quantity of supplies which still remained in the warehouses. After dressing the wounds of the soldiers of both nations in the hospitals, we evacuated such of our own men who could walk, and collected those we could not transport in a strongly constructed building, safe from the fires which constantly broke out in those of wooden construction, either from the men's carelessness or from bivouac fires being lighted too near to the houses: this is one of the calamities of war and is especially frequent in winter campaigns.

"As we were lacking transport, the Commander-in-Chief put his

[2] "They unanimously gave the required promise, and it is known to God alone whether they paid the debt contracted with the best of men." (Thiers).

wagons and carriages at our disposal for the use of the wounded and instructed the physicians and surgeons of his household to go with them and to look after them. I must pay tribute to the zeal and devotion which Drs. Ribes, Jouan, Lherminier and Mestivier displayed at this time: M. Rouyères, the pharmacist, was equally helpful."

* * * * *

"The rearguard, commanded by Prince Eugène, followed immediately behind us as we passed through Wiasma, which was almost entirely reduced to ashes and choked with the debris of burnt houses. This delayed our progress and in particular that of the wagons and artillery, so much so that our rearguard was attacked by a number of Russian divisions before we were clear. This attack was particularly deadly as it took place in a fog, so thick that the troops of the 4th Corps soon became mingled with the Russians and a terribly confused combat resulted. This was one of the main causes of the loss of our wounded, at any rate of those of the 4th Corps, and of a number of the French families from Moscow who were accompanying them. Marshal Ney's corps took the place of Prince Eugène's,[3] which had lost considerably in this affray.

"In spite of everything the army continued to march in fairly good order, but the effects of its privations and of the cold became more and more marked. Already the wounded and the weaker individuals had fallen victims to these cruel vicissitudes, and the horses being without forage and continuously in bivouac died in large numbers; often the men did not wait for them to fall to cut their throats, and relieved their hunger by grilling the flesh at the first bivouac fire.

"We reached the Dnieper and crossed it at a short distance from Dorogobouje. As three-quarters of this town had been burnt it provided us with scarcely any resources; there were, however, many wounded for whom with great difficulty we found some flour and a small amount of bread. All who could walk followed the army—the rest were left behind

[3] The actual rearguard as far as Wiasma was Davout's 1st Corps which was in the rear of Eugène's 4th Corps and the crowd of stragglers, sick, wounded, women and children, who followed it. This corps was attacked outside Wiasma and momentarily cut in two, suffering the severe loss Larrey refers to. The situation was saved by the resolute action of Davout and Ney, though the losses were severe and included the wounded of the 4th Corps. Napoleon criticized Davout severely and replaced his corps by Ney's, although much of the disaster seems to have been due to a failure of Eugène to move as rapidly as the circumstances demanded, thereby adding to Davout's difficulties.

Of Napoleon at this period Thiers says: "In the midst of the Guard, which marched at the head of the army, and consumed such provisions as could be procured from the country they traversed, leaving dead horses as the sole means of subsistence for those who followed, he saw nothing of the retreat, and wished to see nothing of it. . . . Instead of taking an active part in its conduct . . . he remained two marches in advance of the rearguard, and sometimes on horseback, sometimes on foot, but most frequently in a carriage, between Berthier, who was plunged in consternation, and Murat, who was almost annihilated by terror, he passed whole days without uttering a word—only rising at intervals from the abyss of gloomy reflections in which he was sunk, to utter complaints of his lieutenants. . . ."

in the best and most solid of the hospitals. A number of them were, alas, the victims of a fire which broke out during the night in a house near to the ambulance, and made such extremely rapid progress that in a few moments all the houses of the quarter were burnt. I myself only escaped through the flames, after I and my colleagues had used every possible means to arrest the spread of the fire and to save our patients.

"After a number of days of very difficult marching through an uninhabited snow-covered land, we reached Smolensk on November 12th. During this time our men continued to subsist on the dead horses which we found in large numbers on the roads. Here, at the gates of the ancient kingdom of Poland, we hoped to reach the term of our miseries. There were reasons to believe that large stores had been accumulated at Smolensk and that we should be able to rest there for some days; but our hopes were vain[4]. There was scarcely any food even for the sick and wounded who filled the hospitals. The army hardly received anything and was obliged to march on in the same state of destitution.

"Now, indeed, began the horrors of which we were destined to be the victims during this fatal retreat.[4] The soldiers, driven on by hunger and the lack of every necessity of life, having forced the gates of the town and sacked the stores of what small supply of bad biscuit remained, were condemned to the cruellest privations. The position of the medical officers was especially deplorable: obliged to spend every moment of their time in treating the large number of wounded whom we found in the hospitals, they had no opportunity of obtaining any means of subsistence themselves, and were far from finding them in the establishments in which they worked, since these were lacking to the patients themselves. However I was fortunate enough to be able to buy two sacks of flour at a high price and this I distributed amongst those of my comrades whose need was most pressing. I organized the work of the hospitals and myself operated upon or supervised the operations on all who required this. I left behind some fifty surgeons to care for the wounded we were forced to abandon.

"We had barely made ready to resume our march when our rearguard, which had been pursued to Smolensk by the Russians, was attacked by their advance guard on November 13th. The attack was, however, vigorously resisted, and the army had time to evacuate the town and get clear of the mountains beyond. This fresh incident resulted in the precipitate retreat of a section of wagons, and the treasure which had been ordered to move by a cross-road fell a prey to the Cossacks in the confusion.

"The cold had now become intense. The thermometer had already fallen to minus 11°F., and the wind blew strongly from the north-east. Coming so abruptly, this first spell of cold was very damaging to many of our young soldiers, and particularly to the animals which we constantly found dying in the snow at the sides of the roads. Those of us who had formed the wise habit of walking, and who had been able to save a little

---

[4] "Even previous to the Beresina, a handful of gold would have been valueless to procure a crust of bread." (Caulaincourt).

coffee and sugar, were in less danger. The continuous exercise prevented the benumbing of the limbs and maintained the heat and action of the organs; whereas the cold seized on those who were carried on horseback or in vehicles and soon produced a state of torpor and paralysing numbness, which led them to approach too closely to the bivouac fires since they were unable to feel the effect of the heat on the frozen parts. This caused gangrene, which I myself had the good fortune to escape by continuously marching and entirely avoiding the pleasure of warming myself.

"Between Smolensk and Krasnoë, for a distance of about twenty-four leagues, we saw no habitation. Everything had been burnt; the ground was covered with snow and the thermometer fell four more degrees. The army rested for a few hours during the night in the forests we were marching through, but it suffered cruelly from both hunger and the severe cold. During this short march the *cognats*[5] and the bodies of horses were keenly sought for. A loose horse was immediately killed and cut up almost whilst alive. Unhappy the animal which moved a few paces from his master! The sharing of this spoil was sometimes a cause of brawling amongst men of all ranks; even the women were deterred by nothing from getting their share.

"The army, which had become disorganized at the time of its passage through Smolensk, lost heavily between this town and Krasnoë. Cold and hunger were the principal causes of the deaths. The baggage trains and artillery parks were on many occasions cut up and dispersed by the Cossacks, and this was all the easier since the roads were covered with ice which made the march extremely difficult.

"We were hoping to find food at Krasnoë and to stay for at least twenty-four hours, but once again hope deluded us. At daybreak the next day, November 17th, we found ourselves almost surrounded by a large Russian army. We were forced to give battle, as much to be able to continue our retreat as to shew the enemy that we were not as completely without the means of defending ourselves as he had believed. Only the rearguard and the Old Guard were in any condition to fight; the men of the latter corps in particular resisted with the greatest bravery. We had about twelve hundred wounded whom I moved to the hospital at Krasnoë and went there myself to operate on the most serious cases and to see to the dressing of the others. Although a fair number of inhabitants still remained in the town most of them were Jews. We lacked almost everything required for the treatment of these interesting casualties and I had

[5] *Cognats.* I have had great difficulty in translating this word. In its ordinary sense it has no meaning in this context. Mr. Fleurent, of the Royal College of Surgeons, has suggested that it is a gallicism of the Russian word for horse which is transliterated as *kon*, and that *Cognat* is a fair phonetic rendering of this. It seems possible that the French soldiers adopted certain Russian words as their current slang, much as the English did in France in 1914–18 ("*na poo*"—Il n'y en a plus), and that the *Cognats* were the native Russian horses in contradistinction to the French army horses. Larrey saw a colonel's wife who was wearing a sable and white satin dress, thrust her hands into the belly of a dead horse. As she had no knife she pushed her whole head amongst the animal's entrails to reach its liver.

the utmost difficulty even in obtaining first-aid for them; so that they were bound to have suffered much after our departure. The lack of transport allowed us to take away only a very few: all who could not follow were collected in the town hospital where I left some medical officers to continue their treatment.[6]

"After this engagement it was imperative to continue our march, so as to avoid a fresh attack and to reach inhabited places containing provisions as soon as possible. Almost all the army was now without weapons and in utter disorder. Only the Guard, although reduced to less than half of its strength, had kept its arms and spirit of discipline. It was they who protected the stragglers and exacted respect from the enemy who pursued and harassed us unceasingly.

"On our departure from Krasnoë the temperature rose ten or twelve degrees and we suffered much less from the cold; but we were very exhausted by the snow which fell heavily for several days, and much tormented by hunger, the *cognats* having become very scarce and the search for food in the villages more difficult on account of the large number of partisans who hung about our flanks. We only halted for a few hours in the middle of the night at places where we could find some resources, or at least wood for our bivouac fires.

"We soon reached Dumbrona, a small town full of Jews, where we were able to buy a little brandy of bad quality and some bread. There were a large number of patients in the ambulance there. All who could walk followed the army and several medical officers stayed behind to look after the remainder. A violent fire broke out in one part of the town at the moment of our departure, but I have since learnt that it did not spread to the hospital.

"On reaching Orcha we crossed the Dnieper for the last time: most fortunately the bridge had not been destroyed as the river was not entirely frozen over. The whole army, protected by the Guard, passed over without difficulty whilst Marshal Ney with the rearguard held off the pursuing Russians. At the moment when he expected to rejoin us the Marshal was himself surrounded and summoned to surrender. Our communications with his corps were cut and during the twenty-four hours we were at Orcha we had no news, so that our anxiety was extreme. We found here a certain amount of provisions which were of the greatest value to our wounded. I passed the whole of the night of our arrival, as well as the next day, in dressing them and seeing that their other requirements were fulfilled. I also left behind a sufficient number of medical officers to care for them.

---

[6] In this difficult and very perilous situation every individual in the army shewed an imperturbable *sang froid*; the French women who had managed to follow us, and shared our privations and dangers, were courageous enough to help us to dress the wounded under the enemy's cannon. Mme Aurore Bursay, Directrice of the Moscow theatres, otherwise well known for her dramatic talents, was outstanding by her humanity and a steadfastness uncommon in her sex. (Bausset in his Memoirs speaks of Mme Bursay as a woman of forty-five to fifty, witty, strong-minded and courageous, who had for long managed the Théâtre Français at St. Petersburg.)

"The troops continued their march towards Tolecsehyn, but the bridge was kept intact in the hope of seeing the rearguard arrive. Eventually an officer reached us from Marshal Ney to tell us that his brave men, far from surrendering and despite the large number of enemies who surrounded them, had succeeded in breaking through the Russian columns and had reached the river. It was with the greatest joy that we saw them again."

This was one of the most intrepid of Ney's many exploits with the rearguard of this unfortunate army. He evaded the whole of Kutusoff's force which barred his route, compelling the Russian emissary who had come to demand his surrender to direct him to the nearest point on the Dnieper, where he and his men crossed on the thin ice, leaving all their baggage, wounded and artillery behind them. For three days his depleted corps marched and fought their way through a body of Platov's Cossacks and on November 20th came in sight of Orcha. Before him was a plain occupied by a strong enemy force, but Ney sent some of his officers to find if the French were still in Orcha. One of them reached Napoleon, as Larrey has described, and the Emperor then sent Eugène and Mortier to their relief. Out of six or seven thousand men, Ney succeeded in bringing back only about twelve hundred, and these utterly worn out and incapable of active service, but he saved Napoleon the humiliation before all the world of a famous French marshal falling a prisoner to the Russians.

"After all the troops had crossed the bridge was burnt in the enemy's face, which held up his advance for several days as the river was not yet completely frozen. In spite of this advantage our retreat became more and more painful; the artillery horses were in a bad state, the roads impracticable, and it had snowed ceaselessly since Krasnoë.

"We reached Tolecsehyn, a town memorable for the bloody combat fought beneath its walls between Charles XII and the Russians. Here we found a considerable supply of flour and a large quantity of brandy. The twenty-four hours we spent there were of the greatest service to both troops and horses. We left only a few casualties behind us.

"On leaving Tolecsehyn we learnt that the 2nd Army Corps under Marshal Victor had made contact with our advance-guard, but at the same time we were told that Tormasoff's army had reached Borrisow.[7] Marshal Victor checked his movement to let us pass and constituted himself our rearguard in place of Ney's corps which had suffered badly.

"The winds, after having been for a long time in the north-west, gradually veered to the north-east. The temperature dropped suddenly and the cold became more bitter as the wind became fiercer. We reached Borrisow to find that Tormasoff had cut the bridge and occupied the town and suburbs on the right (opposite) bank of the Beresina, and was in an impregnable position and beyond the range of our cannon."

*   *   *   *   *

[7] The vital bridge across the Beresina. On leaving Orcha, Napoleon had abandoned most of his baggage wagons and with these his heavy bridging equipment, and now only had the materials for a light trestle bridge.

"Our road of retreat being cut off and unattainable it was decided to cross the river two leagues higher up, whilst making a demonstration against the enemy's front. The site chosen for the crossing was before a very large village where it was possible to procure almost all the material necessary for the construction of bridges.[8] It appears that Charles XII, when pursuing the Russians before the battle of Tolecsehyn, crossed the Beresina at this same place and thus avoided Borrisow which no doubt was strongly held.

"Whilst waiting for the bridges to be built, General Headquarters and the Guard passed the night of the 24th November in the chateau of Prince Radziwil, which was about a league from the proposed crossing. This castle and its dependencies are on the eastern slope of a hill on the left bank of the river. Its farms were full of forage and stock, which were a great boon to our remaining cavalry and the whole of the Guard. We also found some flour and an abundance of dried vegetables.

"The fear of being burnt in the barns made me bivouac amongst the grenadiers. The sky was clear and the cold intense. Being obliged to pass through the camp during the night to visit the wounded I was able to get a good view of everything round about. It was not long before I noticed a comet appearing almost parallel with the horizon, on the side away from the army and directly north. It descended in the direction of the north pole as a luminous body, elongated vertically and ending in a point, from which a thin lock of hair extended upwards for a great distance. It disappeared the same night and was not seen again. This peculiar meteorite was observed in a number of places in Europe, notably at Leipsic.[9]

"Two bridges were completed without the enemy's knowledge, and the Guard crossed immediately after the 1st and 4th Corps and took possession of the opposite bank without opposition or incident; but during the transport of the heavy cannon one of the bridges broke, and in consequence the passage of the rest of the artillery and of all the wagons and ambulances was brought to a halt. At this critical moment Wittgenstein's corps, which had followed close behind us, came up with our rearguard. The latter resisted as well as it was able, but being driven from its position retired and allowed the enemy to approach, so that cannon balls and shells began to fall amongst the immense crowd which had gathered before the bridges, and although these had been repaired passage had now become impossible on account of the encumbrance and disorder

[8] The ford of the Beresina, opposite the village of Studzianka (about four leagues above Borrisow), was discovered by General Corbinian who was marching to join Oudinot's corps which he believed to be near Bobod. Napoleon made a feint of crossing at Borrisow, and succeeded in deceiving the Russians who left Studzianka practically unprotected. Had the French been more speedy and effective in their bridge building, and had there been fewer of the delays so vividly described by Marbot, it seems that the whole of the army might have crossed.

[9] The Astronomer Royal has courteously replied to my query: "From comet lists, there does not seem to be any appearance in 1812 November and so it is probable that the object was a meteor."

which prevailed.[10] Terror was in every mind; men pushed and jostled from every direction and piled one on top of another; the stronger struck down the weaker who were trampled under the feet of the mob; carriages, artillery limbers and wagons were overturned and smashed; horses and drivers were crushed under the wreckage of the vehicles and over all pitiable cries were heard on every side. To crown this misfortune the weakly fastened bridges broke for a second time. From this moment all hope of safety seemed destroyed. The majority took the council of despair; some jumped onto slabs of ice, hoping to be able to cross the river on the floes which seemed to cover it, but they were held up before reaching the opposite bank or else the ice was broken by the current. Some managed to swim across; others, less fortunate, were drowned or found themselves vainly struggling amongst the masses of ice; they died the more quickly for being already weakened by cold and privation. The most courageous and sensible retraced their steps to throw themselves into the hands of the Russians and to get away from the horrors of the scene which was enacted before their eyes.

"The crossing of the Beresina cost us the lives of a large number of individuals of all classes: one saw mothers deliberately following the fate of their children who had fallen into the river, or drown themselves holding these tightly in their arms. Many other equally touching actions were seen during this disaster.

"In spite of almost insuperable difficulties I had recrossed one of the bridges a few hours before its collapse to bring over some cases of surgical instruments which we urgently needed; this short journey nearly cost me my life. In my turn I was nigh to perishing in the crowd when happily I was recognized and at once everyone tried to assist me; I was carried by the soldiers from one to the other and to my great surprise before long found myself on the bridge. This proof of their affection in such circumstances quickly made me forget the danger I had run and the loss of my equipment.

"The first army corps to cross the river surprised the enemy behind Borrisow. He obstinately opposed our advance and appeared to be prepared to yield the town in order to retain the road, which made our position very precarious considering the heavy losses we had suffered. Nevertheless we took 3,000 prisoners and killed a large number of Russians in the first encounter. We had about 600 wounded, whom I collected together in a nearby village where their wounds were dressed.

"A retrograde movement of Tormasoff's, made as much to facilitate his

[10] Marbot says that Napoleon and his staff crossed the two bridges on the evening of the 27th November. During the night that followed, owing to the failure of the headquarters staff to give the necessary orders, the bridges were deserted, whilst 50,000 stragglers were grilling horse-flesh at their bivouac fires on the near bank. The next day, as the Russian artillery fire began to reach them, they all tried to cross at once and this coincided with the breaking of one bridge. The French, however, still contained the enemy throughout the night of the 28th, when Victor's men forced their way through the struggling mob. It was only on the morning of the 29th that the vehicles remaining on the left bank were burnt and General Eblé set the remaining bridge on fire also. In the passage of the Beresina the French lost between 20,000 and 25,000 men.

retreat as to oppose ours, provoked a second engagement chiefly involving Prince Poniatowski's corps. Amongst the seriously wounded who were brought to the advanced ambulance was General Zayonchek, one of the oldest of the Polish generals in the service of France, who had campaigned in Italy, Egypt, and all the northern countries of Europe. This brave officer had his right knee fractured by a bullet fired at almost point-blank range whilst leading his division. The wound required the immediate amputation of the thigh, which I performed there and then on the snow, under the enemy's cannon fire and in the most intense cold. This operation, which was noteworthy for its unusual circumstances, was followed by a success that I did not expect and Poland is still in the proud possession of one of her most illustrious soldiers, now more than eighty years old.[11] Except for those with mortal wounds, whom I left in charge of some assistants in the village I have spoken of, all the wounded from these engagements were quickly evacuated to Wilna on some sledges which we found amongst the local people.

"We discovered that there was a branch road by which we were told we could reach this town ahead of Tormasoff and without being harassed by his troops. We sent off the wounded first. As for the transport, there was none; it had all been left at the Beresina. After we had beaten off the Russian general, who expected to decoy us onto his route, we entered the defile which had been pointed out. This passes through the most immense forests and marshes and is intersected by many rivers or streams which were very indifferently bridged. A company of Cossacks with a single cannon could easily have held us up, but happily we got through without any important mishap and rejoined the main road at Smorgonie[12] two days in advance of Tormasoff. Here Napoleon left the army to return to France, after confiding the command to Prince Joachim (Murat).

"Although the cold had continued to increase since we crossed the Beresina, the mercury had not yet fallen below between 10° to minus 5°F., but the day we arrived at Smorgonie there was a fall of snow in star-shaped crystals and this was a prelude to the intense cold which came immediately afterwards. In our bivouac that night the mercury went down to minus 8°F. and soon afterwards to minus 15°F., or 47 degrees of frost.

"We marched very early the next morning, December 6th, so that we could reach Osmiana, another large town where we found some Jews from whom we were able to buy some bad brandy and bread. The cold steadily increased. Before we reached Smorgonie all the rivers were frozen. When we entered Osmiana my thermometer registered minus 25 degrees and during the night it fell to minus 26°F. and the cold in the bivouac was terrible. I was fortunate enough to pass that fatal night in a warm room and on a little straw, after having had some food that one of my old comrades of Egypt, M. Pla, had the kindness to offer me. We marched again the next morning before daybreak, the temperature being

[11] He entered the Russian service in 1814 and became Governor of Poland under the Czar Alexander.
[12] Smorgonie is notable for a sort of academy for training bears.

minus 27 degrees. It was difficult to maintain oneself erect, and to make the simplest movements. Whoever lost his balance and fell was at once overcome by a glacial and fatal stupor. On this march we lost a large number of men from the 12th Division which had come to meet us at Osmiana.[13] I left behind in this town all the wounded who desired it, together with a number of medical officers; it was too painful to me to see them die on the march without being able to give them any aid. Except for a number of crack troops of the Guard, who had been sensible enough to keep their cloaks or mantles and their boots and gloves, the whole army was in a frightful state of destitution; jumbled together, without weapons and without any distinctive sign of their corps, they were just masses of individuals who seemed to walk all of a piece. The cold and their weakness made them huddle together and lean on one another. Nothing was more bizarre and deplorable than their clothes. They were clad with the remnants of pellises, cloaks, or bits of stuffs of different colours which had been gradually burnt by the bivouac fires; there was no way to repair them, in fact such a thing was never thought of and we stopped nowhere. All these circumstances explain the state of dilapidation to which the remains of the Grand Army was reduced before it reached Old Prussia.

"Our passage through Miedneski, a place remarkable for the castle which time has blackened and ruined (Rownopoli), was marked by the extremity of the severe cold. Most of the village houses, which were grouped about the foot of the castle, had been burnt or demolished so that the entire army was forced to bivouac. Unhappy the individual who fell asleep! A few minutes were sufficient to freeze him completely and he remained dead where he had slept.

"My thermometer, which I hung from the buttonhole of my coat for a few moments in the middle of the night, registered minus 31°F. There was little difference between the night and day temperatures as the sun's rays were unable to penetrate the dense atmosphere. We were enveloped in a thin fog which covered every prominence of the body and clothes with icy crystals. Some hung like stalactites from the eyelashes, interfering with sight and an infinite annoyance on our difficult march to Wilna, Kowno, and beyond, since the cold continued to be almost as severe during the whole journey.

"The edges of the roads were covered with soldiers who had perished on the march of the night of December 8th. They belonged chiefly to the 12th Division, almost entirely composed of youngsters. Eventually we reached such a state of weakness and torpor that we hardly knew one another. We marched in a heavy silence. Sight and strength were enfeebled to a point at which it was difficult to follow the road and to maintain one's balance. One who lost this fell at the feet of his companions who did not turn their eyes to look at him. Although one of the most robust in the army it was only with the greatest difficulty that I reached Wilna. On my arrival there I was at the end of my strength and my

[13] This division, commanded by General Loison, had 12,000 men when it left Wilna. It reached France with only 360, according to the statement of a number of officers.

courage; I was ready to fall, no doubt never to get up again, like so many of the unfortunates who had perished before my eyes.

"The reception, full of compassion which I received from the Grey Sisters of the *Charité* when I came to their hospital on the night of the 9th, and the unremitting care with which they overwhelmed me brought me back to life. This will remain for ever engraved on my memory.

"The press to enter Wilna, the city so much desired and where we found nothing but misfortune and misery, quickly produced a frightful chaos at its gates. Men fought to get in.[14] Although places of shelter had been assigned and made ready for each army corps, masses of men wandered through the town and speedily crowded the cafés, inns and grocers shops, where they drank and ate so unrestrainedly that in next to no time all the food and drink were finished.

"In spite of the extreme confusion everywhere the night passed uneventfully. Those who were unable to sleep in the convents or houses bivouacked in the squares and streets, where they were much better off than in their previous bivouacs. The Cossacks, however, were already threatening the suburbs: their proximity causing the tail of the column to crowd within the walls of the town on the morning of the 10th, which increased the trouble and confusion. The sentinels placed over the warehouses were forced, the doors thrown open, and the food and clothing pillaged by our troops and the Jews. Disorder reached its height and the voice of the authorities was entirely disregarded. The looting of the stores had made the soldiers free of a large quantity of rum and brandy of which for the most part they drank immoderately; thus increasing the number of our sick and causing gangrene of the extremities and even the death of many of them.

"In the middle of all this confusion, Prince Murat, who was in command of the army, hurriedly left his palace and passing through the mob without escort departed to find himself a lodging on the Kowno road, where he was quickly joined by the Headquarters Staff and the Guard.

"For my part after a few hours sleep I hurried to visit the hospital to attend to my responsibilities. I collected at the *Charité* the principal wounded officers and such of the surgeons as were sick, and confided them to the particular care of the good Grey Sisters. In addition to these medical officers, I left behind in the hospitals sufficient surgeons for the care of all the wounded who had been brought into the town. I provided them with letters of recommendation to the Chief Physicians of the Russian Army, and then made ready to rejoin the Guard and General Headquarters. I left Wilna on the night of the 10th, and instead of

[14] "On December 9th we reached Wilna, where there were still some stores, but the Duke of Bassano (Maret), the Governor of Lithuania, and General Hogendorf, the Military Commander, had retired to the Niemen and there was no one to give orders. There, as at Smolensk, the commissaries required that regular receipts should be handed to them before giving out provisions and clothing, a thing which was impossible in the disorganized state of the regiments, and thus precious time was lost. General Maison had several store-houses broken open and his troops got some food and clothing, but the rest was taken the next day by the Russians. . . ." Marbot.

stopping in the suburb where the former had halted I continued along the road to Kowno.[15]

"On the morning of the 11th the Cossacks entered Wilna and spread terror amongst the large number of French who were still left there. The Jews also treated them very ill, and such who survived this catastrophe and the murderous effects of cold and hunger were afterwards attacked by epidemic diseases.[16]

"On our departure from Wilna the temperature had risen several degrees; but at the same time there was a heavy fall of snow which made the road over a mountain (Ponari) which lay across our route some leagues beyond the town almost impassable. The few wagons and treasure carts which had been saved from earlier dangers were abandoned or burnt on this fatal slope;[17] in fact it may be said that Wilna was almost as deadly as the Beresina.

"During the night of the 12th the temperature again fell and the cold resumed its earlier intensity which continued until we reached the other side of Kowno. Our entrance and passage through this town were as difficult and as harassing as at Wilna. There, too, we lost many of our younger soldiers from drunkenness. It was here that I had the good fortune to meet again my friend Dr. Ribes, whom I had not seen since Wilna. He was in the last extremity of exhaustion from fatigue and the effects of the intense cold which the most robust constitutions could not resist. I have, however, noticed that other things being equal the temperaments which go under the name of hot and sanguine resist its depressing effects much better than those which are generally termed lymphatic: thus many more of the inhabitants of the southern countries of Europe escaped death than those of the northern and more humid lands, such as the Dutch, Hanoverians, Prussians and other Germans. The Russians themselves, according to statements made to me by many of the medical officers who were left at Wilna, lost proportionately more men from this cause than the French. I used all the measures which my affection for him could suggest to reanimate M. Ribes' lost strength and to help him to reach the frontiers of Old Prussia, a country which in spite of all that had happened we looked upon as a second homeland.

"On the day following our arrival at Kowno I busied myself with visits to the hospitals which I found full of patients: all who could walk were evacuated in the direction of Prussia; we provided for the others and left sufficient medical officers with them to ensure their treatment. Here, as at Wilna, the stores were looted, which maintained and aggravated the excesses and disorders in the army, and at the same time we were continuously attacked by enemy partisans. The greater part of the troops

[15] Desgenettes, the Physician-in-Chief, was captured at Wilna, but was liberated by Alexander's orders and reached Magdebourg at the end of March.

[16] Later we learnt that the arrival of the Emperor Alexander had restored order in the city, and that our prisoners had been greatly comforted by his munificence and humanity.

[17] It is commonly said that the soldiers plundered the treasure. Marbot says that Ney, seeing that its abandonment was inevitable, had the chests opened and told the men to help themselves. Here most of the remaining artillery and many of the sick and wounded were also abandoned.

resumed their march on the morning of December 13th: I myself only left at daybreak on the 14th, with my friend and a few soldiers of the Guard; we had great difficulty in crossing the bridge which was blocked and it was only by our utmost efforts that we reached the top of the hill which is beyond Kowno. Almost all the artillery we had brought with us from the town was abandoned on this steep icy road. The passage was fatal to many more of our soldiers, who weakened by constant efforts, cold and hunger, were unable to escape the pursuing Cossacks who had crossed the Niemen dry-shod, the river being frozen to a depth of several feet, which was as much an advantage to them as it was a disaster for us since we had hardly any rearguard to protect our stragglers. Some of the Guard who still had kept their weapons, finding themselves about to be charged by these Cossacks, bravely rallied to repulse them, but the contact with the iron so paralysed their fingers that the muskets dropped from their hands without their being able to load or use them and they were obliged to fall back precipitately and rejoin us.

"Eventually the enemy drew off and ceased to harass us, either because they preferred to capture the remains of our transport and cannon, which were piled in the road on the other side of the mountain, or else that they feared to advance too rapidly beyond their own frontiers; we were therefore able to march unmolested and in security for several days. The soldiers of the other nations made the most of this short respite to desert by different routes to their several homes: only the French continued on the road to Gumbinen.

"Three thousand of the best soldiers of the Guard, mostly infantry and cavalry from the southern regions of France, were the only ones to have truly withstood the cruel vicissitudes of the retreat; they still kept their arms, their horses and their martial appearance. With the Marshals[18], the Dukes of Danzig and Istria at their head, and Princes Joachim and Eugène in the centre, this troop represented the remains of an army of 400,000 men which the local people had seen march through six months earlier in all its strength and brilliance. The honour and the glory of the French armies were in some measure enshrined within this tiny *corps d'élite*.

"The first two days following our departure from Kowno were again very painful. We still suffered from hunger and the bitter cold, but at Gumbinen and afterwards we found shelter and food enough for the troops. Never did a night seem more pleasant than the one I passed in that town. For the first time since Moscow I had a full meal. I slept in a warm room in a good bed. For the first time also we had the good fortune to remain for a period in these better conditions. The interval allowed the troops which had become isolated to continue their march to Königsberg, and a number of stragglers of the Guard to rejoin its colours. We were also augmented by several detachments of Neapolitan guards with some cavalry and pieces of artillery. These reinforcements swelled our *corps d'élite* and made it capable of facing the enemy and even of forming a

[18] Lefebre, Bessières, Murat and Beauharnais.

rearguard. From now on we marched with better order and discipline. Quarters and regular rations were available at each halting place: new uniforms from the French stores in the first towns of Old Prussia were issued to the soldiers, and they entered Königsberg on the 25th–26th December in good order and shape.

"During this march I only left in the hospitals the sick who were unable to walk, along with the requisite number of medical officers. At Insterbourg I quitted the Guard and General Headquarters, so as to get more quickly to Königsberg where my presence was urgently required for the organization of its hospitals. I arrived there during the night of the 21st December, prostrated by fatigue and the great cold which still held, leading by the bridle my one remaining horse; there is no doubt that I only saved this animal by taking the useful precaution of having it rough-shod before leaving Insterbourg."

*　　*　　*　　*　　*

Chapter 22

The Russian Campaign (4). Increase in cold. York's defection. Macdonald's defeat. Murat's desertion. Deaths from cold. Larrey's typhus. Königsberg. Leipsic. Frostbite and the effects of cold. Trench foot.

"On the day after my arrival at Königsberg, in spite of my weak state I visited all the hospitals of the place, in company with M. Gilbert, the Physician-in-Chief. Having done this I gave instructions to the surgeons for the treatment of gangrene resulting from frost-bite and allocated all the medical officers I had collected from the army to these hospitals. Finally, I made a report of this inspection to the Intendant-General and requested him to exert his authority so that the requisite measures for the improvement of these establishments should be carried out.

"The number of sick and wounded already in this town, which had become the general rendezvous of the Grand Army, rose to nearly ten thousand. They overcrowded both the hospitals and private houses. Each army corps was, however, allotted a special place on the banks of the Vistula and the soldiers from the different units gradually made their way there. We evacuated all the wounded who could stand the journey across the frozen Frisches Haff to Elbing and Dantzick on sledges. Only the Guard remained at Königsberg with Headquarters. . . ."

"I had hardly finished my various dispositions when I was suddenly seized with the symptoms of the catarrhal fever of congelation, a form of typhus very similar to hospital fever. . . ."

"On the same day the precipitate retreat of the Duke of Taranto (Macdonald) was announced. The marshal had first marched on Riga, in concert with York the Prussian General-in-Chief, but the separation of the two corps caused Macdonald to retire on Königsberg.[1] On hearing this news we hastily evacuated the hospitals, arsenals and stores, and General Headquarters prepared to leave. This was done the next day, January 1st, and on the evening of the 2nd the Duke's rearguard entered the town and the enemy appeared the same night. I pulled myself together

---

[1] York von Wartenburg commanded the Prussian corps on the left of Napoleon's army and was in cantonments between Riga and Tilsit. He treacherously made terms with the Russians and this forced Macdonald to retreat hurriedly. The King of Prussia, honouring his alliance with Napoleon, had York arrested and tried and condemned for high treason, but in the rapidly changing climate of the time, and with the resurgence of Prussian nationalism, York was later reinstated. Larrey, writing in 1817, is naturally very restrained about this episode.

to take the road and get away, together with Dr. Bourgeois one of my most esteemed colleagues who helped me in every way, and we overtook Headquarters at Elbing. When passing through Framberg I wanted very much to climb up to the observatory of the immortal Copernicus, but my extreme weakness did not allow me to satisfy my curiosity; moreover the cold was still extreme, the thermometer being minus 14 or 15 degrees, and for two or three days after we reached Elbing it became even more severe, falling about another two degrees. Subsequently the temperature began to rise a little between the 10th and the 11th of January, and gradually continued to do so until our arrival at Francfort-sur-Oder on February 10th; even so the thermometer still registered 10–11 degrees below zero. The old men of Russia and Poland told us that they had never seen so long and severe a winter.

"Here the actual retreat from Moscow came to an end. Joachim (Murat) abruptly left Posen for Italy and Prince Eugène, who had the confidence and goodwill of the troops, replaced him in command of the army. . . ."

"It will have been evident, from the brief history I have given of our expedition to Moscow, that the cruel hardships which accompanied our retreat were due entirely to cold and hunger. The cold began to make itself acutely felt during our crossing of the part of Borystène (Dnieper) which is close to Dorogobouje. It increased progressively and almost without intermission up to the time of the passage of the Niemen and continued until we reached Königsberg and even Posen. On the occasions on which the temperature rose for a few degrees snow fell heavily, often in the form of six-pointed stars of different sizes, all the crystals, both large and small, having the same symmetry.

"After our departure from Smolensk, where the mercury in the thermometer had fallen to minus 11°F., the temperature remained at this level, or a few degrees lower, as far as Kowno. During the night at Osmiana it was down to minus 25 degrees and the next day it fell a further two degrees. At the bivouac at Miedneski, where we passed the night of December 8th, it went down to minus 31°F degrees and after that it varied between minus 18 and 24 degrees.

"The whole army being continuously in bivouac it was a matter of great difficulty to shake off the effects of this stupefying and deadly agent. The animals, who were without any sort of covering, were the first to suffer. We found dead horses at every step; the places of encampment were full of them and it was chiefly during the night that they died. The men, most of whom lacked furs, cloaks or coats, were overcome with numbness as soon as they took the least repose. The young ones, more liable to fall asleep, died in the greatest numbers. . . ."

"Between the 6th and the 10th of December men were left frozen to death in every bivouac; they even died from this on the march. The most fatal periods were the days and nights of the 8th, 9th, 13th, 14th and 15th of December. It would be difficult to estimate with accuracy the number of bodies we saw between Miedneski and Wilna.

"The death of these unfortunates was preceded by pallor of the face and a kind of imbecility—difficulty in speaking, and the failure and even complete loss of sight—in this state many of them continued to march for a considerable time, led along by their comrades or friends. Gradually the action of their muscles became weaker, they staggered like drunken men, and their weakness increased until they fell lifeless.

"The continuous rapid march of the soldiers in a solid mass caused those who were unable to keep up to drift out from the centre of the column to the edges of the road: separated thus from the tightly packed column and left to themselves, they soon lost their balance and fell into the snow-filled ditches from which they could only clamber out with difficulty. They were quickly overcome by a painful numbness which passed almost at once into a state of lethargy and collapse, and a few moments later their troubled life was over. Frequently there was an involuntary passage of urine before the end. Some had nasal haemorrhages, which I noticed more especially on the heights of Miedneski, which seemed to me to be one of the most elevated parts of Russia where the barometer would be considerably lowered. The outer air being rarefied, and the elevation diminishing the resistance to the movement of the fluids, which are maintained by internal vital forces and the expansion of the animal heat, these escape at the points where resistance is least, that is to say at the mucous surfaces, and in particular those of the nose where the capillaries are very numerous and liable to rapid dilatation.[2]

"This death did not appear to me a cruel one. The vital forces are gradually extinguished and remove the general sensibility, so that appreciation of sensation becomes lost. It seems probable that at the last moment the heart is paralysed and the functions of all the organs of life cease at the same time. The fluids, already reduced in volume by privation and the absence of caloric, promptly coagulate. Almost all those who perished in this way from the continued effects of cold were found lying on their stomachs; their bodies rigid and their limbs stiff, their skin pale without any trace of gangrene. . . . In general death was fairly rapid, depending on the length of time the victim had been without food. At no great distance from where we suffered so much Charles XII lost a whole division of his army from the effects of hunger and cold. . . ."[3]

"It is clear that the sedative effect of cold acts chiefly on the brain and nervous system: this is strongly supported by the fact that on our retreat from Moscow those who had no fur caps or had very little hair were the most susceptible, since the head in such cases loses its natural warmth the more easily. . . . The snow and ice water the soldiers swallowed to relieve their hunger, or to quench the thirst which came from the irritation of the mucous membrane of the stomach, contributed not a little to their death by absorbing the small amount of heat remaining in the viscera, and was

[2] Mme Blanchard, having ascended in her balloon to a height of 3,900 *toises*, experienced extreme cold (her thermometer fell to minus 25 degrees, presumably Réaumur), which would quickly have ended her life had she not promptly opened the valve of the hydrogen reservoir, and at the same time had a bleeding from the nose. *See the Supplément aux Institutions physiques, du Professor Sages*, p. 224.

[3] In 1939 several Russian divisions perished in the same way in the Finnish forests, when this small country was gallantly defending itself against the brutal aggression and overwhelming strength of the Soviets.

especially fatal to those who were emaciated by starvation. Amongst these death was preceded by cramping pains in the epigastric region, a painful sense of constriction in the throat, and marked mental anxiety, all of them symptoms of hunger.

"I found from experience that a small amount of good wine or coffee relieved hunger and allayed its painful effects. I recall that once when I had gone for three whole days without eating anything, except for two or three cups of black unsweetened coffee, a friend gave me a glass of Bordeaux wine which I drank with unspeakable pleasure and from that moment all the symptoms of the hunger to which I had been a prey for many hours vanished. *Famem vini potio solvit.* (Hipp. Aph., Section II, aph. 21). The horses in particular died quickly after eating snow; to save them from this ice or snow was melted at the bivouac fires whenever we had suitable vessels, and they were given a small amount of this water to drink. Since our return to France we have seen a considerable number of individuals who were in the expedition to Moscow who were left with hemiplegia, due evidently to a form of incomplete or partial disorganization of the brain. I could give details of most of them were I not afraid of being too prolix.

"Unfortunate the man benumbed by cold, and with his animal functions nearly extinguished and his sensibility to external things dimmed, who suddenly entered too warm a room or approached too near to one of the great bivouac fires! His numbed or frozen peripheral parts, distant from the centre of circulation, became stricken with gangrene which appeared at once and developed so rapidly that its visible progress could be followed with the naked eye; or else he suddenly became suffocated by a kind of turgescence, which appeared to spread through the pulmonary and cerebral systems, and he perished as though asphyxiated.

"The chief pharmacist of the Guard, M. Sureau, died in this way. He reached Kowno without mishap, save that he was enfeebled by cold and hunger. He was lodged in a very warm room of the hospital pharmacy, but he had hardly been a few hours in this unaccustomed atmosphere when his benumbed limbs became swollen and bloated, and he soon afterwards expired in the arms of his son and one of his assistants without being able to utter a word.

"We have seen men suddenly fall stone dead into the bivouac fires. All who came near enough to warm their frozen feet and hands suffered from gangrene in the parts in which the cold had deadened the vital functions. This disastrous event, by mutilating the majority of our soldiers, caused them to fall into the enemy's power.

"Let him who can imagine, if this be possible, the sufferings and miseries our unfortunate prisoners endured, dragged or transported with little consideration from Poland or the frontiers of Old Prussia into the most distant parts of Russia. . . .!"

"Although the army had marched great distances, and been exposed to fatigues and privations of every kind and excessive cold, there were no internal maladies. The only reason which forced the soldiers to stop behind in the places we passed through was partial frostbite of the feet and hands. These were also the only forms of sickness we encountered amongst the wounded in the hospitals on the line of communication between Moscow and Königsberg; but once we had reached Old Prussia, where the army rested for several days and received reasonable rations and warm billets, the greater part of the men who had happily withstood the effects of cold and hunger were stricken almost immediately with a disease which we shall call *fièvre meningite catarrhale de congélation*. This disease quickly assumed an epidemic character, and when it reached the third degree became contagious, especially if complicated by gangrenous changes in the extremities.''

No doubt the epidemic at Königsberg was in the main typhus, which at this time had not been distinguished from other fevers, but it is possible that typhoid and dysentery may also have been present, sometimes more than one disease in the same patient. Certain of the cases were complicated by epistaxis and gangrene of the extremities which may have been due to associated scurvy. Larrey, as he tells us went down with the disease, and in the English translation of Thiers' *Consulate and Empire* he is stated to have succumbed: an amusing example of mis-translation of a French idiom!

"This fever which overtook me a few days after my arrival at Königsberg, at the end of a long and exhausting visit to many of the hospitals, began with mild symptoms which developed and increased in intensity until the seventh day, by which time my temperature was at its maximum, the pains in the head extreme and I began to be delirious. After having pleaded in vain to be bled from the jugular vein, a severe nasal haemorrhage occurred spontaneously, which relieved the symptoms and put me out of danger. A mild emetic immediately afterwards, embrocations of camphorated vinegar over my whole body, an infusion of quinine in the morning, good wine, coffee, and some excellent broth, by degrees freed me from this malady and I was happily able to follow the army when it left Königsberg on January 2nd, 1813: my convalescence was slow and difficult.

"Convalescence in all cases of this disease was long, from the prolonged under-nourishment the patients had been subjected to. The intestinal canal, as we have noted, was considerably shrunken and could only regain its original state slowly and gradually. The return of strength and bodily nutrition was also slow, so that the least departure from a proper regimen speedily brought on a relapse, and the smallest excess in diet caused colic and dragging pain throughout the abdomen. One had to eat frequent small meals and to keep the belly compressed by a belt. In many cases convalescence was followed by a loss of hair from both the head and body. An unusual phenomenon in surgeon Adorne, one of my colleagues whom I saw during his illness at Königsberg and again after our return to France, was the loss of the nails of both the feet and hands, as well as his hair, all of which grew again afterwards. This disease was widely prevalent in the border towns of Poland and Old Prussia where very large numbers of our men had been forced to stop on account of fatigue or frostbitten feet.''

*   *   *   *   *

"The Russians, having crossed the Oder on the ice, our communications with Berlin were cut, so that we were obliged to continue our retreat as far as the Elbe. We therefore left Francfort for the capital on February 22nd, overcoming the various obstacles on the way. From Berlin we went to Wurtemburg, where we crossed the Elbe, and from thence to Leipsic, which we entered on March 9th: here we realized that at last the campaign was over. We were informed that we should have several weeks rest and were made welcome and well treated. The townsfolk are kindly, affable and generous; the town itself very pleasant and its environs delightful, particularly in summer. All of this was especially welcome, but to me no less were the important possibilities of instruction the city offered, amongst them the anatomical collection in the University and the Observatory with its excellent telescopes."

Larrey had already written at length on the subject of frostbite after the battle of Eylau, and had expressed the view that the damage to the tissues occurred during the subsequent thaw rather than at the time of exposure to great cold. In the three or four days before Eylau the temperature was between 3° and 10°F., but no case of frostbite appeared and the Guard, which was standing by in the snow and hardly moved for twenty-four hours, did not produce a single case. But on the day following the battle the temperature rose to 39–40°F., bringing thaw and sleet, and from that moment very large numbers of men, both of the Guard and Line, reported sick with "severe pain in their feet and disabling numbness, heaviness and tingling. The extremities were hardly swollen at all and dull red in colour: in a number we noticed a slight redness towards the base of the toes and on the dorsum of the foot; in others, the toes had lost all power of movement and were cold, insensitive, and already black and desiccated-looking. All affirmed that they had experienced no pain during the severe cold they had endured in their bivouacs between the 5–9th of February, and that it was only on the 10th, at the time the temperature rose some thirty to forty degrees, that they felt the first symptoms."

He goes on to point out that the worst sufferers were those who were able to warm their benumbed limbs at the bivouac fires. In them the disease progressed rapidly, although the effects were generally limited to the toes and only occasionally passed beyond the lower half of the foot. He attributed the ill effects of rapid heating, as opposed to the gradual restoration of the circulation by rubbing with snow, ice, or cold camphorated spirit, to a violent reactive congestion which engorged the toneless vessels and led to circulatory arrest with gangrene. He concludes: "Experience has shewn that the ill-effects can be prevented by avoiding going near to a fire, or the too rapid action of heat upon the parts benumbed by cold: all this goes to shew that the cold is only *predisposing* cause of the gangrene. Heat, suddenly applied to parts rendered senseless by cold, may be looked upon as the *determining* one. Once this essential fact is understood it is easy to prevent the effects of freezing."

Larrey compares the gangrenous areas in frostbite with those of burns, and in both encouraged the separation of sloughs by simple and mild local applications, the best being styrax ointment spread on linen. He condemns out of hand the alcoholic liquids and decoctions of quinine then habitually used in hospitals, which, he says, constrict the healthy vessels, inhibit the secretions necessary for the separation of the sloughs, and tan or cornify the surface of the wound. This is interesting teaching when we remember the vogue for tannic acid, silver nitrate, and picric acid so recently in use and so recently abandoned. So do the cycles of therapeutic fashion recur!

In another way his teaching is noteworthy: "... it is important to maintain the utmost cleanliness about the wound and to carry out the dressings gently and quickly, to prevent the contagion of hospital gangrene which the diseased parts easily acquire if the air of the wards is in the least impregnated with the miasma of this form of gangrene: it is also advantageous to carry out *fumigations guitonnienes* during these dressings." These fumigations would appear to be similar to, if not identical with, the Guyton-Morveau process of "nitrous fumigation" mentioned in his Newfoundland voyage as a method of disinfecting ships. It consisted in burning small quantities of sulphur and saltpetre, the effect of which would be to liberate sulphur dioxide. Although empirical, this fumigation of wounds is not so very far a cry from Lister's carbolic spray.

It has been said, by recent writers[4] that Larrey was the first to describe "trench foot", a condition extremely common in the armies fighting in Flanders in the winter of 1914–15, when soldiers were forced to stand for hours in waterlogged trenches in very cold weather. It is doubtful if this attribution is correct, for trench foot was not synonymous with frostbite, or it would from the first have been widely recognized as such. The great difference was the sodden condition of the parts in the former and the absence of actual freezing, although this was no doubt an added element in many cases. Trench foot did not often lead to gangrene but was characterized by great and persistent pain which was slow to resolve and was dependent upon peripheral neuritis.

In his medical report from Königsberg Larrey reverts once more to frostbite and the effects of cold generally. He has, as we have seen, given it as his opinion that the disaster to the French army in Russia was largely due to the great cold of the winter of 1812–13, and this of course was the explanation given by Napoleon, who said that he had defeated the Russians but had been overcome by "Generals January and February". It is, however, accepted that much as the severity of the winter may have contributed to this colossal disaster, his own strategic errors, the failure of morale amongst his troops, the equivocal attitude of his allies, and, above all, the general breakdown of discipline all played their parts.

It has been pointed out recently[5] that old records of the St. Petersburg Observatory shew that the winter in question was not an especially severe one, and argued from this that the weather was not the major factor in the disasters of the Russian retreat. But the writer makes this terminate with the departure of Napoleon from the *Grande Armée*, at Smorgonie on December 5th. However just such observations may be this was before Wilna had been reached, and most of the extremely low temperatures and terrible snowstorms recorded by Larrey were subsequent to this. Even at Francfort, on February 10th, the thermometer registered

[4] King, Parrish and Allibone. *British Med. Journal*, May 10th, 1958.
[5] *The Times*. February 8th, 1961.

over 20 degrees of frost (Fahrenheit) and Poland and Germany suffered one of the coldest winters ever recorded! In any case it remains very clear that the French were in no state to withstand this terrible weather, being provided with no winter clothing, although a little foresight in Moscow might have procured this. A similar lot befell Hitler's men before Stalingrad in the winter of 1942–43.

* * * * *

Chapter 23

The campaign of Saxony. Napoleon at Mersbourg.
Lutzen. Casualties and operations. Bautzen. Death of
Duroc. Armistice of Pläswitz. Accusations of
self-mutilation by recruits. Medical commission of
investigation. Comparison of casualties.

"We had barely been fifteen days in Leipsic when we were threatened on all sides by the enemy who had already overrun Upper Saxony. This made our position insecure and it became necessary to forestall the investment of Magdeburg, where the construction of fortifications and provisioning against a siege were not yet complete. This, no doubt, was the reason for the Prince's leaving Leipsic and moving to Magdeburg, which we reached a few days later. At Halle, where I stayed for twenty-four hours to clear the hospital of our sick, I had the great pleasure of making the acquaintance of the son of the celebrated Meckel,[1] whom I had not seen when I passed through this city in the first Prussian campaign. This young and scholarly professor shewed me a very beautiful and valuable anatomical collection largely prepared by his father. Almost all the preparations are dry: they shew injections of the capillary vessels of the osseous systems and mucous and serous membranes of an excellence attained by very few anatomists. Some beautiful injections of the lymphatic vessels with mercury attracted my especial interest, as well as other striking specimens.

"We reached Magdeburg in the last days of March, being threatened on the Prussian side by the numerous troops which were approaching its advanced fortifications. Prince Eugène crossed the river on April 2nd with his army of about 12,000 to 15,000 men and advanced for a few leagues. We encountered a body of about 30,000 Prussians who at the sight of our troops retreated in order to cross the river (Elbe) at some distance from us. For several days we followed this corps but finally, as we were about to return to Magdeburg, they made a surprise attack on our advance guard during the night of the 6th–7th with superior forces which gave us about 200 wounded, whom I had taken to the hospitals in the town which were comparatively near, it being impossible to attend to them on the battlefield.

[1] This would be P. F. T. Meckel who was professor of anatomy and surgery at Halle. He was the son of J. F. Meckel (1714–1774), the authority on the fifth nerve whose name is remembered in Meckel's ganglion. The Meckel (1781–1833), who was a well known comparative anatomist and gave his name to Meckel's diverticulum, was the grandson of G. J. F. Meckel.

"Being convinced that the Prussians had crossed the river and joined hands with the Russians near Leipsic, Prince Eugène retired from Magdeburg to establish his line on the Saale, after having made provision for the defence of this town. As ordered I did everything in my power to ensure the service of the hospitals, and on this account left General Headquarters for a short time to visit the hospitals and ambulances in the neighbourhood, including those at Halberstat where I remained for several days, before rejoining Headquarters at Mersbourg. On reaching this town, on April 30th, our advanced units had an engagement with the enemy which gave us between 500–600 wounded, who were treated and operated upon in the hospitals which we had previously established when passing through."

"For some days the forces of the coalition had manoeuvred to cut off our small army and advance towards the frontiers of France, but they were checked by the arrival of Napoleon at the head of the fresh troops who joined Prince Eugène's command in front of Mersbourg on the first of May. From this moment the two staffs were united and I received orders to rejoin General Headquarters at Lutzen. I left Mersbourg with the light ambulances during the night of the 1st of May and we reached Lutzen on the 2nd, at 11 o'clock in the morning. Already a heavy cannonade was to be heard on the right of our army and active preparations were being made everywhere for a great battle. This commenced very shortly afterwards with great violence along the whole line. On his way there the Head of the Army[2] saw me and gave me his orders in person: 'You have come at the right moment; go into the town and choose places for the reception of the wounded from the battle which is opening, and see that they have all the care necessary.'

"After having decided where to place the ambulances and having made arrangements for dressing the wounded, I returned to the field to see the early results of the battle and to attend to the posting of the front line ambulances which I placed with the Guard. The fighting was very severe on all sides and for a moment the issue was in doubt. But under the stimulus of the examples of valour which were before their eyes, and encouraged by the presence of the Army Chief, our young soldiers threw themselves on the enemy columns with such impetuosity that they broke and fled. Victory made us masters of the field and left in our hands a large number of prisoners, some pieces of artillery and a great part of the enemy's baggage. The rest of the coalition army hastily retired on Dresden, where they did not stop but contented themselves with breaking the (temporary) bridge over the Elbe, which gave them time to rally and take up a position on the heights of Bautzen.

[2] From here on Larrey no longer speaks of the "Emperor" or the "Commander-in-Chief," nor does he refer to "His Majesty". He is the Head of the Army, or the Chief of the Army. Napoleon, on leaving for Dresden, had conferred the Regency on Marie Louise. "He was anxious, too, after having made the campaign of 1812 in the character of an Emperor, to make that of 1813 in that of a simple 'general'" (Thiers); and, with his customary accuracy in formal matters, Larrey alters his title accordingly.

"The field of Lutzen was covered with dead and dying, most of them Prussians. We brought all the wounded, both the French and those of the coalition, to the small town of Lutzen which became almost one large ambulance. The first two days and nights were occupied in dressing them and I myself carried out most of the difficult operations. Amongst the cases of amputations of the leg through the condyles the most remarkable was that of General of Brigade Chemineau. His lower leg had been shattered by a large cannon ball, the injury extending well into its upper part. Feeling sure that the knee was intact, I hoped to be able to preserve it by amputating through the tibial condyles, in spite of the fact that the damage approached very near to the joint. I marked out the line of amputation from the top of the patellar tuberosity to the head of the fibula in my mind and after dividing the soft parts circularly I disarticulated the latter bone and cut through the tibia at this level; but to my surprise, and that of the assisting surgeons, we discovered a vertical fracture that separated the two condyles and appeared to extend into the knee joint. For a moment we were disposed to amputate through the thigh, but on reflecting on the internal condition of the joint which shewed no sign of effusion we thought that the fracture had not actually penetrated it, and that the more limited operation might be successful. I therefore drew the two condyles together and fixed them in position by a moderately tight bandage. The patient had several stormy periods which were successfully overcome, and made a perfect recovery. This case completely decided the question of the advantages of this amputation over that through the thigh, even when the injury is close to the knee. Where the tibial condyles are not fractured, provided that the soft parts are intact, I should prefer to amputate through the knee joint itself rather than as high as the thigh. The case is different if the femoral condyles are fractured, for here amputation through the thigh cannot be avoided.

"We performed eighteen amputations of the arm at the shoulder, which only differed from one another in detail. In all these men the injury reached to the point of the shoulder, which was usually involved. My method of operating was employed in all of them with the greatest advantage. Reports I have since received from the surgeons of the Leipsic hospitals and from other towns on the line of evacuation informed me that all except three of these patients recovered perfectly.

"After having seen to the first dressing of all the wounded, both our own and the foreigners, I arranged for their subsequent treatment by detaching a sufficient number of surgeons to whom I gave instructions regarding their evacuation. I then hastened to rejoin General Headquarters, which I only caught up when the army halted at Colditz. The enemy might well have awaited us there in security, for this small town dominates a defile high in the mountains through which passage is very difficult. We set up an ambulance at the General Hospital, a well constructed and spacious building which normally received all the cases of chronic disease or incurable infirmity from the province. We noticed several cretins amongst these, mostly females, who were very like those I had seen in the Maurienne valley in Savoy. The customs of this institution are remarkable and in certain respects striking: the livery of the infirmary servants is particularly bizarre, for their costume, including the stockings, is one half yellow and the other a dark violet.

"From Colditz we reached in a few hours the low hills which border the left bank of the Elbe. From the summit one may see the capital of Saxony and the mountains of Bohemia, a magnificent and very varied tableau. Our scouts soon brought back the news that the enemy had evacuated the town and cut the bridge. On hearing this General Head-quarters and the Guard entered and the different army corps encamped in the outskirts. I made haste to visit the hospitals and other establishments, which we found full of Russian and Prussian sick and wounded. The latter's wounds had been dressed and the necessary operations performed, but those who had undergone the latter appeared to be suffering in-tolerable pain. I requested the Saxon surgeons to be good enough to shew me some of the amputation stumps. As I had anticipated they had been sutured in accordance with the method customary in Saxony, and in some parts of Poland and Prussia; in fact every stump in these unfortunate men had two, three, or four sutures, and was covered by very tight adhesive bandages. In all of them inflammation and erythrism had developed to some extent. I advised the Saxon doctors to cut the sutures, to remove the plasters, and to apply emollients to the stumps. They did not at first receive my suggestion favourably, remarking that the dis-turbance was transient, and that the symptoms did not prevent the patients from being cured. I was bound to respect their opinion, but nevertheless I took it upon myself to remove a dressing of this kind from one of our own artillery officers who had been picked up on the battlefield of Lutzen and whose thigh had been amputated. He was very much relieved by the removal of the dressing, but the erythrism was too far advanced and I could not protect him from the gangrene which had already developed in the interior of the stump and made rapid progress, so that he died between the 3rd and 4th days. All the other amputees without exception died in the same manner sooner or later. As there were still many French wounded who required amputation I had them operated upon by the surgeons of our own ambulances. I myself performed the most difficult in the presence of the Saxon physicians and surgeons, who were quick to appreciate the difference between our method of amputa-tion and the one they practised, and they did not hesitate to adopt the former which had advantages easily to be seen. The Saxons cut through the skin and flesh by means of a curved knife at a single stroke, the section of the bone being made at almost the same level as that in the soft parts, whilst the arteries are forcibly compressed by a tourniquet: the wound in the stump is then stitched, without troubling about ligation of the vessels. The exact and tight union of the edges of the wound usually prevents haemorrhage. Simple and rational as the French method was, only experience and success with it carried conviction to these foreign doctors, in other respects very estimable for their social qualities and obvious worth.

"The army halted for some days on the left bank of the Elbe to await the building of two bridges of boats and the repair of the stone bridge (of Dresden), the principal arch of which had been destroyed.[3] I used the time to organize the divisions of our light ambulances, and to have certain surgical instruments made which we lacked. I also gave clinical surgery lessons on the wounded on whom important operations were performed.

"The work on the bridge being finished, the troops marched over. General Headquarters and the Guard, whose movements I constantly followed, left Dresden on May 19th and reached Bautzen[4] on the 21st. We already knew that the enemy had taken up his position on a circular range of low hills on the east and south east of this town, which insensibly blend with the chain of mountains forming the frontiers of Bohemia. The same day the heads of our columns, which were engaged in reconnoitring the enemy's lines, became involved in combat which was broken off by the approach of night and the bad weather. We attended to the needs of the wounded from this fight, and continued our preparations for the battle which seemed to us inevitable for the next day. On going to Bautzen, on the evening of the 21st, I arranged for the positions of our ambulances and entrusted their general direction to M. Fabre, assistant chief surgeon, and at daybreak the next day I betook myself to the battlefield with the light ambulances. The attack had been begun simultaneously by both armies and fighting had been very severe in places. A number of our battalions had been severely shaken by the masses of the coalition, which might have had some success but for the able and rapid manoeuvres of our generals which soon succeeded in arresting the advance of their wings, driving in their centre and capturing the principal redoubts, in which our young soldiers shewed unequalled bravery. Never, since the campaigns of 1792, 1793 and 1794, had the French troops shewn such ardour! They overcame every obstacle and obtained a signal victory which resulted in the capture of a line of redoubts on the heights of Wurchen, some forty cannon, wagons, carriages and a large number of men. We had six thousand five hundred wounded, both of the Line and Guard.[5] After administering first aid to the most urgent cases on the field, I went into the town with the greater number of my assistants to continue our work on those who had been taken there. I spent the first three days thus, in collaboration with my esteemed colleague M. Fabre. I attended in particular to Generals Laurancé, Laboissirère, and a large number of officers and soldiers whose wounds required important and difficult operations. The first of these had the condyles of his left femur broken immediately above the joint by a spent cannon ball, without

[3] By Davout, contrary to Napoleon's wishes.
[4] Although Bautzen was a tactical victory for Napoleon, it was far from being the strategic one it might have been if he had sufficient cavalry. Unfortunately too many of the horses had been eaten during the retreat through Siberia, whilst their riders lay dead along its frozen roads.

It is stated (André Castilot's *Napoléon*, p. 531) that Colonel Hudson Lowe saw Napoleon through his field-glasses at Bautzen.
[5] Probably many more: it is said that the French lost more than the Allies.

there being the least solution of continuity of the soft parts, and, in addition, a simple bullet wound in the right thigh, the ball being buried in the flesh and out of sight. After attending to the latter wound I proceeded to deal with the fractured thigh with the help of M. Fabre. A carefully prepared and applied 18-tailed bandage maintained the alignment and configuration of the general's leg. This extremely serious condition is one of those where surgical judgement is most difficult: nevertheless, the patient recovered. The second of these officers had been struck in the left leg by an exploding shell, which had removed a part of the tibia a short distance from the malleolus. I deferred the amputation which seemed inevitable and the general was so fortunate as to retain his leg, which is a little deformed and has about two fingers' breadth of shortening.

"As the army was in continuous contact with the enemy and pursuing him with all possible vigour, I was ordered by the Chief to rejoin him as speedily as possible.

"On reaching General Headquarters, a short distance from Hainaut, I learnt the sad news of the death of Generals Kirchener and Bruyères, and of the mortal wound of Marshal Duroc, Duke of Frioul. The latter had asked for me repeatedly and was in a state of great impatience. He had been taken to a villager's cottage at the place where he was wounded. I found the Marshal lying in his uniform on a heap of straw, and was seized with a sudden fear that I might find his wound mortal. My evil presentiment was only too fully realized. He could scarcely utter a few words. The nature of his wound could be seen through the dressings which covered it and the pallid hue of death was on his face. The wall of his abdomen had been shot away by a large ball and the intestines ruptured in a number of places and extruded from the abdominal cavity. With the keenest sorrow I realized that all the resources of our Art could not snatch him from the inevitable death which awaited him, and a few hours later this general officer, one of my honourable companions in Egypt, ended his brilliant career. His name, with those of Desaix and Lannes, is deeply graven on my heart, with the consciousness of the friendship which these illustrious soldiers who attained to the highest honours, always retained for me.[6]

"On reaching Hainaut we found three hundred and sixty wounded as the result of an unfortunate engagement on its heights, in which a large body of the enemy had surprised and overwhelmed one of our divisions (Maison's). Amongst them were three female *cantinières* and two children. In one woman the sabre, after removing a portion of the left parietal bone, had cut into the dura mater and the cortex of the brain. I attended to her with the other wounded, and commended her and her companions to the

---

[6] Géraud-Christophe-Michel Duroc, Grand Marshal of the Palace under Napoleon, was born at Pont-à-Mousson. He was mortally wounded on May 22nd in a successful cavalry action against the Russian rearguard at the small defile of Reichenbach. The ball which struck Duroc first killed General Kirchener, Marshal Lannes' brother-in-law. Bruyères was killed in the same engagement. Duroc was universally beloved and was probably Napoleon's oldest and best friend.

care of the surgeon of the hospital and I have since been informed that she recovered. Three amputations of the arm at the shoulder and a number of other important operations which I carried out were equally successful. Most of these wounded were evacuated to Dresden, and those incapable of being moved far were taken to a hospital which we set up at Hainaut. These events did not delay the advance of our army which pursued the enemy with the greatest vigour. It would have been easy to push them back beyond the Oder, where we could have relieved the garrisons which had been left there, composed of excellent troops who were more than capable of replacing our losses at the battles of Lutzen, Bautzen and Wurchen, but at Neumarck, about ten leagues from Breslaw, the French accepted an armistice and the proposal of peace preliminaries."

It is widely thought that by accepting the armistice of Pläswitz Napoleon threw away the opportunity of a major victory. He was, however, strongly pressed by Berthier and Caulaincourt, and was in no doubt of the growth of feeling in France that the army had done enough for glory and that the country was sick of slaughter and unending levies. Once having agreed he found himself trapped. The armistice was used by both sides to prepare for the resumption of hostilities. By the allies to cement the alliance and to ensure Austria's ultimate adhesion to it and by Napoleon to strengthen his forces by every possible measure. It seems likely that he realised to the full that he must conquer now or that his Empire would collapse, and that Thiers was wrong in believing that the acceptance of moderate losses, such as that of the Confederation of the Rhine, the Hanseatic towns and Illyria, could have led to a permanent settlement and pacification. In this critical position Napoleon's policy during the armistice (June 4th to July 20th) was one of delay and prevarication: to prolong the negotiations and to gain time. This was not altogether unacceptable to Metternich, who had his own hand to play and not too much time either, so that the armistice was eventually prolonged until August 10th. On the day following its expiry Austria declared war and rejoined the coalition. In the meantime the wily Austrian diplomat had succeeded in spreading abroad the suggestion, which until recent times was very generally accepted, that Napoleon "in his mad pride" had "refused an advantageous peace".

*   *   *   *   *

"The armies remained facing each other and we returned to Dresden. During the short time we were at Neumarck, a small town full of Jews, we had to suffer from a shortage of good food, bad water and wet inclement weather which caused an intractable diarrhoea and hepatic affection amongst a large number of our men.[7] We also lost many of our horses from a peculiar disease (*vertigo*), which they no doubt acquired as a result of the wet and unhealthy climate; furthermore the water they drank from muddy fens was full of insects and animalcules.

[7] No doubt dysentery: a recurring scourge of armies.

"I hurried on my journey so as to have time to revisit the wounded from Bautzen. Two-thirds of them had been moved to Dresden by the inhabitants, who were full of humanity and eager to assist them, and on my advice they had used a kind of hand barrow which is very convenient and much in use in the country for the carriage of goods and merchandise: each house had a number of them. As the road from Bautzen to Dresden slopes downwards there was no obstacle to these barrows, and we have seen as many as a hundred to a hundred and fifty filing along it, one behind the other. No means of transport could be better or quieter. This shews how important it is for the Surgeon-in-Chief to study the countries in which the armies operate, so as to know how to employ the local resources for the benefit of the wounded.

"In the early stages the progress of these was disturbed by the appearance of a dangerous complication—tetanus—which attacked in particular those with compound fractures involving joints, or with wounds of the fleshy part of a limb with loss of substance, as well as many of those who had undergone amputation at the thigh. With one exception all who were affected by this cruel malady succumbed. The solitary exception, a man who was wounded in the foot, owed his recovery to his leg being amputated as soon as the first symptoms of tetanus appeared. Operations for removal of the arm or leg were generally less liable to this complication than those of the thigh.

"On reaching Dresden and General Headquarters my first preoccupation was the organization of my service and the distribution of the wounded. I started a course of practical clinical surgery which the French and Saxon surgeons attended assiduously, and I followed with great care the treatment of our sick. The Chief of the Army being satisfied with the performance of our mobile ambulances, although this was far from perfect, and wishing to establish an honourable position for the army surgeons, commanded that a Council composed of the Quartermaster-General, the Adjutant-General, and the Chief Surgeon to the Army, should examine under the aegis of the Minister, Count Daru, a project for a law relative to a Corps of Military Surgeons, similar to the Corps of Engineers.

"During the armistice the King of Saxony returned to his capital[8] and received the most touching proofs of affection and esteem from his subjects. The French joined in the acclamations of the people of Dresden, and they have not ceased to admire the generous conduct of this virtuous prince, who constantly and with a tender solicitude interested himself in the lot of our sick and wounded, and ensured that the civil administration of the hospitals provided them with everything they had need of.

"Whilst I was actively supervising the hospitals and continuing with my clinical work and lessons on external medicine, I was also working

---

[8] Frederick Augustus, King of Saxony, had signed a treaty with Austria at Linz. After Lutzen he disowned this and returned to Dresden. He was one of Napoleon's more loyal allies and after Leipsic he became a prisoner of the coalition whilst his army was absorbed into theirs. He was stripped of most of his territory, which was added to Prussia at the Congress of Vienna, but retained his title of King.

at a new organization of our ambulances and on the classification of the regimental surgeons. In addition I submitted a report on the results of my operations during this astonishing campaign to the two ministers, the one with the army and the other in Paris, with whom I was charged to correspond.

"The weather having become settled and fine and the temperature at night much the same as in the daytime, there were no further cases of tetanus, and the gangrenous affections also quickly disappeared: all wounds continued to heal without any complications of note.

"In order to conceal from Napoleon the considerable number of casualties which had resulted from the battles of Lutzen, Bautzen and Wurchen, certain persons who were accustomed to hide the truth gave him to understand that many of the men had deliberately wounded themselves to escape from service, including all who had lost fingers or been shot through the hands. On this information orders were given to assemble these men and to confine them in an isolated camp allotted to the customs officers, at a quarter of a league from the town on the main Bautzen road. There were nearly three thousand in all.

"Being personally questioned by the Chief of the Army on the difference between self-inflicted wounds and those acquired in battle, I replied that, other things being equal, no doctor could be sure of the least difference between them. My opinion did not agree with that of some of my colleagues, nor did it prevail, and an order was given at once for the formation of a surgical jury over which I was to preside. This jury was charged with deciding which of these soldiers it considered culpable in this matter, so that they could be put at the disposal of the Provost-Marshal of the Army."[9]

This was for Larrey neither an easy nor a pleasant task, for it is evident that the matter aroused strong feelings between those powerful senior officers who made the accusation and the surgeon, whose strong sense of justice was mingled with a certain irritation that his professional opinion on the possibility of deciding on the mode of infliction of similar wounds was called in question. The board of five senior surgeons spent three days in examining 2,632 suspected soldiers, all of them wounded in the hands or fingers, under the critical eye of a superior staff officer and an officer representing the Provost-Marshal. After a most detailed review of the wounds the board reported that most of them had been caused by fire-arms, but that in the majority of cases the men had other wounds as well, or else multiple tears in their clothing due to the passage of bullets, and finally that the few to whom this did not apply were old soldiers whose devotion to duty could not be doubted. They went on to say that they believed that lack of experience in handling arms was a main reason for the high incidence of wounds in the hands in young conscripts, since when advancing in three close ranks and ordered to fire the men in the second and third ranks, in raising their muskets hurriedly and without due deliberation, were liable to wound the hands of their comrades in the ranks in front, which were not far from their muzzles. They also pointed

---

[9] Equivalent to condemning them to be shot.

out that in assaulting heights the muskets of the advancing troops, being held before them, presented the first object to the fire of the defenders above, and that this had been noted as a cause of wounds of the hands in the first Polish campaign as well as in Spain, where it had also aroused a like suspicion. After reiterating that there were no certain signs to differentiate a self-inflicted wound from one due to an adversary the board concluded:

"The jury in summing-up protests that it is physically impossible to establish the least proof that any of the soldiers it has examined mutilated himself voluntarily, and it believes that the perusal of these detailed statements, which it has drawn from all the wounded submitted to this examination, whilst explaining the reasons for so apparently large a number of these mutilations, will help to dispel the unfavourable opinion spread about by those who have drawn attention to them."

"I presented this report to the Chief of the Army and declared to him that the blame attributed to these soldiers was wholly false, and it appeared to me right that the men should be returned to their respective corps or sent to their ultimate destination in accordance with our reports on their invalidism."

It is related[10] that Napoleon was at first so furious on being told that many of the wounds at Bautzen were self-inflicted, that he determined to make an example and to shoot one out of every four of the suspects. On hearing this, Larrey rushed impetuously to him, his hands held out, exclaiming: "Sire, you are mistaken. These boys are innocent. They ask nothing more than to serve their country!" Napoleon rounded on him, pale with anger: "You presume too much! I give you forty-eight hours to prove it. Go!"

The Emperor accepted his report and published an army order which ended the matter as far as it concerned the wounded. But it was to have a consequence for Larrey, for Soult, who seems to have been a chief mover in the accusation, took the result as a personal affront and was later to give vent to his spite in an unworthy way.

In the August of 1813 Larrey sent a report to the Commander-in-Chief on the casualties of the first Saxon campaign, including the battles of Lutzen and Bautzen. A stricter supervision of the wounded had been imposed since the ordinance of June 30th, and most of them had been examined by medical boards to assess their fitness for duty or degree of invalidism, so that we may suppose his figures to be of a fair accuracy. Of 22,000 who had been recorded as passing through the ambulances roughly a tenth had died. The mortality amongst the amputees, of whom there were 972 was 24 per cent. Some had been double amputations, and 22 had been disarticulations at the shoulder joint. It is interesting to compare these figures with those in Wellington's army at Waterloo,[11] where amongst 15,000 wounded only 146 primary amputations were performed, the mortality being 27 per cent[12]—no great difference. But

[10] *Eloge du Baron Hippolite Larrey*, by Paul Reclus, 1898.
[11] Guthrie. "*On gun-shot wounds of the extremities*, etc." 1815.
[12] Gordon-Taylor and Walls. *Life of Sir Charles Bell*. 1958.

clearly there was much greater readiness to resort to amputation amongst the French than amongst the British. It is arguable that the former were more light-hearted in the matter, but equally that the latter's reluctance resulted eventually in greater loss of life. In either case the amputation results compare very favourably with those in civil hospitals or in other armies, for Ehrichsen, at a much later date (1861), estimated the mortality for primary amputations for injury in London and English provincial hospitals at 61 per cent for the thigh, and 40 per cent for the leg; whilst the overall mortality for thigh amputations in the British army in the Crimea was 65 per cent. Great though the sources of error in comparisons of this sort may be, it is clear that Larrey's results were excellent by any contemporary standard.

Another duty of Larrey's during the course of the Pläswitz armistice was the selection of surgeons for the regiments. This seems to have been rather a haphazard impressment, symptomatic of the urgency with which the organization of Napoleon's new armies was being pushed forward, which he complained of as being a trying and difficult task. How much better, he wrote, would it not be to establish schools of military surgery in which young surgeons could be trained for this special vocation and to leave the country folk with their own doctors? The project of a school of military medicine had always been in Larrey's mind, and as far back as 1797 he had remarked upon the desirability of establishing one in Paris for the surgeons of the Guard. He was ever an ardent teacher, and we have seen how the records of his campaigns are full of notes of the courses of instruction which he gave in any number of places. These were attended not only by the surgeons under his charge but also by those of France's allies, when her armies happened to be quartered in their cities, as well as by local civilian surgeons and even by enemy surgeons in the occupied countries. This was the case in Vienna, where he treated the wounded of Wagram, and in praising the Academy Josephine he made a strong plea to the Emperor for a school of military surgery in Paris, which seems to have been ignored. The convent of Val-de-Grâce had been converted under the National Convention to a school of military surgery, but it does not seem ever to have adequately fulfilled this function, although it exists today as a famous post-graduate school in the subject.

*   *   *   *   *

Chapter 24

Defeats of Oudinot, Ney and Macdonald. Battle of Dresden. Casualties. Vandamme's defeat at Külm. Battle of Leipsic and French retreat. Wrede's defection and defeat. Case of young Robsomen. Arrival at Mayence.

"On the 15th August, 1813, the date of expiration of the armistice when we were hoping at every moment to hear the cannon which would announce the conclusion of peace despite the considerable preparation that had been made for a new campaign, we learnt that our advanced posts had been attacked by the Austrians. Threatened with an almost immediate advance from Bohemia, the army and General Headquarters marched towards Lovemberg on the 19th of the month. We passed once more through Bautzen and Gorlidtz and in four days were at the gates of Lovemberg, which is on the bank of the Bober at the foot of the first chain of the Bohemian mountains. This really picturesque country is rendered even more agreeable by the gentle character, generosity, and extreme kindness of its people; I have met with none more humane and more hospitable: they gave our soldiers a truly generous and cordial welcome.

"After passing through the town and crossing the river our advance guard met that of the Austro-Russian army in an obstinate and inconclusive engagement, from which we had about eight hundred wounded of all ranks. It was with much difficulty that I ensured that they received first aid, as the supplies for the ambulances had not been able to keep up with the rapid movements of the army. Nevertheless, as I always carried with me the instruments necessary for major operations, I was able to perform all which were most urgent, and the Lovemberg people readily brought us the linen and fine tow needed for dressings.

"We had hardly repulsed this column, which had advanced through the mountain pass, when the Chief of the Army was informed by special courier on the evening of August 22nd, that a second column had invested Dresden (garrisoned by Gouvion-Saint-Cyr) and that a considerable army had inflicted a reverse on two of our most able generals in front of Berlin.[1]

[1] Oudinot, advancing on Berlin, was defeated by Bülow at Grossbeeren on August 23rd–24th and had to retire with heavy loss towards Wittenberg. Macdonald, who had been entrusted with the pursuit of Blücher, was defeated on the Kutzbach on August 26–27th and lost some 13,000 killed or drowned, 20,000 prisoners and 50 guns. Ney, who succeeded Oudinot, was in turn beaten at Juterbock by Bernadotte on September 6–7th, and was compelled to abandon the right bank of the Elbe and to give up Napoleon's projected march on Berlin.

We turned about and moved by forced marches on the Saxon capital, leaving a rearguard at Lovemberg which a few days later was surprised by the enemy and almost completely routed, thus endangering our position as from this time on we found ourselves between two strong enemy forces. On reaching the vicinity of Dresden, on the evening of the 26th, we learnt that the Austrian troops had already occupied the suburb of Pirna, so that it became necessary to dislodge them by a vigorous attack as soon as we entered the town. This was in every way successful; the enemy retreating to a position on the edge of the hill to the west of this suburb, where he decided to make a stand. We took advantage of the extreme darkness of the night to push forward the Guard and other army troops and took up positions for the attack which was decided upon for the following day. At daybreak the artillery of both armies opened a heavy fire from all quarters; the battle was joined and bloodily contested, but we gained a complete victory in the face of the greatest obstacles and amidst heavy and continuous rain. The result was the capture of a large number of Austrians, about twenty colours, some forty guns and a large quantity of equipment.[2] From this engagement, in which we were exposed to the greatest dangers, we received six thousand five hundred wounded who were taken to the Dresden hospitals and treated as soon as they arrived. The enemy wounded who fell into our hands were given the same succour as our own men. Almost all our operations turned out well, but many of the wounds of joints or those with fractures were invaded a few days later by tetanus; a fatal complication which we have seen so often, more especially in wet seasons or when the temperature changes abruptly from one extreme to the other. Of all the measures we used to combat this cruel disease only the actual cautery of the wounds or the amputation of the injured limb saved the lives of a few patients. I was unable to make a record of these cases, being obliged to follow the movements of the army. But though we were victorious at the centre of operations, Vandamme's corps was surprised and defeated in the Toeplitz gorges[3] at the moment of success, and the advance on Berlin also suffered a serious setback, with the result that we did not long enjoy the victory won on the 27th, and it became necessary to abandon the plan of campaign which had so far been followed.

"The unexpected reverses of our corps in front of Berlin encouraged the coalition powers, to whom our position at Dresden was a serious obstacle, to concentrate their forces upon our road of retreat to Leipsic where they no doubt hoped to cut us off. Our communications with France were already being interrupted, our convoys captured, and the sick exposed to the hostility of partisans.

"The Chief of the Army, after concentrating a number of divisions of Line troops and the different Guards corps, gave the order for departure, which I myself received on the previous evening from the Intendant-General. I hastily designated the surgeons required for the care of the six

[2] This was the Battle of Dresden; the last major success in Napoleon's offensive against the Allied Powers.
[3] Vandamme's disastrous defeat at Külm was on August 29th–30th.

thousand patients whom we still had in the Dresden hospitals and reconstituted the staff of the headquarters ambulances from such medical officers as remained available. The command of the troops left to defend the capital was entrusted to Marshal Gouvion-Saint-Cyr, who from all reports was well deserving of the army's confidence. We marched off during the night of the 6th October. The King of Saxony and his family accompanied us, which caused much consternation amongst the people of Dresden to whom it seemed like the passage of a *cortège*. For some time we followed the course of the Elbe. The fertile and smiling lands which border this river, and the resources which we found amongst the agreeable and generous people in the villages and towns we passed through momentarily dissipated the gloomy and unhappy thoughts which our departure from Dresden and our general situation might otherwise have aroused. After several days march we reached Leipsic. Here we had reliable news of the forces and disposition of the coalition army, and learnt that it was advancing from Halle towards Leipsic where they hoped to cut off our retreat. Nevertheless we occupied the latter town and took up positions on the most advantageous points of its line of circumvallation. So far we had only encountered some detachments of Cossacks which our scouts held off or dispersed at the slightest attempt to attack. I passed through the town on October 15th, and stayed for several hours to visit the hospitals and to prepare other places suitable for the reception of the wounded from the battle which I foresaw would be inevitable. I gave my orders on this matter to M. Multon, an army surgeon acting as Chief Surgeon.

"Having done everything necessary to ensure the hospital service in Leipsic, I returned in the evening to local headquarters, which was in the centre of our army on the Dresden road, and here I spent the rest of the night in seeing to the preparation of the materials required for first-aid to the wounded. I then went round the greater part of our line of battle to find the most suitable sites for the ambulances, and placed the one which was to serve General Headquarters at Tomberg.

"Although our army had been marching through part of the night to reach its positions the movement was still incomplete when we were attacked at daybreak on the 16th by the more numerous forces of the coalition, which had also advanced during the night. A heavy cannonade broke out all along the line. We hurried on our manoeuvres and engaged the enemy everywhere. The shock of the encounter was terrible and the result would have been decisively in our favour had not the forces of the coalition been so numerous and so advantageously placed. (Their army had swelled to nearly three hundred thousand men.) Even so, after eight or nine hours fighting, the enemy's advanced troops were repulsed, their columns thrown into confusion, and we remained masters of the battlefield. A few more hours of daylight, a fresh effort on our part, and this large army would have been defeated; but darkness and the extreme fatigue of our soldiers, who had come from Dresden by forced marches, resulted in contact between the two armies being broken off.

"We had six thousand five hundred wounded whom we treated close beside the battlefield, and often under the enemy's cannon fire. The sixth echelon suffered wounds from artillery fire, all of them requiring some form of major operation, which we performed as they occurred. A number of those who underwent amputation at the shoulder joint were fortunate enough to be evacuated to France almost at once, and teached her without any delay en route: some made the journey on foot.

"I treated Generals Cammas and Latour-Maubourg, both of whom were grievously wounded, during a day on which Generals Vial, Delmas and Friderich, were killed in the thick of the fighting. The death of these three great soldiers was a grievous loss to the army and caused me the keenest regrets as they were all my old comrades and friends.

"General Cammas lost a large part of the flexor muscles of the right leg from a cannon ball. The wound was a terrible one and appeared to require amputation; however I had some hope of saving the limb, as I had succeeded in doing in certain similar cases. I therefore excised all the shreds of tissue to simplify the wound as far as possible and to enable me to bring the parts together. The missile had not injured the popliteal artery, which could be seen pulsating. I applied some perforated linen soaked in salt water to the wound and by its aid brought the severed edges together and fixed them in the most suitable position, placing on top some soft lint compresses and a suitable bandage. The General was put in the care of an army surgeon and recovered, with only a little interference in his walking.

"General Latour-Maubourg,[4] upon whom I operated practically under cannon fire, had been hit by a large grape-shot in the left knee which removed the greater part of the external condyle of the tibia, the head of the fibula with its attached tendons and a part of the calf. The knee joint was open on its outer and posterior side, the corresponding condyle of the femur fractured, and the peroneal artery torn close to its origin from the popliteal. After fully ascertaining the extent of the damage and shewing it to several assistant surgeons, including MM. Bigarrée, Devergie, Bourgeois and others, I announced that it was absolutely necessary to amputate the thigh which was also the wish of the wounded man and was considered indispensable by the other medical officers. The operation was effected in less than three minutes. The general was evacuated to Leipsic and from thence to Mayence. All the wounded were moved during the night or in the course of the next day to Leipsic, where they were humanely received by the inhabitants who gave them all the succour in their power.

"I spent the day and night of the 17th at the ambulances, attending to the dressing and evacuation of our wounded. Our forces began to obtain the rest which they so much needed, but at the same time the enemy received considerable reinforcements under a capable general, and we were again attacked on the following day, the 18th, at daybreak.

"This sudden assault was unexpected especially as the engagement of the 16th had caused such heavy losses to both armies. The battle quickly spread along the whole line and was at the point of being decided in our favour when the Bavarians and other troops of our allies deserted us and

[4] He recovered.

went over to the enemy.[5] In spite of this total defection the French bravely sustained the onslaught of their innumerable foes. The latter were time after time repulsed in their vain attempts to break our line, weakened though it was by the losses we had suffered. The valour of our soldiers overcame the almost invincible force of the serried ranks which pressed upon us from all directions, and they attacked with a sort of frenzy which surprised and staggered their opponents. Eventually, after twelve to fourteen hours of the most desperate fighting, the French army retained almost the whole of the ground it had occupied on the 16th. But information was received of the junction of a strong body of enemy troops around Leipsic and of fresh movements to cut off our retreat to France, with which our communications were once again interrupted. A retreat was ordered and carried out during the night of the 18th the fatal anniversary of our departure from Moscow.

"This bloody battle[6] provided us with many wounded; it was the only occasion on which I have been unable to find out the exact number. The greater part came from the Guard which sustained the shock of the main attack. A large number of serious wounds required difficult operations, and I was operating continuously during the first twenty-four hours, whilst also directing the treatment of the whole of the wounded. Many who underwent amputations at the shoulder were hardly out of my hands when they took to the road, and making the most of the period in which communication with France was still open succeeded in returning there. They made the journey from Leipsic to Mayence without stopping, being dressed only at long intervals at the hands of the earlier comers, and eventually reached their own country perfectly cured. These extraordinary successes seem to me conclusive proof of the advantages of the method I have adopted for this operation. Most of the wounded in the battle of the 18th, like those of the earlier one of the 16th, were evacuated to Leipsic; many of the Guard were carried in the administrative wagons in the train of the army and in this way escaped the disaster which occurred in the town. These brave men owe their safety very largely to the energy of Baron Dufour, quartermaster to this corps.

"The retreat began at midnight and continued in an orderly fashion until the following morning. To facilitate the crossing of the numerous canals outside Leipsic which intersect the road to France, it would have been desirable to have built bridges over them and to have provided additional exits through the weak walls on this side of the town. But it is not within my province to decide whether such measures could have been taken.

"As soon as the enemy learnt of our retreat he attacked us violently and driving in our rearguards pursued them to the gates of the city. The hostile

[5] The Saxons on meeting Bernadotte's troops deserted, and fired upon the Druette division with which they had served for two years.
[6] The battle of Dresden was particularly murderous, and though the French acquired some tactical advantage on October 16th, they failed to defeat their more numerous and continuously increasing foes. Strategically the result was a disaster, since it made their retreat through Leipsic inevitable.

artillery fire now reached to centre of the town, so that the retreat became precipitate and our men, being forced to go into action in the very narrow defile of the main street whilst in the act of withdrawing, were soon in great difficulties. The confusion became frightful, as the enemy advanced from all sides and threw the whole column into a state of panic. Many of the gates which had so far been kept closed were thrown open by our allied troops who formed a part of the garrison, and this hastened the disaster which overtook a portion of the French army a few hours later. An order had been given to destroy the main bridge over which we were retreating as soon as our troops had passed and at the first appearance of the enemy. Only the latter part of this order was given heed to, and the fatal error was made of blowing up the bridge whilst large numbers of our comrades were still in the town, together with all the transport and a large park of artillery. I myself had made the fateful passage only a few moments before this happened. Most of my colleagues of the mobile ambulances were also saved, but the whole of the ambulance equipment remained in Leipsic.

"This news spread consternation through the rest of the army, now in the throes of a difficult and painful retreat. Nevertheless Hanau was reached without encountering any great obstacles. We had a few hours pause at Erfurt, which was used to distribute rations and supplies and to arm the citadel. The advance guard was about two days short march ahead of us and had just passed through Hanau, when General Wrede[7] advanced across the Main to cut us off and placed his army astride of our route between the river and some marshy ground. Our position was extremely critical and none of us dared to hope to escape from it. A way by which the army could pass on one side or the other and avoid an engagement was sought in vain, so there was nothing for it but to attack the opposing force in this almost impregnable position.

"The regiments which led our advance succeeded at first in driving back the enemy's outposts, but on attacking their main lines failed to break them and were themselves forced to retire at some points. A heavy rain of shells and cannon balls from the enemy artillery fell upon our ranks and the danger was pressing; it was imperative to force our way through at the peril of our lives or to surrender to the Bavarians.

"In this difficult situation the Chief of the Army advanced personally at the head of his Guard and after a number of skilful movements launched it against the enemy. The infantry broke through his battalions, which were concealed in the forest or entrenched along the road, whilst the cavalry charged the numerous bodies of infantry and enemy cavalry who opposed our passage to the left of the town, with an energy and impetuosity which was remarkable. The shock of the first encounter was terrible, but it resulted in the almost complete defeat of the enemy who was every-

[7] Wrede, who commanded the Bavarian army on the Inn, went over to the coalition and with the acquiescence of the King signed an offensive and defensive alliance on October 8th, 1813. As soon as this had been done, Wrede advanced by forced marches with 60,000 men to bar Napoleon's retreat at Hanau, by which time the latter's army was reduced to only 40,000–50,000 men.

where forced from his position and thrown back in disorder. A great number of Bavarians were left on the battlefield; the rest took to flight and precipitately recrossed the Main destroying the bridges behind them. A part of their artillery fell into our hands and our communications were once more fully opened. As the engagement lasted until late in the evening we had to pass the night where we stood. The soil here is damp and sandy and there are numerous large oaks which we could not get to burn. We were far from any habitations, without shelter or food for the men or forage for the horses. The weather was cold and misty, and so this bivouac was one of the most wretched we had ever known. In spite of this horrible state of affairs, and the absence of the whole of the ambulance equipment which we had lost in the disaster at Leipsic, our wounded, who fortunately were not numerous, were all dressed and operated upon. We performed these operations with my own instruments which I had saved, since I always carried these upon my horse, and we managed to find sufficient linen in the haversacks of the wounded men or in our first-aid panniers. I had with me only a few surgeons who had been so fortunate as to escape the dangers of the campaign, and these I must praise for their energy and devotion. Amongst them were several belonging to the Guard who had long been habituated to the fatigues of war, such as Army-Surgeon Zink and Assistant-Surgeons Desruelles and Meunier.

"Amongst the severely wounded from this engagement whom we operated upon on the battlefield, I must mention a lieutenant of foot chasseurs of the Guard who lost two limbs. This young officer, Robsomen by name, the brother-in-law of General Gros, was marching at the head of the column when he was struck by a ball which removed his left fore-arm at the elbow joint. He was taken behind the line where I saw him, and whilst only a few paces distant from me he was hit by a second ball which carried away almost the whole of his right leg near the knee joint. His father, a captain of chasseurs of the ex-guard, had run to his son's assistance on hearing that he was wounded, and found him stretched out almost dead on the sand. The shock to the internal organs caused by the two cannon-ball wounds, with the blood he had lost and the cold and privations to which he had been exposed, had reduced him to this alarming condition. His father, however, who was a man full of courage and sensibility, lifted his son onto his shoulders and hurried with him to me to ask my help.

"He was pale, blanched, cold and almost pulseless, but in spite of his state of extreme prostration and exhaustion I felt it imperative to amputate both the injured limbs forthwith. As we were very close to the actual fighting I was alone, except for one of my pupils and the young soldier's father. I did not dare to suggest that he should hold his son during the two serious operations I was about to perform and looked around in vain for assistance. "You can count on me, Sir," said the captain, "since it is a question of saving my son's life." The latter did not utter a cry during the operations and the father shewed a rare fortitude.

"I immediately amputated the arm in continuity; the vessels had been torn so that there had been only a little haemorrhage. Directly afterwards

I removed the leg through the condyles, instead of going as high as the thigh which the nature of the wound seemed to require. I found sufficient linen on the patient and of my own to dress the two amputation wounds.

"I did not expect much success from my operations in view of the weak state of the officer. However, I advised M. Robsomen, the father, to find some soldiers to carry his son to the nearest village. I recommended him to become a prisoner and to stay with his son until he had recovered, or until he was able to find him a suitable lodging in one of the neighbouring towns.

"My advice was taken; and to my great surprise this young soldier came to visit me on his return from the German prisons in October 1814. This case, which is very remarkable both for the gravity of the wounds and the way in which they had been caused, confirms how necessary it is to operate at once if an operation is required. A little delay and young Robsomen would have been dead.

"I disarticulated the arm at the shoulder in a number of other patients who also recovered: two amongst them followed us to Mayence on foot. The next morning we sent into Hanau men and means to carry the wounded from the battlefield into the town which was speedily done. The greater number were evacuated to Francfort. I have since learnt that they were very well treated in these two towns, as were the medical officers whom I left behind with them.

"The army continued its march to Mayence which we reached during the night of November 1st, 1813."

*   *   *   *   *

Chapter 25

The last campaign. Napoleon's strategy. Brienne.
Champaubert. Montmirail. Château-Thierry. Vauchamps.
Nangis. Montereau. Treaty of Chaumont. Soissons.
Craönne. Laon. Advance of Allies. Fall of Paris.
Napoleon's abdication. Larrey's account.
Defence of wounded at Craönne and Soissons.
End of Vol IV of Memoirs.

On November 4th the retreating remnants of the Grand Army entered
Mayence and gained the protection of the Rhine, whilst the Emperor left
for Paris to prepare for his last campaign. Although the army in the field
was now reduced to 40,000 effectives, some two hundred thousand troops
were left behind in the fortresses of the Vistula, Elbe, Oder and Rhine,
destined either to die of pestilence in their overcrowded garrisons or to
be led away into captivity. The severity of the typhus and other fevers
affecting the exhausted and ill-cared for troops was extreme. At Mayence
the 4th Corps lost a half of its number in a month, and the ravages of this
disease also spread widely amongst the civil population and caused great
suffering and consternation.

The allies for their part hesitated at the Rhine; uncertain of themselves
and of their ability to continue to command the success against the Great
Captain which had so suddenly come to them after years in which they
had known nothing but defeat, and doubtful also of the issue of an advance
onto French soil itself. But their inclination to temporize and an early
spirit of accommodation lessened as the winter of 1813 became expended;
and a passing moment, in which France might have accepted the Francfort propositions and been granted peace and her natural frontiers was
lost. Anxiously viewing Napoleon's fresh military activity the will of the
allies hardened and they encouraged each other in a determination to
make an end. On December 21st the commander of the army of Bohemia,
Napoleon's sometime ally, Schwarzenberg, crossed the Rhine at Bâle, and
taking advantage of Swiss internal divisions swarmed across that country
and invaded Franche-Comté. At the same time Bülow in the north entered
Belgium and occupied Mons. The signal had been given for the general
invasion of France to commence.

To meet this situation Napoleon reacted with the utmost energy. He

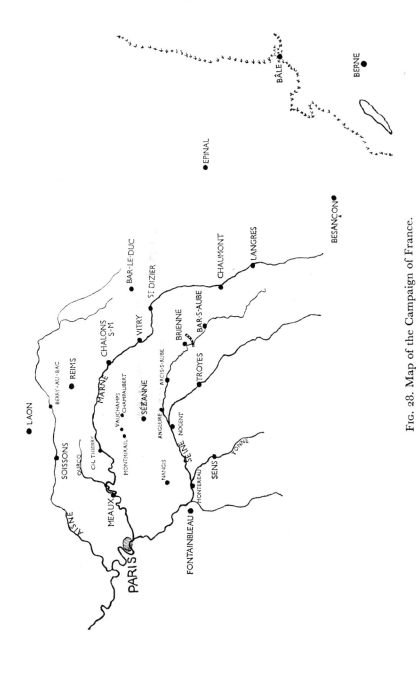

Fig. 28. Map of the Campaign of France.

ordered a gradual withdrawal of the marshals from the frontier towards the capital, and reinforced them by all available means with freshly conscripted levies. He cut his losses in Spain and withdrew some of his best troops across the Pyrenees. Before long he had assembled a force of some 60,000 men between Epinal and Langres to dispute the invasion from the east, whilst with 20–30,000 in front of Paris, another 15,000 falling back from Cologne and 20,000 returning from the Pyrenees, he formed a mass of manoeuvre with which he hoped to attack the advancing enemy armies separately and defeat them in detail whenever the circumstances were propitious. On January 25th, having confided the regency to Marie-Louise, and instructed Joseph to defend Paris to the end should this be necessary, he set out for Chalons-sur-Marne and joined the army that evening.

It is widely agreed that in the campaign which followed in which he faced overwhelming odds Napoleon's genius was superb. Paris, as Thiers points out, forms the apex of a triangle of which the Marne and Seine form the sides (Fig. 28). Blücher, with the army of Silesia, was advancing along one side in the direction of St. Dizier on the Marne, whilst Schwarzenberg was pursuing Mortier along the Seine. It would be possible for Napoleon, who though inferior in numbers was well equipped with artillery, to ascend the Marne as far as St. Dizier and by turning right and combining his forces with those of Gerrard and Mortier, to come down on Schwarzenberg's column with 50,000 men. Whilst he was manoeuvring between the Seine and Marne, the Duke of Valmy (Kellerman) was to occupy the Marne bridges and Pajol those on the Seine. Furthermore there is an intermediate line between these two rivers, the Aube,[1] which would increase the invader's difficulties by making him divide his forces, and if he were denied the river crossings Napoleon might anticipate many opportunities for fighting which he would not fail to seize. Whilst he employed these delaying tactics time would allow the arrival of troops from Spain and the fortresses, whilst Augereau from Lyons and Besançon would threaten the enemy in the rear.

On January 29th Napoleon attacked Blücher at Brienne, and threw him back on Rothière in disorder. But on February 1st he was himself attacked at this village by both Schwarzenberg and Blücher and fought a desperate defensive battle, resisting with 32,000 men 100,000 of the enemy for a whole day before falling back on Troyes in good order but with the loss of Oudinot's artillery. The French position was now one of great danger, but at this juncture the allies made the mistake Napoleon had hoped for and divided their forces, Blücher following the Marne to outflank him on the left whilst Schwarzenberg descended the Seine to encompass his right, hoping between them to force him back upon Paris

---

[1] The famous revolutionary Georges-Jacques Danton was born at Arcis-sur-Aube on the 26th October, 1759. He was guillotined on the 16th Germinal at the age of 34. Alone on the scaffold, the last of Sanson's batch, his feet in the blood of his friends, he was overcome by a moment of weakness on realizing that he would never see his young wife again. But pulling himself together he exclaimed: "Allons, Danton, pas de faiblesse" and turning to the executioner: "Tu montreras ma tête au peuple, elle en vaut la peine."

and to crush him beneath its walls by sheer weight of numbers. Seizing this opportunity Napoleon attacked the army of Silesia between February, 10–14th, at a moment when it was divided into four corps, and fought the engagements of Champaubert, Montmirail, Château-Thierry and Vauchamps, by which he accounted for some 30,000 of the enemy with slight loss to himself. He then turned upon Schwarzenberg who had crossed the Seine, and driving him back over the river fought the battles of Nangis and Montereau on February 18th and 19th, so roughly handling the enemy as to force an armistice.

The terms of the allies, conveyed by the Prince de Liechstein at the Chatillon conference, were such as might have been imposed upon a defeated nation, and Napoleon, in view of the recent considerable successes of French arms over the greatly superior numbers of the enemy, declined them, whilst re-occupying Troyes by a convention agreed with the Russians.

The internal feeling in Paris at this time was complex and cannot be disregarded in an otherwise purely military survey of the events of the spring of 1814. Many were weary of the Imperial régime, with its seemingly unending wars and perpetual demands for men and money which brought no prospect of a lasting and favourable peace. The supporters of republicanism and of the Bourbons, who had reared their heads the moment defeat threatened, were for a time driven underground but they still existed and their subterranean murmurs helped to swell the growing body of general discontent. France, in fact, was preparing for the fall of the régime, in a feeling of uncertainty and apprehension no doubt, but none the less preparing.

The victorious Napoleon was however in no mood to allow negotiations to rob him of an advantage which might be further exploited, and the discussions dragged on, bogged down over the interpretation of "natural frontiers" and protracted from the desire of both sides to use the suspension of hostilities as a time for further preparations. But the tangle was straightened and the allies' differences resolved, by Castlereagh's forthright intervention which resulted in the Treaty of Chaumont (March 12th, 1814), later to become the basis of the Holy Alliance. Blücher in the meantime had resumed his march on Paris, crossing the Aube on February 24th at Anglure and reaching Sézanne the next day. On the 27th he was before Meaux which was defended by Marmont and Mortier who had retired behind the Ourcq. Here he nearly met with utter disaster, for whilst he lingered there Napoleon bridged and crossed the Marne and drove him back on the Aisne, from which his sole route of escape was across the river at Soissons where the town and bridge were held by a French garrison. The Emperor's grand idea was to hold and destroy Blücher in this trap, and then to advance into the country beyond and free the numerous garrisons of the blockaded fortresses of Belgium, Luxembourg, Lorraine and Alsace thereby swelling his army by perhaps 50,000 trained men, and thus reinforced to fall upon Schwarzenberg's rear. Blücher, as soon as he realized his danger, retreated with all speed but was successfully shepherded by Napoleon towards Soissons. Further retreat began to appear impossible and he was for the moment numerically inferior to the French. His destruction seemed certain and his army was beginning to shew early signs of disintegration, when General Moreau, who commanded at Soissons, allowed himself to be intimidated into surrendering the city, although explicit orders had been sent to him to hold it. Blücher was able to cross the river and join hands with Bülow and Wintzingerode, who had been detached from the Northern Army (Bernadotte) and were waiting to reinforce him. Instead of the prospect of a crushing victory Napoleon now found his 50,000 men opposed by 100,000 of the enemy, protected by a river over which the allies held the all-important bridge. The Emperor did not delay, but seized a minor bridge at Berry-au-Bac, higher up the Aisne, as he had to fight and deal with Blücher before turning against Schwarzenberg and time pressed. Blücher had established himself in a position of great strength on the Craönne plateau before Laon, and the French were at a great disadvantage, in that they had not been able to transport much of their artillery across the single bridge at Berry-au-Bac. After a tremendous struggle, in which the losses were about equal, the French possessed themselves of the plateau. But their success, such as it was, led to the attack on Laon itself, which failed after a prolonged and bloody engagement and forced them to disengage and to retire on Soissons.

Once more there was a pause whilst the negotiations of Chatillon still dragged on. These to the reader suggest real willingness on the part of the allies to come to an accommodation with Napoleon whilst he on his side deliberately temporized with a fixed determination to retain for the Empire, Antwerp, Cologne, Mayence, Chambery and Nice. The unfortunate Caulaincourt, negotiating from weakness, displayed the utmost persuasiveness, obstinacy and persistence, but the *pourparlers* were unreal and in the end came to nothing, and the conference broke up on March 19th.

On March 17th the Emperor had resumed the offensive. His strategic object continued to be to rally to himself the garrisons in the fortresses behind the allied armies and by operating in the latter's rear to relieve the threat to Paris. To this plan there were two great obstacles: the lack of fortifications around Paris itself, which made it difficult for the city to withstand a siege, and the political situation in the capital. Circumstances, however, left him no choice, for his plan of operating alternately against Blücher and Schwarzenberg had now become too obvious for repetition, and moreover his army was pent in the apex of the angle between the Seine and Marne where he had conducted his earlier offensive. He therefore moved to Epernay to gain freedom of manoeuvre, and whilst there learnt that Schwarzenberg was well beyond the Seine and that something approaching panic was developing in Paris. This state of mind in the Parisians was aggravated by Soult's failure to arrest Wellington at Orthez and his retreat to Toulouse, whereby he uncovered Bordeaux which the English promptly occupied and where the Bourbons were forthwith proclaimed.

Meanwhile Schwarzenberg, aware of Napoleon's movements on his right flank, took the precaution of withdrawing his advanced troops and of concentrating them around Troyes and Bar-sur-Aube, which left Napoleon a little in advance of him and temporarily freed his road to Paris. At this juncture the Emperor decided to concentrate his own rather scattered forces at Arcis-sur-Aube and from there to advance to the Marne, Vitry, St. Dizier and perhaps as far as Bar-le-Duc. But matters took a very different course. On reaching Arcis on March 22nd, Napoleon found that instead of retreating on Troyes, as he had anticipated, the army of Bohemia had been concentrated at Arcis and his 20,000 men had run into 90,000 Russians and Austrians. A desperate battle fought before this town was the Emperor's last major engagement. He successfully disengaged his force and recrossed the Aube breaking the bridges behind him. Still sustained by the prospect of joining the fortress garrisons and falling on the enemy's communications he moved on St. Dizier to pick up such troops as were available and in the hope of drawing his opponents after him. But other counsels prevailed amongst the allies, and for once the fundamental military precept of assuring an army's communications whilst advancing was abandoned. There can be little doubt that in reaching this decision the allied rulers and their commanders were fortified by the knowledge that the political situation in Paris favoured them, and the belief that once the capital was occupied the Empire must collapse. Napoleon did not expect such a decision from the cautious Schwarzenberg and was deceived. Whilst he manoeuvred in their rear the armies of Silesia and Bohemia united. Their march upon Paris began on March 25th; the meagre remnants of French resistance were overwhelmed and on March 30th the Battle of Paris was fought at odds of three to one under the walls of the city. After a short defence, characterized by many acts of signal bravery, a capitulation was signed on March 30th and the allied sovereigns made their formal entry the next day. Napoleon reached Fromenteau on April 1st, where he learned of the fall of Paris, and signed his abdication at Fontainebleau on April 6th, 1814.

*   *   *   *   *

But to return to Larrey's narrative. After his short stay in Mayence, Larrey was occupied to the full in the problems of the organization of the ambulance depôts and hospitals, and in doing what was possible to arrest the formidable epidemic of typhus which was ravaging the towns on the line of evacuation. Something of the state of affairs is revealed by his report to the Minister of War.

To H.E. The Minister of War.

Metz, December 10th, 1813.

"My Lord,

After having completed my administrative duties and organized the medical service of the Mayence hospitals as far as was within my province, I received orders from the Intendant-General to proceed to Metz and inspect the lines of evacuation between these towns. I have given the latter an account of the measures I have taken or have requested from his department for the amelioration of the ambulances at the principal stations I have inspected, and I now wish to give Your Excellency a summary of the result of my observations.

"I assure you, My Lord, that between Mayence and Sarrebruck I have found all the ambulance depôts in a very bad state. I have been forced to spend a part of each night in removing with my own hands or in superintending the removal of the dead bodies which for several days had been lying buried beneath the rotten straw on which many living patients were still lying: in having the dead buried and the places in which they were concealed disinfected. I have written to the Intendant-General to request him to send these ambulances all the assistance they lack, since the inhabitants on the other side of the Sarre no longer appear able to meet their requirements. At Landstoul, for example, at the risk of their all becoming victims of the prevailing epidemic, they left twenty-five corpses which had been dead for many days lying in the church in the middle of their town, which is of itself extremely insanitary: nothing had persuaded them to remove these from the building (in truth very noisome) for burial.

"I anticipate that the Intendant-General, Baron Marchand, will undertake the improvement of these establishments with the zeal and energy you know to be his. I have interviewed the doctors of the communes through which the troops are passing, and have given them my views on the nature and causes of the epidemic and the measures which I think should be put in hand to arrest its progress and prevent its worst effects. (These I shall deal with below). I have visited the people of the towns and country and have given them all the encouragement and consolation in my power.

"Before quitting these places I have had the satisfaction of seeing that the inhabitants were everywhere reassured and disposed to follow strictly the regimen prescribed for them, and I have since been informed that my advice has not been without good effect. From Sarrebruck to Metz I have found all the hospitals in the best possible state. The citizens and the administrative authorities are worthy of the highest praise for the vigilant and assiduous care they have bestowed upon our sick. In particular we are under a great obligation to Baron Marchant, Mayor of Metz, who has supplemented his wide knowledge of medicine and administration with a splendid philanthropy. . . ."

"During the few days I spent in Metz I did everything I could to improve the hospital services. I first caused the different patients whom circumstances had brought together in the same wards to be classified and separated. I paid special attention to the wounded, and carried out a number of difficult operations with a success which might hardly have been expected. In connection with these I gave a number of lessons on clinical surgery to the young medical officers who were quartered at Metz.

"The epidemic continued to make progress in the country in the vicinity of General Headquarters, and I was ordered by the Intendant-General to visit these regions and to find out both the condition of the sick and the state of the military hospitals which had been established, or were about to be established, in the principal places through which the troops passed. The effects of this epidemic had been much exaggerated as the young doctors sent from Paris considered it to be pestilential and eminently contagious, so that they proposed, as a first step, *the strict forbidding of any communication between the soldiers and civilians in the towns and country.*

"This measure was not only impossible at the time, but it would have spread alarm amongst all classes of citizens without affecting either the means by which the disease was spread or the conditions predisposing to it. I shall not permit myself to comment on the different forms of treatment advised or practised by these zealous doctors; but I can say, to the credit of those of the army, that the methods used by the latter in properly equipped hospitals gave all the success to be hoped for. No one was in a better position than the army doctors to give valuable advice and to suggest suitable measures for dealing with this epidemic, but it was not considered proper to consult them. However, the leading physicians of our army, MM. Gorcy, Maillard, Baulac and Monceau, sent personal and collective reports to the Intendant-General and the Minister of War, from which it was easy to compile a general instruction characterizing the disease, detailing its causes and treatment, and advising how to minimize its effects and arrest contagion when present; the latter a feature we had rarely observed.

"During my last inspection I visited the hospitals and the sick inhabitants of Pont-à-Mousson, Nancy, Thiaucourt, Saint-Benôit, Manthul, Verdun, Etain and Malatour. Everywhere the epidemic appeared to be essentially an asthenic catarrhal inflammatory affection of the mucous membranes, often complicated by gangrene of the limbs due to the wet and cold bivouacs of the retreat from Saxony. In most of our patients this catarrh was accompanied by a tiresome and painful expectoration, and by diarrhoea or dysentery: in some there was evidence of congestion of the cerebral membranes or the brain itself, but in general these symptoms developed slowly and were not very alarming, so that there was always time to undertake appropriate treatment. The unhealthy state of the towns and villages, and the overcrowding and bad conditions of life, spread the epidemic with special intensity in some places, aggravating its severity and preventing the salutary crises. Thus, for example, in places where the mortality was much greater than elsewhere, I discovered foci of infection in certain houses or in others not very far off; and the stupid prejudice which led to the patients being shut up in rooms heated with charcoal or coal stoves contributed to this mortality. The usual treatment had been to give sudorifics and drastic purgatives. At first it was very difficult to alter this, but the improvement which was daily seen in the patients treated by our army physicians gradually inspired confidence and overcame prejudices. Everywhere I took or advised measures which I thought proper for the general health, the improvement of the hospitals, and the treatment of patients of all classes."

*   *   *   *   *

"On my return to Metz I obtained leave to go to Paris, where I spent a few days with my family which I had not seen since I left for Russia in February 1812.

"General Headquarters soon moved from Metz to Chalons-sur-Marne where shortly afterwards the Chief of the Army arrived in person. Being ordered to follow him, I left the capital hurriedly and reached that town on January 25th, 1814, just as he was leaving to attack the enemy who were advancing by forced marches from all parts.

"Having learnt the direction of General Headquarters I set off again the next day, and after two more days travelling I reached the outskirts of Brienne on the morning of the 30th, where I found five hundred wounded, the result of an engagement with our advance guard before its gates. This fight, which cost us the life of Count Baste, colonel of the marines of the Guard and one of our bravest and most accomplished generals, had resulted in the capture of the Château of Brienne and the precipitate retreat of the enemy.[2] Our scouts advanced several leagues beyond the town and we took up our position on the heights above it.

"The 30th and 31st were occupied in reconnaissance. I used the time to organize a stationary ambulance in the civil hospital, into which I put the most severely wounded of the 29th. Amongst them were two Russian officers, on one of whom I operated for empyema and have no doubt that this was successful, for the patient was very well at the time of our departure. I performed many more important operations, such as amputation of the arm at the shoulder and of the upper part of the thigh by flaps.

"Measures were in hand for a movement from Brienne towards Troyes, when our forward troops were surprised on February 1st by a superior force. A part of our effectives were captured, but the rest rallied and checked the speed of the enemy's advance. The engagement developed and became general. A continuous heavy and icy snowstorm fell throughout the day and badly interfered with our manoeuvres, and to this and to the small number of our troops our lack of success was due. Nevertheless we held the enemy and prevented him from entering the town.[3] The retreat to Troyes was effected in excellent order. We attended to the wounded during the night and I had the most serious cases moved into the church and hospice of the *Charité*. I was instructed to give the sisters at the latter

[2] This engagement was fought on the 29th with Blücher's troops who outnumbered the French by almost two to one. Blücher had a narrow escape from being taken prisoner in the Château.
[3] Vide p. 221.

fifty gold pieces to be expended on the men's needs. I evacuated the rest of our casualties to Troyes which they reached ahead of the army. We ourselves arrived there on the evening of the 3rd without meeting much opposition. Here we found the Old Guard (under Mortier) which we had badly needed at Brienne, and from this moment the army felt itself invincible; in fact wherever afterwards it encountered the enemy a more or less brilliant success was obtained.

"I pass quickly over the memorable and glorious combats of Champaubert, Montmirail, Château-Thierry and Montereau to pause for a moment at the battle of Craönne.

"After Montmirail and Château-Thierry we reached Guignes by forced marches, and here we ran into the head of the Austrian column which was advancing on Paris. No sooner had our advance guard of dragoons from the army of Spain recognized the enemy than they fell upon them like lightning. Never was there a fiercer attack and it met hardly any resistance. In the twinkling of an eye they broke the squares of Austrian infantry and scattered them with great loss. The cavalry captured the whole of the artillery defending the enemy's column and took five or six thousand prisoners. The rest of the Austrian army retreated precipitately on Montereau, which is in an impregnable position. Here they halted, but Marshal Victor ordered them to be attacked at once, as we were pursuing them literally with our swords at their backsides. The enemy, however, maintained his position until the arrival of the Guard, led by an infantry battalion of gendarmes of rare courage. Together with the marshal's troops they broke down the defence of the bridgehead and made themselves masters of the town. The position in the castle was abandoned and the Austrian force responsible for its defence was overthrown. Many were killed in the impetuous charge by which our soldiers captured the bridges, as well as in the centre of the town, so that the streets were full of dead and dying. On our side we had only a few wounded but some of them of high rank, including General Château, commander of the advance guard of the Duke of Bellune (Victor). He was leading his column in the first charge and received a musket ball at almost point-blank range which shattered his right arm very near to the shoulder joint, the bullet remaining buried beneath the scapula. I proposed to disarticulate the limb, since this seemed to me to be unavoidable, but he angrily rejected my advice and would hear no more of it. At this refusal I called one of my colleagues into consultation, who was of the opinion that the operation should not be performed. I was therefore forced to limit myself to applying a simple dressing, after doing whatever else was necessary, and I had the general evacuated to Paris. The dangerous complications which I had foreseen developed and led directly to his death. I brought all the other wounded into the hospices of Montereau, where I had their wounds dressed and by degrees evacuated them to the capital.

"We vainly pursued the enemy in different directions but it was not possible to come to grips with him. There was marching and counter-marching. One of his columns occupied Méry when we were hoping to pass through it to reach Arcis-sur-Aube, which had become the focus of

military operations. On our attacking the enemy burnt the bridge and
set fire to the town so that it was no longer possible for us to pass, and
we retreated towards Troyes. The affair at Méry gave us some hundreds
of wounded, amongst them Baron Gruyer, one of the generals of the
advance guard, whom I attended on the battlefield. He was shot through
the right arm, the ball fracturing the bone at its middle but doing little
damage to the soft parts. This wound was much less serious than General
Chateau's and although he asked me to amputate the limb I refused. He
was carefully dressed and evacuated to Paris accompanied by my nephew,
Auguste Alexis Larrey, assistant army surgeon, who continued to treat
him until at the end of four months he was well.

"After many movements and manoeuvres, which were so rapid as to
be difficult to follow, we at last succeeded in forcing the enemy to halt
and accept battle. The greater part of his force took up a position virtually
on the Craönne mountains, with his advance guards pushed out as far
as Corbini on the main road, in which position they were attacked by
several detachments of the Guard. This preliminary engagement gave us
a few wounded including General Cambronne, whose wound although
serious had no special features of interest.

"After forcing the enemy's front line we took possession of Craönne
and the two armies faced each other on the morning of the 7th, on the
plateau which lies half a league from the town. Both sides attacked simultaneously; the battle was bloody and continued until night approached.
At the outset the enemy's resistance was very tenacious, but although in
superior numbers he was forced to give way before the tried valour of
our soldiers, who forced his lines, disorganized his columns and compelled their retreat.

"This battle gave us a thousand to twelve hundred casualties, of whom
at least a quarter were severely wounded, and amongst them about
ninety suffered one or two amputations. (Amongst the wounded were
Victor, Grouchy, and de la Férière.)

"After having collected the wounded at the ambulance at the mill,
where I attended to their treatment throughout the battle and operated
on Generals Victor and de la Férière,[4] I betook myself into Craönne
itself to organize an ambulance for those who had taken refuge there
and had so far received no aid. It was only with the greatest difficulty
that I could give even the most urgently needed treatment. I moved other
wounded from the various parts of the commune into some deserted
private houses, and put them in charge of a division of surgeons whose
actions I cannot praise sufficiently.

"This task finished, I hurried to the front-line ambulance which had
been stationed during the battle in the Hurbise farm. More than two
hundred wounded, almost all of them mutilated by artillery fire, had been
left forgotten in the farmyard. They could barely be seen, some being
hidden in the manure and others covered with snow. Although we were
at some distance from the army, and surrounded by Cossacks, I thought

[4] Victor lost his thigh and de la Férière his lower leg.

it my duty to risk being taken prisoner with my assistants rather than to abandon these unfortunate men to the grim fate which awaited them. A good many of them had already perished from haemorrhage, or the suffering caused by the laceration and complete destruction of their limbs. Nevertheless I took certain precautions. To begin with I had all the peasants of the adjacent village called together, asking them to bring bread, meat, wine and beer for the wounded. Next, I ordered M. Desrouelles, one of the most intelligent of the medical officers, to issue the wounded men's arms to the peasants, and to place them at the gates of the farm to protect the place whilst we were attending to our patients.

"Some linen sheets, window curtains, tow and rags which we found in the farm served as dressings. Everything being made ready, I began the operations and performed all those which presented some difficulty. As soon as the wounded had been dealt with they were taken into the stables or the farmhouse and the peasants who had protected us gave them the nourishment they required. I left a number of medical officers to go with the wounded when they were evacuated, and during the night rejoined General Headquarters at Champignon.

"On our arrival we found that the troops were marching on Laon which was held by the Prussians. We attacked in vain and some useless engagements were fought: Laon, from its position, is almost inaccessible and its seizure had to be abandoned.[5] These obstinate engagements, which might perhaps have been avoided, provided us with many wounded almost all belonging to the Young Guard. They were treated on the spot and evacuated to Soissons to which we ourselves hurriedly moved. Whilst there I visited the hospitals and was able to effect several improvements. I reorganized the distribution of the sick, who had been brought indiscriminately to different places, and condemned some of these on account of their unhealthiness. In particular several hundreds of Russian wounded were badly in need of treatment: these I collected together and after superintending their dressing I specially commended them to the hospice administration and the Muster Master General.

"From Soissons we moved to Rheims, where we were once more heavily engaged. The Guards of Honour[6] under General Count de

[5] In discussing this campaign with Bertrand at St. Helena Napoleon said: "The second mistake I made was in marching on Laon after the Battle of Craönne. I should have returned to Rheims at once, and immediately done what I did not do until several days later. . . . I was unfamiliar with the position of Laon." (*Napoleon at St. Helena.* Memoirs of General Bertrand. Paul Fleuriot de Langle. Cassell & Co., London, 1953). No one who has visited that town can fail to be impressed with its naturally strong defensive position.

[6] Amongst one of the shifts resorted to by Napoleon for the creation of a new army after the retreat from Moscow, was the conscription of men who had quite legally paid for substitutes to serve in their place. According to Marbot this was done on the advice of Clarke, the War Minister, and Savary, the Minister of Police, who persuaded the Emperor that it would be advantageous to the regime to get the sons of influential families out of the country and send them to the army, to act in some sort as hostages. To reduce the odium of this measure the Emperor created four cavalry regiments, designated Guards of Honour, which were formed of such young men of good education. They wore a brilliant hussar uniform and had generals for their colonels.

Ségur, covered themselves with glory in the attack on this town, and captured the outer defences and the batteries of the main gate with incredible rapidity and rare courage. We had only a few wounded, amongst them de Ségur himself. We found about four hundred Russian and Prussian casualties in the town hospital: I took care that their medical officers should be treated with respect and left them in charge of their own patients, who received from them and from us all the attention they required. I performed several delicate operations, two being extirpation of the arm at the shoulder and I have since learned that both of these patients recovered. I was full of admiration for the zeal and activity of M. Noël, the surgeon to the military hospital in which these foreign patients were. I must also praise the devoted attention given us by M. Quesnel, surgeon at the *Hôtel-Dieu*, and the other medical officers of Rheims.

"The enemy had retreated to Arcis. We pursued him by forced marches and came up with his rearguards at the bridge. Although the position was a strong one and easy to defend, there was hardly any resistance, the foreign troops abandoning the town and taking up battle positions at the lowest part of the plain. Our advance guard moved forward rapidly, believing no doubt that it was meeting with only a part of the coalition troops, and after deploying outside Arcis they advanced. I followed this rapid movement with two or three of my pupils but soon we saw with astonishment clouds of Cossacks descending upon us who speedily covered the whole plain. We were on the point of being enveloped when the Chief of the Army ordered the small detachments in his immediate vicinity to form squares against the walls, where they were under the protection of some pieces of artillery. Had our advance guard been captured it would have opened the gates of the town to the enemy and have led to a massacre inside. The resolute bearing of this small body of troops allowed the rearguard to deploy behind the squares. At the sight of our grenadiers' bearskins the Russians withdrew to their original position and the whole army advanced in expectation of the regular battle which we had unsuccessfully sought throughout the day. In the meantime I went back to the town to continue to attend to our wounded, whom I had lodged in the hospice and a large house. At night-fall we retired along the road we had come by and recrossed the river. In this retreat, which was quite orderly, we had some further wounded who were dressed and evacuated to the ambulances of the interior.

"Instead of retiring on Paris the French troops marched in the direction of Saint-Dizier, and by so doing uncovered the way to the capital. The coalition army took advantage of this to occupy the roads, whilst at the same time they pursued us with a corps of cavalry.

"From Saint-Dizier we marched to Vassy and then returned again to Saint-Dizier, where we encountered the cavalry I have just spoken of. After we had engaged and dispersed them, the plan of operations was suddenly changed and we marched with all speed on Troyes with the intention of advancing from thence into the interior.

"On our arrival at Troyes the rumour we had heard at Saint-Dizier of the movement of the coalition forces on Paris was found to be true. We marched with all speed towards the capital, but as the bridges over the Seine had been cut we were forced to go by Sens and Pont-sur-Yonne. This detour delayed us by twenty-four hours and Paris had surrendered by the time our advance guard reached Fontainebleau."

*　　*　　*　　*　　*　　*

"Here ends my twenty-fourth campaign. On learning of the occupation of Paris our armies determined to capitulate. The whole of France was quickly overrun by the numerous troops of the foreign powers. The political government was changed. Napoleon abdicated the supreme authority and retired to the Island of Elba, and the ancient family of our kings was restored to the throne. I reached at last the term of my labours and of the painful vicissitudes which until this moment I had endured without respite.

"To acquit myself of the whole of my responsibilities, I hastened to render a report to the Minister of War in which, as First Surgeon of the *Grande Armée*, I gave an account of the work of my service during the last campaigns. This army being now disbanded I returned to Paris with the principal members of the Administrative General Headquarters whose functions had come to an end. On my arrival I resumed my duties of Inspector-General, and Surgeon-in-Chief of the health service of the army at the Gros-Caillou hospital.

"However painful it has been to me to lose one of these employments,[7] I am no less dedicated to the pursuit of fresh enquiries into the little known causes of the many diseases I have spoken of; being well persuaded that esteem and public appreciation is the most gratifying reward for a man of sensibility and the most worthy of his ambitions. I am happy if I am deserving of this by the zeal I have brought to the performance of my duties and the efforts I have never ceased to make to advance the progress of the science to which I am consecrated. Happy, above all, if I can still be useful to my country by offering it the results of my work, my observations, and thirty years of honourable service."

(End of Vol. 4 of Larrey's Memoirs).

[7] The office of Inspector-General was suppressed on January 15th, 1816, and replaced by a Health Council.

Chapter 26

Preamble. Napoleon's escape from Elba. Larrey at Waterloo. Jealousy of Percy. Departure for Belgium. Ligny. Waterloo. Grouchy's absence. Louvain. Guthrie's hip amputation.

"How far is St. Helena from a little child at play?"
"What makes you want to wander there with all the world between?"

*   *   *   *

"How far is St. Helena from the field of Waterloo?"
A near way—a clear way—the ship will take you soon.

*   *   *   *

"How far from St. Helena to the Gate of Heaven's Grace?"
That no one knows—that no one knows—and no one ever will
But fold your hands across your heart and cover up your face,
And after all your trapesings, child, lie still.

Rudyard Kipling

English traveller. South across France to the Mediterranean sun, you are taking the *Route Napoléon*. The Route Napoleon—what memories it evokes! The moon rising over Elba. The excited gathering on the quay; the gruff shouts of men tending the mooring ropes, the creaking of spars and cordage as they warp her off and clear the harbour to catch the rising breeze.

Europe sleeping securely with the Tyrant safely tucked away in Elba, whilst the Man of Destiny breaks his bonds to precipitate himself in superb gamble upon that Europe which was once his vassal. The Golfe-Juan . . . the road to Cannes. We stumble ashore . . . the word flies from mouth to mouth: "He is here!" Disturbance in the Tuileries. Doubts and anxieties assail Paris. M. de Talleyrand in Vienna is glancing anxiously over his shoulder. M. Fouché in Paris is in no better plight. Ney boasts to the Bourbon that he will return with the Monster in a cage! And in the far south the Route Napoleon is being christened: its name to endure long after our ephemeral kings and marshals lie blent with the common dust that is the soil of Europe.

Grasse . . . Digne . . . Gap . . . and then Laffrey where a Line Battalion offers a firm front and blood is to be shed and the contemptible group of adventurers halted in their tracks.

There they stand in the road, the gruff, slightly bewildered *vieux moustaches* of the Fifth of the Line. Let us do our duty! ... And yet, my comrades, Glory goes for nothing in this restored kingdom and a starveling half-pay is poor recompense for the sacrifices of the Moskova, the flames and frosts of Russia, and the burning deserts of Syria. We were there, my comrades, ... and now we stand uncertainly waiting to do our duty in this dripping road and on this March morning. *Allons!* A moment's firmness. ... A volley. ... And the business is done and destiny settled! But as we stand doubtfully fingering our muskets, the halted ranks opposite are broken and a man advances. A man alone. What has he to say? What has he come to offer? ... Well, comrades, let us listen to him at any rate.

That short thickset figure; the pale brow. ... "It is he!" Too much for these *vieux moustaches*. To hell with the Bourbons! Away with a France in chains and tutelage to the hated Prussians, the despised Austrians, the perfidious English. "It is he!" *Vive la Gloire! Vive l'Empereur!* ... the old words spring magically from hoarse throats ... a better cry that than *Vive le Roi!* Austerlitz and Jena are come back to us. "Fall in behind him!". And the column grows as it moves forwards. ...

The Emperor desires the King to send him no more soldiers; he has enough already.

And here is Ney ... the Bravest of the Brave. "I shall greet you as on the morning of the Moskova." And Ney, poor Ney, falls for the magic of the words and his die is cast. There is not long to go, Ney ... the gathering for Waterloo, with the men looking up as you gallop past ... *"Voilà la rougeaud ... we shall be all right now!"* And so you gallop on to Waterloo, and those fatal charges against the English infantry stubbornly forming squares behind their hill. ... *See how a Marshal of France dies.* But he dies not. Desperate and despairing attacks and losses that cannot be stood. ... The last charge of the Guard. ... "Ney behaved like a madman" ... and then it is the Prussians instead of Grouchy, and *sauve qui peut!* Better to have found death in the field than in a corner of the Luxembourg gardens maladorous with ordure. The shade of d'Enghien and a broken oath weighed too much in the balance. It was expedient that a man should die.

*　　*　　*　　*　　*

As the valour of France drained away that misty autumn night from the slopes of Mont St. Jean the avenging Prussians slew and gave no quarter. These, after all, were not the soldiers of France, but rebels and mutineers who had sworn obedience to the legitimate sovereign! Yet groups of tired men toiled on at the work of healing and mercy, which mingles so incongruously with battle's destruction—their actions a feeble protest against the incompatability of civilization and war. No mercy to be expected from the Prussians. Kill the French dogs! One is the same as another! Suddenly a group of them appears in the gathering darkness. Their leader, a big man, draws his pistols and fires at the pursuing cavalry, then wrenches round his horse and spurs away. But he is cut down, his horse falls and he is taken prisoner. He is disarmed, despoiled of his weapons, his valuables and part of his clothes, and hustled before the nearest officer. The Prussian has little time to spare. Let him be shot like the other rebels! But another officer interposes. It is a doctor, who in Berlin had studied in the School of Surgery set up by the most famous of the French military surgeons. He recalls the crowded lecture theatre and the ardent disputations presided over by his teacher, and recognizes in this dusty, wounded and abused Frenchman, sustained by dignity and courage in the presence of death, Baron Larrey, surgeon to the *Grand Armée*.

He expostulates with his superior. Well, let the order be suspended: Blücher will decide. And so Larrey is brought to Blücher. Old General *Vorwart's* son had once been wounded and captured by the French and cared for by Larrey, and Blücher had not forgotten. A debt is to be paid: a debt of gratitude and something for humanity. The prisoner is honourably treated and sent with an escort to Lourain and a new chapter opens.

*　　*　　*　　*　　*

In 1841, twenty-four years after the publication of the fourth volume of his *Campaigns and Memoirs*, Larrey produced a fifth volume, entitled *Campaigns and Travels*, covering his activities in the years 1815–1840 (Fig. 30) and including the Hundred Days and the fateful campaign of Waterloo.

By this time Louis XVIII was dead and Charles X fled, and the July Monarchy of Louis-Philippe was dragging on halting feet towards its close. The ashes of Napoleon had returned to France and been laid within the Invalides on a day of bitter cold in the previous December: a day on which the old surgeon had marched behind the cortège wearing the uniform he had worn at Wagram, nigh on thirty-three years earlier. He was now 75. It was time to finish the chapter whilst time remained.

The events with which this volume opens must be read in Larrey's own words:

"On my return from the *Grande Armée*, or rather from Fontainebleau, a few days prior to the departure of the Emperor for Elba,[1] I resumed my former duties of Inspector-General of the army medical service and at the Guard's hospital. It was only by the determined exercise of my will that I was able to discharge these arduous and difficult tasks, as my health had been seriously affected by the cruel conditions we had experienced in the terrible campaigns in Russia, Saxony and France, and by my anger at the exile of the Emperor. For a long time I was the victim of black melancholy which might have had unfortunate results had it not been that I was sustained by the hope of seeing once again my illustrious protector. I had even made plans to join him on his island, and was about to put them into execution, when suddenly we had the news of his unexpected return—in fact he had already left Elba—and he reached Paris

---

[1] I offered to accompany His Majesty in exile, but he refused: "You belong to the army and you should remain with it; it is not without regret that I part from you, M. Larrey."

on March 20th, 1815. One of his first acts on returning to the Tuileries was to send for me.

"At this interview he gave me the most affecting proofs of his pleasure and expressed his regret at having left me unprovided for financially. 'Continue with your work, M. Larrey,' said His Majesty, 'I hope at some time to be able to reward you for the sacrifices you have made and the services you have rendered to our wounded.'[2]

"Important and far-reaching arrangements were going forward and orders were issued for the organization of the army and the Imperial Guard and its attached ambulances, whilst at the same time preparations were pushed on for the fête of a *Champ-de-Mai*, an inappropriate cere- mony and one little suited to the existing circumstances. This, like other equally ill-considered ideas, was suggested to the Emperor by the secret triumvirate who held the reins of government and had already schemed his fall.[3]

"At the ceremony of distribution of new national colours to the heads of the deputations from the Departments, Napoleon delivered that of the Hautes-Pyrénées (my native country) into my hands, saying: 'Gentlemen, I am pleased to hand you this flag through your compatriot Larrey, who honours humanity by his disinterested zeal and courage. In the deserts of Lybia he saved many of our soldiers by sharing with them his own meagre supply of water and spirits of which he had so great a need himself.'

"The reappearance in France of this famous soldier spread terror amongst the European powers, who immediately formed a coalition to attack us and to forestall any fresh invasion of their lands by a sudden offensive. These ill-armed powers advanced towards our frontiers with so much speed and confidence that it was clear that they counted upon finding assistance from certain eminent personages who owed their elevation and fortunes to Napoleon. History has yet to expose and deal faithfully with these acts of ingratitude.

"The repeated representations made by my colleague, Baron Percy, that I should be displaced from my position of Chief Surgeon to the *Grande Armée* at the Emperor's headquarters having achieved the result desired,[4] I decided to betake myself to some quiet retreat where I could

[2] In this volume Larrey once again reverts to the Imperial title, coincident with the change in national sentiment at the time it was written and the return of Napoleon's body to Paris. Napoleon is once more "The Emperor" and "His Majesty," although these titles were dropped in Volume IV, published after the banishment to Elba, and this usage continues throughout the book. But he takes more liberty to criticize than when he wrote in the days of the Empire.
[3] The chief actors in the Emperor's fall were Fouché, first and foremost; Talleyrand, at this time spinning webs at the Congress of Vienna but with many agents in Paris, and Lafayette, holding aloof but awaiting his chance to play a decisive role after Napoleon's defeat.
[4] In spite of the cordiality with which Napoleon greeted him on his return from Elba, Larrey, who had been Surgeon-in-Chief to the *Grande Armée* in 1812–1814, found himself replaced by the aged Percy who had not been in good health during these campaigns. Percy had social graces which he used to good purpose during the restoration

rest and recover my health, and at the same time put together the materials for the fourth volume of my *'Campaigns'*. But just as I was on the point of departing General Count Drouot, the commandant of the Imperial Guard, came to request me in the name of the Emperor to join the army in his personal entourage and to direct the ambulances of the Guard. I felt bound to agree to this and made my preparations to leave.

"The armies and administrative staff were already on the march towards the most important points of the frontier, and with a *décurie* of surgeons of my ambulance I followed the Guard, which formed a part of the force destined to defend the gates of Belgium, putting the ambulances under the direct charge of Dr. Zink, acting chief surgeon.

"On quitting Paris on June 9th, 1815, I was seized with the presentiment that this campaign would be disastrous, both for me and for France. These feelings were intensified when at the end of our first day's march I saw one of our grenadiers of the Guard lying stretched dead in the corn by the roadside, shot through the head with his own musket which lay by his side, and it was by a considerable effort that I forced myself to continue the journey to the frontier.

"Fighting began, and we soon reached Fleurus, a place made famous by the victory gained by Marshal Jourdan at the time of the conquest of Belgium. On June 16th Napoleon engaged in another battle on the same ground but without Jourdan's success, either because the initial advantage was not pushed home or because those who desired our defeat dissuaded the Emperor from the plan he unquestionably intended of pursuing the

---

and had stood well with Louis XVIII. It was not politic for Napoleon to rid himself of all the trimmers, and so it happened repeatedly that these gained employment in preference to others whose devotion was unquestionable. Davout, the minister of war during the Hundred Days, may have had much to do with this situation. Larrey withdrew disgruntled, leaving the ambulances to Zink and Paulet, and was only persuaded to march by Drouot's visit on June 6th. "I must have Larrey for the Guard and General Headquarters," the Emperor said, "he sulks because he has been replaced by Percy. Go and tell him that he is indispensable and that I count on him."

[5] This was the engagement with the Prussian army about Ligny. Various events caused the French attack to be delayed until the afternoon, and the decisive advance of the Guard was not made until 7 p.m. But still more important for the whole campaign was Ney's failure on the 15th and 16th at Quatre Bras, where Napoleon had anticipated that he would brush the English aside, secure the important cross-roads, and then march to take the Prussians in the rear. The French gained a victory at Ligny, but not a crushing one, and an undisturbed retreat, for which Grouchy has always been blamed, enabled a part of Blücher's force to join battle again two days later at Waterloo on the English left and play its part in that overwhelming defeat.

There has been much discussion and more speculation about Napoleon's alleged lack of energy on the 17th—the day following Ligny—and his responsibility for Grouchy's failure. Certain it is that on the morning of that day the right wing of the French army, where Napoleon was in person, hardly moved and Grouchy did not depart in pursuit of the Prussians until 11 a.m. It is even stated, by a recent medical writer, in an otherwise most erudite book, that this was due to the Emperor's suffering from thrombosed piles, and that this painful disability caused him to spend most of the morning pottering about with Berthier on the battlefield of the day before.* Unfortunately for the French,

* James Kemble, *Napoleon Immortal*; London, John Murray.

enemy with his accustomed vigour.[5] As it was the army remained inactive during the twenty-four hours after this engagement, and the enemy turned it to his profit by rallying his troops and taking up fresh and more advantageous positions. Eventually we faced him at daybreak on the 18th on the road to Waterloo. The signal for battle is quickly given: the Prussian and English columns are shaken and signs of retreat are once again seen amongst our enemies, when a violent storm breaks and is succeeded by torrents of rain which interfere with the movement of our artillery and disintegrate the roads, so that wagons and guns are bogged down in the clayey earth and swamped ground on which the battle is fought.[6] The creatures of the traitors in our midst, and the agents of the foreign generals profiting by this setback, hurry through the ranks and infiltrate the batteries, shouting to the drivers: '*Sauve qui peut!* Cut the horses' traces and get away. You are surrounded.' I was a witness of

---

Berthier was dead in Belgium, and his place as Chief of Staff had been taken by Soult. When all the evidence is weighed it seems that Napoleon's immobility on the morning of the 17th was largely dictated by the exhaustion of his troops, who had been fought to a standstill by the Prussians before Ligny and had slept on the battlefield. Time was needed for them to be fed and redeployed. The balance of blame over Grouchy's ineffective pursuit will never be fairly apportioned, but the consequences of a loyal but unimaginative commander weighed down by unaccustomed responsibility, and the obscure instructions issued by Soult were disastrous for the French.

Certain it is that later in the day, when Napoleon galvanized the hesitating Ney at Quatre Bras (over five miles from Ligny as the crow flies), and organized and energized the attack on the British rearguard over muddied fields and through a deluge of rain, he shewed no signs of mental or physical weariness.

[6] The story of Waterloo as given by Larrey is not in accord with most descriptions of the battle. The heavy rain had been on the afternoon of the 17th and throughout the following night, but it ceased on the morning of the 18th, and Napoleon, on the advice of Drouot, delayed his attack until the ground had dried somewhat. The battle began at about 11.30 a.m. with a bombardment of the English right wing at Hougoumont by 40 cannon. At this moment the nearest Prussians were some miles away and it was not until 4.30 p.m. that Bülow's leading divisions opened fire on the French cavalry opposing them. Larrey's ambulance was well forward at the farm of *La Belle Alliance*, but he himself was at times up in the fighting line, and it is notorious how difficult it is under such circumstances to form any sort of broad picture of the events that are passing. It is said by Triaire that he was actually seen by Wellington who asked:

"Who is that bold fellow over there?"

"That is Larrey," said someone.

"Tell them not to fire at him. Give the brave fellow time to pick up his wounded." And so saying he raised his hat.

"Whom are you saluting?' asked the Duke of Cambridge.

"The honour and loyalty you see yonder," Wellington answered, pointing to the surgeon with his sword. It is also recorded† that Colonel Samuel Waymouth, then a lieutenant in the 2nd Life Guards, was carried during one of the English cavalry charges through the front ranks of the French and found himself surrounded. Covered with the blood and brains of his corporal, who had just been killed at his side, he was pulled from his horse and a Frenchman had levelled his musket at his head when it was knocked aside by an officer who was attending to the wounded. This was Larrey, who exchanged a few words with his prisoner in broken English and shewed him that the knife he had in his hand came from Cockspur Street, London.

† *Lancet*, July 4th, 1863, p. 25. *Lancet*, July 11th, 1863, p. 52.

these traitorous actions and wished to inform the Emperor, but everywhere there were wounded men crying out for me, and besides I had to see to my ambulances and protect them from these false alarms. And so I gave myself wholly and entirely to the treatment of our brave fellows, wounded by shot and steel. But before I continue my own story of this fatal day I shall say something of our casualties of the battle of the 16th.

"Leaving out of account the attention my pupils and I gave to the Guard, whose casualties were in any case few because this select reserve corps did not take part in the mass charge against the enemy, I performed a large number of operations on the men of the Line, often almost amongst the combatants. One of these operations (the extirpation of the arm at the shoulder) was done in less than three minutes on a battalion leader who was the son of a professor at the University of Montpellier. I advised him to return home at once without touching the dressing; it being sufficient to prevent the wound from being invaded by maggots, and to facilitate its healing, to sponge the surface daily and moisten it from time to time with a few drops of camphorated vinegar, which he could easily procure from the nearest pharmacist. He was also instructed to be careful to cover the stump with a piece of thick wool. I learned later that on arriving home and removing the original dressing he found the wounds completely healed. A second senior officer (Colonel Sourd), a worthy distinguished warrior, was one of the most remarkable casualties of that singular day. For many hours this brave colonel had fought at the head of the 29th Mounted Chasseurs and during one of its many charges he received a number of sabre blows on the right arm, almost simultaneously. Two of these laid open the elbow and severed the brachial artery. Dangerous harmorrhage had been arrested by the application of a tight bandage on the battlefield, where it was thought that amputation of the arm would be inevitable. Convinced that this was so the colonel asked me to do it, and since my colleagues and I recognized the necessity it was done immediately. Whilst the operation was in progress Colonel Sourd dictated a letter to the Emperor asking that he might be allowed to keep the command of his regiment. Not only did he shew no sign of pain, but as soon as the stump had been dressed he remounted his horse and rode away. In a very short time he was well.

"I also attended to many other wounded on whom I was not able to make notes, no more than I could in the disastrous battle of the 18th which, as has already been said, began under the most unlucky auspices. Torrents of rain and repeated cries of alarm unfortunately announced the charges of the enemy's cavalry, which were made with all the more confidence as they knew with certainty that ours were far from the battlefield. In fact Marshal Grouchy and his thirty thousand men were at some distance from our army, which struggled in vain against the united forces of the coalition. The disorder continued to increase, and wounded were brought to us from every side, but however great our zeal and our courage our efforts were rendered fruitless by the cavalry charges, which reached as far as our ambulances, and by the failure of daylight. We were forced to join in the Army's retreat and, following the advice sent me from the

Emperor by one of his aides-de-camp, I tried to reach the frontier by a lateral road which was pointed out to us as the shortest and best route. We had hardly covered a league or two in complete darkness when we were cut off by an advanced party of Prussian lancers. I was leading my little band, and feeling sure that there were only a few of them I did not hesitate to force a way through, sabre in hand. After I had fired both my pistols at the horsemen who barred our road, I noticed a gap leading to open country through which my companions and servant slipped at full gallop, but my horse was hit by a bullet and came down, and at the same time I received a couple of sabre blows on the head and left shoulder which rendered me unconscious.

"Believing me dead and hastening to cut off my unfortunate companions the cavalrymen set off in pursuit and ultimately overtook them, and all were more or less severely wounded and taken prisoner. For my part I was fortunate enough to recover consciousness, and to be able to remount my horse, which had got onto its legs and was standing by me. There was no one to be seen about, so I quickly made my way westward through the cornfields in the direction of the frontier. I had almost reached the Sambre when as day broke I was again surrounded by another detachment of the same cavalry. Here all resistance would have been useless, and I was forced to yield. In spite of the fact that I had surrendered I was mercilessly disarmed and plundered of most of my clothes. The officers themselves shared my purse, which contained about forty *napoléons*, and took possession of my weapons, my ring and my watch. My build, and a grey overcoat I was wearing, gave me a certain resemblance to the Emperor, and at first I was taken to be he, and in this belief they hurried me before the Prussian general who commanded their advance guard. He, not daring to make a definite decision, had me taken, my hands tied together, to another general officer of a higher rank who realized the mistake and in a fit of rage decided to have me shot. But just as the soldiers detailed to carry out this execution were ready to put their bullets into my head, I was recognized by the regimental surgeon,[7] who protested to the general and begged him to suspend this act of barbarism. The order was accordingly given for me to be taken to the Grand Provost of the allied armies, General Bülow. This general, who had seen me in Berlin, also recognized me and was distressed to see me in the unfortunate and semi-nude state to which I had been reduced. I was bare-footed and only partly clad in my overcoat and pantaloons, for the lancers who captured me had stripped me of all my belongings of any value, even to my boots: my hands were tied behind my back and my head enveloped in bloody rags. The Grand Provost at once ordered me to be freed from my bonds and sent me to the generalissimo of the enemy armies, Field-Marshal Blücher, to whom I was known by name since I had saved his son's life at one of the battles of the Austrian campaign in which he had been severely wounded and taken prisoner. The Marshal treated me generously, and after having made me take luncheon with him and presented me with twelve gold

[7] This medical officer had been ordered to put a bandage over my eyes: it was an adhesive plaster.

frédérics he sent me by coach to Louvain in the company of one of his aides-de-camp. This officer merely asked the municipality for a billet for a wounded Frenchman, whose name he was unable to give, so that I was lodged with a poor woman who had barely sufficient subsistence for herself and her children. It was only with difficulty and for a gold piece that I was able to get some onion soup and to obtain the privilege of a visit from a young surgeon to dress my wounds. In a short time the young man arrived and was preparing to do this, when he suddenly recognized me and cried: "You are Baron Larrey!" I had barely assented when he rushed to the stairs and disappeared without another word. In fact he had gone to the municipality to tell them who I was and to ask for a better lodging. He soon returned accompanied by a municipal officer, and together they took me in a carriage to the house of one of the most highly respected citizens of the town, M. Yonk, a well-known advocate, where I was given every care and the utmost attention. It would be difficult to recall all the marks of friendship and high esteem I received from this respected old man during the time I was in Louvain. I can affirm that in general the Belgians sympathized with the French in their hearts, and there is no doubt that they deeply and sincerely regretted that they could not re-enter this great family.[8]

"After several days of nursing and rest, my wounds being on the way to healing, I was anxious to visit or to work in the military hospitals where there was a large proportion of our wounded, but my weak state did not allow me to carry out the many complicated and difficult operations so urgently necessary, so I had to limit myself to assisting the Belgian surgeons with my advice. I cannot sufficiently praise the zeal, intelligence and skill they brought to bear on their difficult and important duties; the result being that almost all of the primary amputations I saw performed had the success we hoped for.

"From Louvain I moved to Brussels where the English had their hospitals. During the first few days it had not been possible to separate the soldiers of the different nations who had been wounded in this terrible combat, and they were inextricably mixed up in the ambulances. Nevertheless there were a number of these set aside entirely for the English wounded. Almost all of our own men were in the town's military hospital, in charge of one of my former colleagues, Dr. Sentin, an active man full of zeal and of unusual intelligence. Together we performed a considerable number of major operations, such as amputation of the arm at the shoulder joint and others equally difficult which were generally successful. In the English ambulances, which I was also anxious to see, I contented myself with expressing my opinion on the nature of the men's wounds and upon what operations appeared to me to be urgently required. One

[8] An Antwerp lady, Mme Standaert, a cousin of my wife's, learning from the Belgian newspapers that I had been seriously wounded at Waterloo, set out to come to my assistance. After having searched for me in vain on the battlefield she went to Louvain where she eventually found me. No visit ever gave me more pleasure or touched me as much: all my life I shall remember the generous and courageous journey of this excellent and true friend.

of our own soldiers had been brought in with the English wounded, with his right thigh almost completely shattered by a cannon ball and needed an amputation at the ilio-femoral joint. I made bold to suggest this to the English doctor who was present during my visit, and to commend the patient to my honourable *confrère* M. Guthrie, Chief Surgeon to the English armies, whom I was unable to meet as I had to return to Louvain urgently. The operation was satisfactorily performed by this celebrated surgeon a few days later and the patient fortunately recovered and is now at the Invalides. [9]

"At Brussels, as in Louvain, the inhabitants vied with one another in taking in as many of the French wounded as they could; they lacked for nothing, and the most tender care was lavished upon them. Never was there greater and more disinterested hospitality.

"On my return to Louvain I quickly obtained permission from the heads of the three allied powers, by then established in Paris, to return to my family. On reaching the capital on August 15th I found every barrier and military post occupied by foreign troops; a sad spectacle for a mind already depressed by so many misfortunes. Alas, yet more were in store for me! As I was looked upon as one of the most devoted partisans of Napoleon, I was deprived of the office and emoluments of Inspector-General of the army medical service, as well as those deriving from the funds of the Legion of Honour. I only kept my post as Surgeon-in-Chief to the Guard's hospital because of the difficulty in replacing me, and the fear of the resentment which might be aroused amongst the whole of the Royal Guard who had the greatest faith in me. In addition, my family had to support the presence of foreign soldiers who were billeted on them, so that I was practically ruined. In spite of this unfortunate situation and my personal distress I applied myself to my work with all the zeal and activity I was capable of. The soldiers had not changed, nor could my devotion to them. But for this philanthropy, which may perhaps have been excessive, I might have taken advantage of certain offers which at the time would have mended my fortune. I was invited in the first place to go to the United States; whilst the Emperor Alexander, who had seen me at Tilsit, was anxious to give me an important appointment in his armies with the opportunities and honours pertaining to the rank to which I should be raised. Finally, I was asked by the Emperor of Brazil, Don Pedro, to become director of the medical service of his armies and professor of surgery at the University of Rio-Janeiro. I could have dictated the conditions of my new position, but I felt it my duty to make yet another sacrifice to my country. All the same it was not without a great deal of distress that I surmounted the various obstacles I had to contend

[9] Charles Bell, in his notes on the wounded at Waterloo, refers to a French soldier, François Gay by name, whose thigh Mr. Guthrie amputated at the hip-joint at Brussels on July 7th, contrary to Bell's advice. John Boggie, reporting to Bell on September 12th, says: "Mr. Guthrie's case of hip-joint amputation is, I am told, likely to recover." It appears, therefore, that Larrey, who had been a persistent advocate of this operation, and of whose work Guthrie was aware, may have contributed indirectly to its success on this occasion. See p. 129.

with and all the perils of the counter-revolution which operated secretly
in 1816 and 1817. Moreover my life between 1815 and 1818 was full
of difficulties, and crowded with every kind of setback and misfortune;
the worst to me being the loss of my devoted mother, who died less of
old age than of grief caused by the news of my death, which had been
announced in a number of newspapers as a result of the wounds I received
at the disastrous battle of Waterloo. This bereavement was followed not
long afterwards by the loss of a brother, a very able surgeon of Nîmes.
To these irreparable losses were added that of my entire income and a
life pension given to me by the Emperor Napoleon as a reward for my
service to the wounded in the famous battles of Lutzen, Bautzen, Wurchen
and Wagram. This however was restored to me in 1818 by solemn decree
of the *Corps législatif* (see the *Moniteur* of the 10th of that year).

"This act of honour and justice revived my courage and ambition. I
was able to write the account of my last campaigns in Russia, Saxony and
France, and to look forward to a happier future. But whilst I was drawing
encouragement from the cordial reception accorded to these *Campaigns*,
which form the fourth volume of the present work, we learned in 1821
of the death of the Emperor Napoleon, which plunged France into
mourning and profoundly affected my whole family. Who could mourn
this irreparable loss more than we, after the glorious remembrance this
illustrious sovereign accorded me in his will?

"I strove to overcome this depression by occupying myself with my
medical researches and by constantly working at a book on the *Elements
of Clinical Surgery* which I had long contemplated; but before putting this
into its final shape I wished to visit the English hospitals to learn about
the operative procedures of their surgeons, and to compare them with
those on which our military surgery is based. . . . In order to consolidate
my ideas on the principles I should establish in my *clinique* I desired to
see the practice of the surgeons of one of the most civilized of the European
nations, where the Art has made great progress in the last century and
which has produced such capable and celebrated surgeons. With this in
view I applied to the Minister of War for three months leave. I proposed
to take with me my son Hippolyte, who was barely eighteen years old
and had just finished a course in the English Language.

*   *   *   *   *

Chapter 27

A Surgical Miscellany. Breadth of Larrey's experience. Wounds of the skull and trephining. Head pierced by a ramrod. Treatment of wounds of the head and face. Of the throat, thorax, empyema, bladder. Surgery of the abdomen. Hernia of the omentum. Suture of the intestines.

The range of Larrey's surgical practice had no limits; a state of affairs now strange to us, accustomed as we are to the ever-increasing specialization of the Surgical Art with the coincident contraction in scope of its parts. He devised his own operative procedure for fistula-in-ano; he treated with some success cases of tuberculosis of the spine, the hip and other joints, and although unaware of their true nature and attributing them to a *vice rheumatismale* he recognized their kinship. It is noteworthy how large a part rest played in his successes, and that when a tuberculous abscess demanded evacuation he recommended that this should be done with a red-hot bistoury and with precautions against the entry of air—thus minimizing the dangers of secondary infection. He treated hydrocele by evacuating the fluid by trocar[1] and cannula, introducing a short length of gum-elastic catheter into the sac and leaving it in position for some twenty-four hours to set up an obliterative inflammation: a line of treatment with which he credits Monro of Edinburgh[2] (presumably *primus*). He operated on the eye as confidently as he did upon the limbs; on one occasion successfully replacing the protruded iris in the eye of his daughter Isaure, who had accidentally penetrated the cornea with a bread-knife. He operated upon elephantiasis (in Egypt); sarcoceles (some tuberculous, others probably malignant) which appeared as illustrations in Cruveillier's Atlas of Pathology, strangulated hernia, hydatid disease, as well as the many other conditions that have been mentioned elsewhere in these pages, and in civil practice on cancer of the breast. *It is all too easy to forget that these operations were done in the appallingly difficult circumstances of an absence of anaesthesia.*

In a period when bleeding was a panacea for the most varied ills Larrey was no enthusiast for it, in certain cases roundly condemning it although he constantly employed wet cups for local engorgement. He mostly bled when he had reason to believe that there was dangerous cerebral congestion, and on such occasions was apt to open the temporal artery. On the other hand he was something of an enthusiast for cauterization, especially in the form of the Moxa[3]—an instrument said to have come from China, in which small lengths

---

[1] Trocar, I think this word must be derived from "trois-quarts"—the early instrument being a three-cornered one.

[2] I have not been able to find a reference to this in Monro's work.

[3] Larrey devoted the greater part of his *Recueil de Mémoires de Chirurgie* (1821) to the popularizing of this remedy. Robley Dunglison, F.R.C.S. published a book, *On the*

of pith, or in some cases dried cylinders of cotton which had been soaked in nitrate of potash (rather like short lengths of a cigarette), were allowed to smoulder whilst held in a special insulated container and kept alight by a blow-pipe, and thus produced small circular burns on the patient's skin. Ammonia was applied afterwards to limit the inflammation. Larrey's *porte-moxa* is illustrated in Fig. 4. But although an enthusiast for the moxa and resorting to the actual cautery in certain conditions (he cauterized the wounds in tetanus), Larrey was sceptical enough to refuse the interpretation of its effects offered by a German surgeon, who claimed a favourable result from its very brutal application in a case of hip-joint disease, basing this upon an immediate reduction in the length of the diseased limb: an effect he rightly realized to be due to spasm.

*   *   *   *   *

Many of Larrey's writings on surgical matters are interspersed amongst descriptions of the wholly military aspects of his campaigns, and of his administrative and other day-to-day activities. In order to lessen this historical discontinuity we have taken a good many of these observations from their context to form the subjects for the present chapter. Another habit of Larrey's was to expand a description of one or two interesting cases, perhaps incidental to a battle, into a full-scale discussion of a particular problem, in the pursuit of which he drags in later examples with scant reference to chronology. This does not make for continuity, neither does his frequent reversion, at a later stage and under the stimulus of a new and interesting case, or of more extended experience, to a subject he has already fully discussed. But such irregularities are inevitable in a journal covering a space of some thirty years.

In spite of these small liberties it is hoped to have presented a balanced and undistorted version of his views in what follows and, as far as possible to have given them in his own language.

Wounds of the Head and the Operation of Trephining.

Larrey gave much consideration to these problems. The operation of trephining, a formidable one in any case, must have been a terrifying experience both to patient and doctor in the days before anaesthetics, and have demanded great skill from the one and fortitude from either party, moreover the mortality in pre-antiseptic times must have been alarming. Nevertheless, it is remarkable what results were sometimes achieved in the most unpromising conditions.

Larrey considered the use of the trephine imperative in wounds of the skull in which a foreign body had penetrated or partly penetrated the skull and had not passed out; or where bony fragments were forced into its interior so as to damage the dura or brain, or where there was evidence of compression of the brain by the effusion of fluid. In any case ". . . and I repeat this, if foreign bodies pass beyond the inner table of the skull into the substance of the brain, it is better to leave the patient to the results of expectant treatment than to attempt to explore the interior of this pulpy organ, as we have seen some practitioners do." The trephine in his opinion was not to be used in cases of fracture of the skull, no matter how extensive, if the bone was not depressed

---

use of the Moxa as a Therapeutical Agent, in 1822, which is a translation of Larrey's article, with a long preface by Dunglison on its history. An example of such an instrument is in the Museum of the Royal College of Surgeons.

and unless there were clear evidence of the presence of a foreign body or of cerebral compression. He proceeds to illustrate this teaching by a remarkable case of a Russian who was wounded in 1812 at Witebsk by a canister shot which penetrated his forehead above the eyebrow, fracturing the bone and lodging on the right anterior lobe of the cerebrum. It was hardly visible from the exterior and the hole of entry was too small for its direct extraction, although attempts had been made to do this. The wounded man complained of extreme discomfort and a feeling of weight in the head, and held himself in a semi-sitting posture with his head between his knees; when this was pulled backwards be became faint. Probing revealed that the ball was an iron one and since it was larger than the breach of the skull trephining was proceeded with. Three small trephine holes were made above the opening in the frontal bone, and their edges being cut away an iron ball, seven ounces in weight, was removed and subsequently sent to the School of Medicine in Paris. A considerable quantity of blood clot and some bone fragments were scooped out by a wooden spoon, when the pia mater was found to be ecchymosed and the brain itself indented. Improbable as it may seem the patient recovered, and in Moscow Larrey heard that he had been evacuated to Poland as a prisoner of war.

Larrey was emphatic about the avoidance of the unnecessary use of the trephine, and goes on to say: ". . . for the rest, the relation of the following facts will decide the cases where the trephine is useless and harmful better than the most learned discourse.

"On our occupation of Berlin in May, 1812, Monsieur . . ., a storekeeper in the Clothing Department of the Army, was knocked down by a carriage which was passing him very fast. His head struck the sharp edge of a large stone; the skin of the forehead and the scalp as far back as the occipital protuberance were detached, so that an enormous flap hung down over his neck and ears. The entire skull was denuded and in many places deprived of its periosteum. There was a stellate fracture on the left frontal eminence, one limb of which extended to the parietal bone of that side but the bones were not depressed or displaced. The injured man did not lose consciousness, although he bled considerably from the nose and ears. He was immediately given a first aid dressing.

"The next day, being very ill, he was moved to the Officers Hospital at the Charlottenburg Gate where we saw him for the first time. His pain was severe and continuous, he was delirious, mentally aberrated, and exhibiting nervous twitchings; his pulse was hard and his face suffused.

"Preparations had been made to trephine him, which it was thought was indicated by the fracture. I caused the operation to be suspended and directed my attention to the treatment of the wound. It was first necessary to turn back the scalp which had been replaced with too little precaution, so that some large wisps of hair and lint lay between it and the cranium. After shaving the whole of the outer surface and removing all the foreign material we made a number of incisions through the contused and inflamed parts of the pericranium and the flap, one being at its base to aid the drainage of fluids, and one opposite to the fracture. The wound was washed with warm sweet wine and the soft parts replaced in their natural relation and maintained by a number of adhesive bandages and a fine perforated linen dressing soaked in the same fluid; some lint pads, compresses and a Galen's bandage completed the dressing. The patient was bled from the foot and refreshing and mildly laxative drinks, clysters and footbaths were prescribed.

"The relief of congestion in the flap and adjacent parts produced by the incisions and the other treatment got rid of the pain and delirium; calm was re-established and continued until night when inflammatory symptoms appeared afresh and increased in severity. A bleeding from the jugular vein with sedative and anti-spasmodic mucillaginous drinks gave relief and the patient felt better and passed the rest of the night quietly. The next two days were again stormy; nevertheless the intensity of the symptoms diminished, a sero-purulent discharge developed from the third day onwards and the dressing was removed on the fourth. The flap had become adherent in a number of places and suppuration was in process around its edges. A fresh dressing of perforated linen, impregnated with styrax ointment to encourage the separation of the sloughs which were forming at the circumference of the flap, was applied and the other treatment continued.

"The suppuration became very copious and the patient lost strength and was seized with an adynamic fever, which began with rigors, colicky pains, nausea and great anxiety. The shivering was succeeded by burning heat, thirst and headache. We were called to him during this paroxysm and prescribed iced acidulated mucilaginous drinks, and ordered his whole body to be bathed with iced camphorated vinegar. The wound continued to be dressed with camphorated styrax ointment.

"The alarming symptoms gradually diminished and were succeeded by complete calm and general improvement. He vomited some bilious material several times and had an involuntary bowel movement; this favourable moment was seized upon to administer an emetic composed of a scruple and a half of a strong infusion of ipecacuanha, prepared in the cold, and a grain of tartar emetic.[4] This was followed by copious effortless vomiting and abundant very foetid bowel movements.

"During the following night there was a severe exacerbation with delirium, and pain localized to the occiput near the base of the flap; this being the part of the head which had suffered the greatest amount of traction. The application of two wet cups to the area relieved the pain as though by magic; the scarifications and the whole occipital region were again covered with a double compress soaked in iced camphorated wine. At our visit the next day all the feverish symptoms had disappeared, but the patient was very weak and I feared the onset of a pernicious fever. As there was still some tenseness in the neck and difficulty in movement of the head we applied a large blister to this part and prescribed a drachm of quinine every hour in an infusion of arnica and Virginian snake root, together with some sulphuric ether; the patient was also given in the interval some small glasses of Hungarian wine.

"The fever that night was slight and the next day, the nineteenth after his accident, the patient who up to then had been in a drowsy condition regained the use of his senses. Except for some portions of the frontal bone, which appeared to be necrosed, the whole of the wound was granulating and on the point of healing.

"As I was obliged to leave with General Headquarters on the 21st of May, I confided the patient, who was now out of danger, to the care of M. Billequin, one of our medical officers of the first class who was in charge of the surgical direction of the Berlin hospitals. He reported later that the progress continued after our departure and that several small pieces of bone were exfoliated leaving the dura mater exposed at one place. The wound gradually healed and M. . . . left hospital completely cured, ninety days after his admission.

"We have seen this man since our return from Russia. He was perfectly well

[4] Drastic treatment indeed!

although a scar, about half a finger's breadth wide, runs around his head from the frontal eminences, across both temporal regions to the insertion of the flap, which is about an inch from the occipital protuberance. He is left bald and has almost entirely lost his memory for proper names. All his other mental faculties are intact and appear to function with exactitude.

"This singular case and its cure are both worthy of notice. If, according to the opinion of authorities and the view of many of the doctors who saw the patient, I had used the trephine there is every reason to think that he would not have survived the operation. In fact if the dura mater, which without doubt was inflamed by the third day of his illness, had been exposed and irritated by the trephine, it is probable that a gangrenous condition would have supervened, which in cases of this sort is the main contra-indication to the operation. If an operation must be performed one should at least defer it if there are signs of inflammation of the cerebral membranes."

*   *   *   *   *

Amongst his descriptions of wounds of the head, Larrey records the strange case which follows. Although he did not treat it himself he found it of great interest from many aspects and it forms a text for some further remarks upon the use of the trephine.

"The following observation shews the unexpected resources which nature may bring into play to preserve life, even in the worst conditions.

"A soldier of the 61st Infantry Regiment, returning from firing practice on the 3rd March, 1801, shot in fun at Christophe Cross a man of the same regiment, believing that his musket was not loaded. Cross fell at once, and to the great surprise of his comrade his head was pierced through by a long piece of a ramrod which had been carelessly left in the weapon. The soldier was promptly taken to the ambulance at Grosgerau where he received first aid from M. Caizergues, an assistant surgeon.[5] The wounded man had made the journey from the place where he was shot, a matter of a league and a quarter, partly on a cart and partly on foot. He had not bled from the nose or ears, nor had he been noticeably deranged in his bodily functions during the journey.

"A long piece of the ramrod had traversed the soldier's head from the middle of the forehead to the back of the left side of the neck, and the ends, which were of equal thickness, stood out for about two inches beyond the skull (Fig. 29). The unique nature of the case, and the difficulties M. Caizergues encountered in his first attempt to pull out the foreign body, caused him to summon all his available colleagues at the hospital.

"It was decided after consultation that it was necessary to extract the ramrod from the forehead end. After several attempts a piece of the iron rod came away with the pincers, when it was easily seen that the break was due to a flaw. According to M. Caizergues the piece of metal, which was subsequently lost, was about fifteen centimetres long and shewed no trace of blood or brain substance. A number of vain attempts were then made to pull out the remaining piece by the end which protruded from the neck. It seems that very strong pincers were used and great efforts made, as the rod is bent and shews the marks of the tools. The next suggestion was that the skull should be trephined as close as possible to the point where the ramrod emerged. This was against all the precepts of our Art, but despite the dangerous nature of the operation it was done, at the edge of the occipital foramen and a few lines distant from

[5] I owe the details of the case to this surgeon, who sent them to me together with the skull.

the posterior condylar foramen. To reach the bone it was necessary to divide the thick mass of the trapezius, splenius and complexus muscles, with their nerves and vessels. M. Caizergues has told us nothing of the difficulties which must have been met with, or of the events occurring during and after the operation; he simply remarked that trephining was of no use, and that it was necessary to give up the extraction of the ramrod and to leave the patient to the resources of nature. He mentioned, however, that the soldier stood the operation with the greatest courage and did not even lose consciousness. He died on the 25th of the same month. There is no mention of the symptoms which preceded his death, nor of the result of the operation.

"The post-mortem examination revealed that the frontal bone was pierced between the sinuses by a round opening, unassociated with any fracture, which was of about the size of the ramrod; the latter had passed horizontally between the two cerebral hemispheres without causing them damage, merely tearing the front end of the falx. It then entered the body of the sphenoid bone below the left optic foramen, and passing in succession through the substance of this bone, the apex of the petrous bone and the cuneiform part of the occipital, it pierced the left condyloid process of the latter at its base and emerged through the occipital foramen, finally reaching the exterior through the adjacent soft parts (Fig. 29).

"In its track the rod had not damaged any essential organ. After passing between the two cerebral hemispheres, without touching them, it had slipped beneath the cavernous sinus and the carotid artery without piercing either, and was actually separated from the sinus by a plate of bone which was barely detached from the body of the sphenoid; it was at some distance from the third pair of nerves and the internal jugular vein.

"The resistance and elasticity of the bony parts caused the projectile, once its force was spent, to be arrested and to remain in part embedded in the bone.[6]

"Two questions naturally arise from the examination of the skull:

"(1) What would have happened to the man if he had been left entirely to nature, whilst being appropriately treated in other respects? Death would appear to have been inevitable, but when would it have occurred? We cannot say, not having seen the patient and not knowing the extent to which his vital or organic functions were damaged. This enquiry seems to have been entirely omitted.

"(2) What advantage was to be gained by the operation of trephining, supposing that it could be done without danger? Since the measures used to extract the rod, such as pincers, etc., were unsuccessful, the trephine could not increase their efficacy and therefore was useless. But, apart from the fact that its application to the most deeply seated part of the occipital region was difficult, was it not perhaps injurious?

"The cerebellum was bound to be damaged by the teeth of the instrument, or at least the dura mater, for the portion of bone trephined varies very much in thickness at the different parts of the opening, and we know that the smallest wounds or damage to the cerebellum suffice to cause death. It is therefore with good reason that writers forbid the application of a trephine to the cranium below the circular line that divides the vertex from the base.

"Without suggesting that the patient's death was due to the operation, I think that it would have been wiser and more rational, after all the attempts

[6] See Fig. 29. The head transfixed by the ramrod is in the Anatomical Museum of the Medical Faculty at Paris.

which had been made, to have left the foreign body and await developments. Furthermore, the danger was due not so much to its presence as to the damage which it may have been thought to have produced within the cranium; and the post-mortem showed that it might well have stayed there for some time longer without killing the patient, since in fact there was no such damage. This case justifies the aphorism of the divine old man: *Experimentum periculosum, judicium difficile*."

Cerebral Hernia. This distressing complication of wounds of the skull was familiar to Larrey, who relates how he saw a man die in the Dresden Hospital within a few minutes of such a tumour being trimmed off by the surgeon in charge. He condemns the then current remedies, such as progressive compression by sheets of lead and the use of astringent and irritating fluids, and advises a simple expectant régime, with protection of the extruded brain by gentle dressings, together with such medicines as seem likely to diminish internal irritation. So treated, he states, a small hernia may spontaneously disappear.

"To complete my consideration of wounds of the head I shall say something about the treatment of wounds due to gunshot and to steel weapons, which injure the membranous coverings of the cranium and not the bone itself.

"In general all wounds of the head due to the cold steel should be closed, but not so as to exert too much traction on the edges. Fine perforated linen, soaked in hot sweet or honeyed wine, is the best form of dressing for ordinary incised wounds. If these are very extensive, or if there are loose strips of tissue, some adhesive bandages should be applied first, and in certain cases—such as wounds of the back of the head with large detached flaps—some sutures are advisable. The suturing should be preceded by a counter-opening at the base of the flap to allow the drainage of fluids, and the sutures supported by appropriate bandages.

"Contused wounds of these parts should be dressed similarly; that is to say that after shaving the head and removing any foreign bodies they should be covered with perforated linen soaked in a tonic liquid, such as wine, oxycrat, or salt water. It is not necessary to debride these wounds as long as there are no blind pockets, or tears or severe contusions of the periosteum; otherwise simple dressings are the best. There is almost no muscular action and the coverings of the head are not very irritable; *débridement* is therefore unnecessary and the wounds do not heal any quicker for it.

"Wounds of the ears demand special attention. If the external ear is cut through, no matter in what direction, the edges should be reunited as quickly as possible by means of interrupted sutures, using my special needles of a suitably small size. The stitches should be protected by a dressing or bandage which fills the hollows of the ear and holds it in a correct position. As long as the severed portion adheres to the remainder by the smallest pedicle healing is accomplished perfectly, no matter how extensive the wound. The same rules apply to wounds of the eyelids, nose, and other parts of the face.

"Amongst the wounds of the face from cutting or bruising certain very remarkable examples have been met with. I have already mentioned some in which there was an almost complete severence of the nose, so that it was only attached to a very small pedicle, in spite of which reunion took place very well.

"When the walls of the mouth are laid open, no matter whether by a cutting or bruising weapon, the wound should be made into a simple one and closed by sutures aided by bandages. We have reported several successes with this, even in gunshot wounds, in the course of our campaigns. I shall add one further:

the case of a *garde-du-corps* who was treated at the military hospital of Gros-Caillou.

"M. de R . . ., of the Royal Life Guards, was brought to this hospital in the winter of 1815 with a serious gunshot wound of the face. He seemed in a dying state when I saw him at my first visit twelve hours after the injury. The barrel of a double-shotted pistol had been placed inside his closed mouth against the vault of the palate, and tilted slightly forwards at the moment of discharge. A violent explosion occurred in the mouth and the two bullets passed out through the palate and nose. The anterior part of the former was destroyed, and the bony walls of the nasal fossae and the parts between these and the cranial cavity were smashed. The nose was split into three strips; a central one consisting of the end of the organ with the lower part of the septum, and two others of each nostril with the attached parts of the lips. The septum was completely destroyed, leaving a hole of about two inches in circumference with ragged edges. The veil of the palate and the base of the tongue had been split from before backwards, and a cleft filled with clotted blood was present in the inner side of the left cheek. The whole of the face and neck were swollen and covered with ecchymoses, and the eyelids so much so that vision was obstructed. The other senses were lost; the pulse was fluttering and almost absent, and the patient was in a state of continuous muscular spasm and pain so that we had every reason to fear his speedy death.

"It was urgently necessary to explore all the parts of the wound and to remove any foreign bodies and cleanse it as much as possible so as to obtain a fairly close approximation of the edges.

"After having prepared a suitable dressing I first extracted a number of fragments of the bones of the palate and nasal fossae and trimmed some parts of the edges of the wound and refreshed others which were ragged. I then inserted eleven interrupted sutures so as to bring the three strips of the nose and the irregular and widely separated edges of the upper lip into exact union, taking care to bring the lower part of the nasal septum into a central position. A number of additional sutures were placed between the primary ones and by this means the parts were brought into the most perfect apposition. To encourage the approximation of the maxillary bones I passed a platinum wire round the canine teeth which were at either side of the gap. I passed pieces of a large gum-elastic catheter into each nostril, with a thread through the ends to keep them in place. These allowed air to pass for respiration and helped very much to preserve the shape of the nose. Small graduated compresses were placed on the sides and in the canine fossae and were approximated and kept in place by a retaining bandage; thus completing a tedious and difficult operation.

"No sooner was this done than the patient felt relieved and the nervous symptoms which seemed to threaten tetanus promptly disappeared. I made use of this respite to put him into a warm hip-bath and to get him to swallow some refreshing and antispasmodic iced drinks by means of a feeding cup: swallowing was extremely difficult, but by patience and perseverance it was gradually accomplished. The night passed quietly; the next day there was some fever, which could be called traumatic, with headache and the threat of suffocation. We sedulously applied a dozen leeches round the throat and wet cups to the neck and over the chest; he was bled from the foot and we continued with the same drinks and some purgative enemata.

"All these symptoms quickly disappeared and the patient recovered the use of his senses, except that of smell. The dressing was not removed until the eighth day when the union of the wounds was everywhere found to be almost complete. A few adhesive bandages were all that was required for the remaining period of cicatrization; but the interior of the nasal fossae and the palatine vault were the source of abundant suppuration for some time, which was followed by the exfoliation of a number of sequestra from the nasal bones, the cornets (concha of the ethmoid), and the part of the maxillary bone damaged by the bullets. The crushing of the bony vault of the nose caused a watering of both eyes, with a lachrymal fistula due to the displacement or temporary blockage of the nasal duct. The use of the catheters already mentioned, the daily replacement of some bone fragments situated at the root of the nose by means of a blunt probe, and a few injections of the lachrymal orifices by an Anel's syringe,[7] re-established the flow of the tears and the fistulae disappeared. The maxillary bones gradually came together to close the gap between the mouth and the nasal fossae, so that the patient had no need for an obturator.

"Eventually, after two and a half months' care, M. de R . . . was sent back to his family in good health and without noteworthy deformity."

Wounds of the Throat.

"At the battle of Dresden we saw two men with gunshot wounds of the throat which were in many respects unusual.

"The first was a light infantry officer. His wound was on the left side of the larynx and about the size of a centime. It was directed downwards and inwards, passing below the thyroid cartilage, which I thought was slightly grooved, and then appearing to track beneath the trachea towards the chest, where the missile became lost. The wounded man was suffering from continuous oppressive pain and had difficulty in breathing; his face was permanently suffused and his whole neck engorged; he was quite unable to swallow solids and the taking of liquids was difficult and painful.

"Neither by a sound nor other means could we determine the exact situation of the ball. The patient himself always indicated the region of his cricoid cartilage, and even believed that in certain positions he could feel it, but my own endeavours were unsuccessful. However I decided to make a thorough exploration of the whole larynx near to the wound, and in spite of the proximity of the branches of the thyroid artery to debride it above and below: this was of no avail and we were unable to find the foreign body. I could not believe that it was lying in the laryngeal cavity itself; for had this been so the patient should have been suffering from serious and fatal symptoms. He had not lost his speech and had no suffocative attacks. Everything led me to think that the ball had come to rest behind the trachea at the point of its bifurcation and, in fact, a few days later, it shewed up at the bottom of the wound and we were able to seize it with forceps and to pull it out. From this moment the patient became steadily better and before long he left hospital perfectly well.

"The second subject was a young sharpshooter of the Guard, Jacques Brisnot. He was wounded on the day before the battle of August 27th and was one of a small group of wounded in the care of M. Emangard, one of our surgeons. He was suffocating and in obvious danger: his voice was completely lost and he was a prey to the miseries of death. He was scarcely breathing and only a few bubbles of air, and a great deal of frothy blood escaped from a bullet wound on the left side of the larynx, between the thyroid cartilage and the hyoid bone, which was fractured. The ball had passed through his throat and come out

[7] Dominique Anel (1679–1730). The originator of lachrymal duct catheterization.

behind the angle of the jaw. The patient had lost a lot of blood and his suffocation was due to this filling the cavity of the larynx, from which the epiglottis
had been shot away and the surface of the thyroid cartilage grooved. The
difficulty facing the surgeon was to clear the larynx of blood and to re-establish
respiration, and happily he had the idea of dividing the thyroid cartilage. The
moment this was done the pent-up air in the bronchi was forcibly expelled,
blowing out the clots which had filled them and were suffocating the patient.
The engorgement of the nearby parts was relieved, the breathing re-established,
and the patient's life no longer in danger. The wound gradually became clean,
the bodily functions were duly re-established, the edges of the wound came
together, the scar quickly closed and in a short time except for some residual
hoarseness the patient was cured.

"This shews the necessity of giving free exit to substances retained in the
cavity of the larynx; and in order to effect this most easily in cases of contused
wounds of the organ with penetration and an effusion of fluid or the presence
of foreign bodies, it is preferable to follow the advice of the celebrated Spanish
surgeon Virgili[8] and to enlarge the wound in the direction of the trachea, in
so far as the chief vessels or nerves allow of this, rather than to make an opening
at one of the sites of election for laryngotomy or bronchotomy; which would
result in there being two openings into the larynx instead of one and might
further harm the respiratory functions."

Elsewhere (p. 41) a description is given of Murat's wound in the throat,
with severance of the epiglottis by a bullet, and of a similar and rather graver
wound in a grenadier who ultimately became a pensioner at the Invalides
(p. 42).

* * * * *

Larrey wrote a good deal about wounds of the thorax and their consequences.
It was a type of wound regarded as highly deadly until long after his time. Thus
out of 147 cases of penetrating gun-shot wounds of the chest in the British army
in the Crimean War, 120 died; whilst of 200 similar Russian cases at the siege
of Sebastopol only 3 recovered (Ericksen). Larrey appreciated the pathology
of surgical emphysema and has given us an account of a gross example of this
from a lance wound of the chest (Vol. IV) with survival. From his Egyptian
experience he recommended two measures for dealing with penetrating wounds
of the thorax without lesion of the intercostal artery, which were contrary to
the then current practice; viz. closure of the wound and keeping the patient
lying on the wounded side, quoting three cases in which this was successful.

He investigated the effects in the chest of effusions, and was well accustomed
to evacuate these by a simple incision through the intercostal muscles, and in
a memoir: *"On the effects of the operation for empyema"* he analyses in detail the
changes in the thoracic cage and its contents in long-standing collapse of the
lung (Vol. III, pp. 442-491). In one case, in which he operated for the relief
of an effusion with haemopericardium, he deliberately opened the pericardial
sac and felt, and allowed his assistant to feel, the beating heart within.

In reviewing the casualties of the first campaign in Saxony he returns again
to wounds of the thorax, with especial reference to gun-shot wounds and the
presence of missiles in the chest cavity, and goes on to give accounts of the
operative removal of such foreign bodies. Not only does he do this—a procedure
which Ericksen condemned in 1861—but in one such operation he performed

[8] Pedro Virgili (1699-1776). Performed a successful tracheotomy for quinsy.

an almost complete resection of a rib. It is to be remembered that damage to the intercostal artery was very much feared as a source of haemorrhage, difficult to control and sometimes fatal. Although Larrey did not deliberately complete the resection (accident completed it for him), nor did he attempt the subperiosteal operation which was later devised to obviate the danger to the artery, he may fairly be regarded as its pioneer.

In pleading for a bolder attitude towards thoracic wounds he wrote:

"The observations I am now about to record, whilst confirming the principles laid down in my memoir, seem to me suitable for the guidance of young practitioners in the new road they will have to follow for the removal of foreign bodies from the chest, the extraction of which would otherwise have appeared impossible.

"Amongst the many soldiers who are shot in the chest, with damage to the internal organs and lodgement of the projectile in the cavity, any who escape the usual fatal outcome are continuously tormented by the presence of such bodies, which produce an inexhaustible supply of purulent matter from the cavities in which they lodge, which forms a collection or empyema. If the wound made by the ball is kept open and fistulous the pus may be so situated that it only escapes with difficulty and this makes the outlook more or less gloomy.

"From the beginning nature invariably tries to expel the foreign body, or to prevent its interfering with the functions of the parts with which it is in contact. First, an abscess forms around the site where the body lodges; by the effect of the suppuration it becomes loosened and then by its weight moves downwards, leaving a sinus in its track. This movement continues, provided it meets with no effective resistance, until it becomes arrested at some site where the parts are incapable of this form of reaction. Here it starts a new focus of suppuration which is the source of fistulae or a localized empyema. This cannot go on without the patient suffering from pain and fever from the reabsorption of morbid products, leading to wasting, marasmus and death.

"On the other hand if the bullet does not enter the chest cavity it lodges in the wall and may make its way into the intermuscular spaces, or become arrested in the gap between the ribs, where it may remain stationary for a long time without causing any notable effects (I have seen several examples of this). It is only rarely that it makes its way to the exterior spontaneously.

"Once a focus of suppuration has developed the foreign body remains free in the thoracic cavity and will eventually encompass the patient's death should not Art promptly come to his aid, but before anything is undertaken it is important to recognize clearly its presence and position. In the early stages of the disease the lower intercostal spaces may allow room for the removal of the bullet; but when the collapse of the chest walls has advanced the ribs come so close together that it can no longer pass between them, especially if it be of large calibre.

"It therefore becomes necessary to enlarge the space selected so as to allow the passage of suitable instruments to seize the foreign body and remove it without the exertion of great force. To achieve this we must remove a part of one of the ribs; and the question is whether to do this with a saw, a trephine, or by some quite different means. The saw, however modified, and the trephine, however small its crown, are equally unsuitable on account of curvature of the rib and its closeness to its neighbour. The only solution remaining is to cut the rib; this can be done more easily than might be thought, especially if the patient be not too old, by the use of a lenticular knife, an instrument devised for trephining.

"The two cases I shall report will serve to confirm these principles, and to demonstrate the course of the disease due to the presence of foreign bodies in the thorax and the phenomena which follow their removal[9]. The latter I have already described in my memoir on the operation for empyema; that is to say, once the cause of suppuration is removed the walls of the infected cavity become clean and come together by the laws of contractility, elasticity, and the force of the tissues. The latter develop in every direction, both the adjacent and even more distant parts co-operating in this work; the cavity is gradually closed by the growth of capillary vessels from the pleurae, mediastinum, diaphragm, and perhaps also from a part of the lung. The intercostal muscles, which have become useless, lose their contractile action; the ribs come together, the cartilages lose their curvature and become drawn in towards the thoracic cavity. The growth of the sternum and ribs becomes modified, so that these arches lose their curvature, their bones become flattened and increased in thickness and assume a cylindrical form which contributes to the reduction in the size of the cavity; in fact all the forces of organization unite in this work of convergence, and by degrees the considerable space left within the chest by the effusion of blood, pus or serous fluid is obliterated. The vessels come into contact and contract adhesions and mutual anastomoses; healing extends from the interior to the exterior and the wounds disappear so that the patient becomes perfectly cured.

"*First Case:* A former young sharpshooter of the Guard sustained a gunshot wound at the foot of the Sèvres hill during the battle of Paris. The ball had passed downwards and punched clean through the upper half of the fourth rib, about an inch and a half from the sternal cartilage. It entered the chest and after traversing a part of the lung struck the spine near the eighth or ninth thoracic vertebra, where it appeared to be arrested. The wound was accompanied by haemorrhage, effusion of blood, frequent attacks of fainting, oppression, spasms of pain and spitting of blood; and, as he told me himself, he had been in the greatest danger.

"He was first taken to the ambulances which had been set up in the Paris abattoirs and there he remained until August (1814) when he was transferred to Gros-Caillou, where he was found to have a fistulous wound in the upper and right side of his chest, with a collection of matter in the pleural cavity of this side. He was worn out by the active suppuration and reabsorptive fever, and was extremely thin and suffering from moderate pyrexia with exacerbations. Each time the wound was dressed it discharged one or more dishes—full of pus, which the patient himself produced by lying on his right side with his head and body inclined downwards. To discover the direction and extent of the wound I introduced a flexible and slightly curved catheter which readily passed down to the lowest part of the chest cavity where I was able to feel a hard metallic body which I suspected to be the bullet. Its position corresponded very nearly to the site of election for the operation for empyema, and by means of the catheter the distance could be measured on the outside of the chest. Having found all this out I thought it imperative to make a counter opening in the thorax near to the lowest point of the diseased cavity in which the foreign body was.

"The very much widened space between the eighth and ninth ribs seemed to me to be the most favourable site, and all the more so as this was the spot at which the patient said that the bullet lay.

"The operation for empyema being decided upon by a consultation of doctors I had specially called for this purpose, I performed it according to the principles

[9] Vol. IV. pp. 250–269.

laid down in my memoir. Through this counter-opening I obtained about three dishes of pus and discovered the bullet, which I easily extracted with a polypus forceps, the intercostal space being very wide and the missile flattened. This operation was followed by several exacerbations which subsided before the third day: the suppuration was free but pus no longer came from the upper wound which quickly healed. To assist nature in closing the cavity I gave the patient various preparations of quinine. The flow of pus diminished daily; the general functions re-established themselves visibly, the patient recovered his appetite and ability to sleep. The affected side of the chest, which before the operation had been the more prominent of the two, daily diminished in volume and the ribs closed up to each other to such an extent that the space through which I operated had entirely disappeared before the end of three months and the level of the right nipple had gone down to two fingers' breadth below the left. At this stage a probe could scarcely be passed into the wound which now discharged only a small quantity of pus of good quality: everything suggested a speedy and complete cure, when suddenly the young soldier, having drunk brandy to excess, contracted an acute febrile enteritis and died in December, six months after being wounded and about a hundred days after the operation.

"At the post-mortem, we found the upper wound healed externally and the interval between the ribs filled at this point with a cellular tissue which could be easily separated with the handle of a scalpel; there was no longer any communication with the disease cavity, which extended only a short distance from the lower wound which was very much contracted and its edges close together.

"The costal pleura had become immensely thick; the mediastinum was depressed on the diseased side and a fleshy mass, constituted no doubt by the tissue of the obliterated lung, filled the upper part of the thoracic cavity. The specimen, which I presented to the Medical Society of the Faculty, is to be found in its anatomical collection and bears out most of the facts I have just described.

"*Second Case:* Louis Claye, twenty-six years old, a native of Monchy in the department of l'Oise, a corporal in the former 61st regiment of the Line, received a bullet wound at the engagement at Moïllow in Russia, on July 22nd, 1812. The ball entered his chest between the eighth and ninth ribs on the right side and came to rest in the thoracic cavity. The soldier fell unconscious onto his wounded side and lay for two days on the battlefield, all the time threatened with suffocation. He was, however, picked up on the second day and taken to one of the hospitals at Moïllow.

"Three days later he was at death's door from an enormous effusion in his chest, but fortunately was saved by the action of one of our surgeons who skilfully inserted a probe-pointed bistoury into the wound and enlarged it in a direction parallel with the upper edge of the lower rib. This operation, which we may call an empyema of election, in contrast to that practised at the usual site, greatly relieved the patient who rallied and after passing the rest of the season at Moïllow was evacuated to the hospitals of Kowno, Königsberg and Thorn.

"After being for some weeks in the latter, with his wound temporarily closed, the patient once again developed symptoms of pain and tension, which were relieved by the spontaneous bursting of an acute abscess which had formed under the edges of the false ribs. After giving exit to some fragments of clothing and a large amount of purulent matter, this slowly closed, but at the same time the wound between the ribs reopened and discharged a fresh collection of blood-stained pus: it was now kept permanently open by means of a strip of linen. The ball, which the patient said was buried inside his chest, had been searched for in vain. But in spite of the seriousness of his wound and all these varied complications he had dragged himself from hospital to hospital until he reached Paris.

"At the end of 1814 he was invalided as incurable by a health council and went back to his commune; but his constant suffering and desire to be rid of the ball, the weight of which alone was a great inconvenience to him, brought him again to Paris. He at first applied unsuccessfully for admission to a military hospital and, not without some difficulty, I obtained permission to treat him in a private room at the Gros-Caillou, where he was eventually admitted on June 15th, 1816. At my first visit I succeeded by means of a sound in detecting the ball at the botton of the right thoracic cavity. The fistulous wound was situated exactly at the point where the operation of election for empyema is performed: its orifice was very small but the suppuration was profuse and the patient was suffering from the early symptoms of hectic fever.

"Having debrided and enlarged the wound along the line of the ribs, I made some unsuccessful attempts to extract the foreign body. The intercostal space was much too narrow and the two ribs did not allow of the least separation. I was able to seize a part of the surface of the ball with forceps and bring it close to the opening, but it quickly escaped and fell back to the bottom of the thoracic cavity. It was too distressing to leave the patient in this condition, since nature had no means of expelling the foreign body from his chest where it was provoking a purulent empyema, and it was clear that this would ultimately bring the unfortunate man to his death.

"But how was I to extract it? The problem was difficult of solution. I had thoughts of sawing through the lower rib of the opened intercostal space to allow room for both the forceps and ball to pass, but the idea was negatived by the difficulty or impossibility of doing this, since the closeness of the two ribs (no doubt ankylosed to their corresponding dorsal vertebrae, for they did not yield at all to the forcible opening of the forceps or other instruments I tried), made it impossible to use a saw (even one specially made) on the convex surface of one rib without damaging the other: moreover, how would it be possible to saw through the whole thickness without lacerating the soft parts within? The use of a trephine involved the same difficulties, as I found later when I made the attempt.

"I then cast about for a better procedure than either of these. I believed that in subjects who were not up in years the substance of the ribs, especially in disease, would be amenable to a cutting instrument. The lenticular,[10] which is used to cut off the projecting angles left after the use of a number of trephine crowns on the skull, appeared to me to be perfectly suitable for my purpose, and this instrument was the basis of the procedure I finally adopted. The patient being resolute and all preparations made, I undertook this unique

[10] The lenticular of the ancients was a vertical chisel cutting on one edge and struck on the other with a hammer, whilst the end carried a rounded button which being smooth, did not injure the brain. Ambroise Paré explains the lenticular as it was then understood: "After the round piece of bone has been removed by the trepan, if any roughness should remain on the edge of the inner table that might injure the dura mater, when it makes its movements, the roughness must be made plane with an instrument called *lenticulaire*." (Catalogue of Surgical Instruments in the Museum of the Royal College of Surgeons of England compiled by A. H. G. Doran, F.R.C.S. 1922). The instrument figured on the left of Larrey's Plate 1, Vol. 1, is his lenticular. Vide Fig. 4.

operation (at least I am not aware of its having ever been performed since) on the 22nd of July.

"The patient was placed on the edge of his bed with the assistants in convenient positions. I first enlarged the wound between the ribs and then made a vertical incision in the parts over the lower one, and retracted its edges exposing its convex surface for a matter of an inch and a half. Two bleeding arterial branches were tied and I then passed the lenticular knife (from which the lentille had been removed) between the ribs and cut away the upper edge of the lower one layer by layer, so that I succeeded in forming a semi-lunar gap of five to six lines deep in the substance of the bone.

"Wishing to avoid damage to the intercostal artery, which runs on the inner side of the lower border of the rib, I stopped at about the middle of the bone and made fresh attempts to extract the ball; but as it was of large calibre[11] I could not force it through the opening; it either slipped out of the strongest forceps or else these gave way. Eventually I was forced to cut more deeply into the rib, until I was about three-quarters of the way through it. For fear of touching the intercostal artery I finally stopped two lines from its lower border, and arming myself with a fresh pair of polypus forceps I seized the projectile and at length succeeded, not without difficulty, in extracting it. The obstacles we had overcome could well be appreciated from the scratches seen on the ball.

"The extraction made, I injected two or three syringefuls of warm marshmallow water into the thoracic cavity and covered the wound with some fine perforated linen soaked in this; an ordinary bandage completed the dressing. I prescribed for the patient, who had withstood the operation with the utmost courage, an antispasmodic potion, mucilaginous refreshing drinks, emollient and anodyne clysters, and embrocations of camphorated oil of camomile to his abdomen, with a low diet.

"He was comfortable during the first hours following the operation, but during the night he had some stormy periods. At my visit the next morning I found him in a low state and fevered, with a weak pulse; he was suffering from much throbbing pain in the liver region and around the wound. After having removed the first layers of the dressing I applied several wet cups to the painful areas and continued with the acidulated and iced drinks and antispasmodics.

"The inflammatory symptoms moderated and the patient felt better. During the night of the 22nd one of the ligatures of the muscular arteries became detached and a haemorrhage occurred which was controlled by light pressure. The inflammatory phenomena appeared to have been overcome, but the patient remained depressed and inquiet and his pulse although weak continued febrile. I substituted mild tonics for the refreshing medicines, and added extract of opium to the antispasmodic potions.

"The next two days were calm, suppuration was established and everything promised a favourable course, but on the 25th he went alone to the lavatory at two o'clock in the afternoon, and there broke the thin and brittle part of the partially divided rib by a sudden and violent flexion of his body on the side of the wound. This fracture was immediately followed by rupture of the intercostal artery and a haemorrhage which brought this interesting patient to death's door. Being called in at once I was fortunate enough to deal with this accident and prevent a recurrence by means of Desault's most ingenious com-

[11] Larrey tells us that the Russian balls weighed an ounce and a quarter (against three-quarters of an ounce for the French). The ratio of their diameters would be 1–1·19.

pressive bag. By now his pulse was barely palpable and his limbs cold, so that everything made me fear a speedy demise. As soon as the dressing was finished I prescribed cordials, aetherated frictions, good wine and absolute rest.

"The day passed off without further incident. Warmth and the vital forces gradually returned, but towards evening there was some fever with a sort of indefinite malaise and much pain in the wound and round about. For fear of starting the haemorrhage again I did not touch the dressing, but prescribed a strong antispasmodic potion with opium, and a mucilaginous acidulated drink with spirit of nitre.

"On the 26th adynamic symptoms appeared, the pains in the wound and particularly those in the region of the liver became worse. I did not disturb the dressing but applied large blisters to the part and to the area all round the wound and continued use of the medicines prescribed on the day before. A violent exacerbation of fever occurred during the night of the 26th. The following day he was prostrated, his tongue coated and he now appeared to be threatened from a different direction. I cautiously removed the dressing. A large amount of pus escaped from the wound, which was extremely inflamed and appeared in danger of hospital gangrene. Without worrying about the effect of spasms of retching which must accompany an emetic, which I thought to be urgently required, I prescribed a mixture of 25 grains of ipecacuanha and a grain of tartar emetic to be taken on the following day. This treatment, which caused copious evacuations both above and below, effected an abrupt improvement in his condition. From this moment he began to progress and we were able to pass readily to quinine and other tonic medicines. The wound was dressed with styrax ointment sprinkled with camphor. For three or four days the disease appeared stationary, but then he began to recover his strength and at once I became more hopeful. The wound became cleaner, the suppuration plentiful and better in quality, all the nervous and inflammatory symptoms disappeared and thirty days after his operation the patient was well on the way to recovery: on August 22nd he was shewn to members of the Society of Medicine.

"The space which had originally resulted from the evacuation of the effused fluids from the chest had, except for the sinus, gradually become filled by the contraction of all the parts of the walls of the chest cavity during the four years which had elapsed since he was wounded. That is to say, the ribs had lost their curvature and become cylindrical, as in the case I have described earlier, the sternum had sunk in on this side and the mediastinum and pericardium were markedly pulled over to the right, so that the heart's beat could no longer be felt in its usual situation. The diaphragm and liver were appreciably drawn up into the thoracic cavity and this unopposed retraction rapidly increased after the operation, as did the contraction of the other parts. The result of these changes was a flattening of the whole of this side of the chest and the displacement of the right nipple relative to the left, as well as the development of a hollow below the false ribs on this side, where a prominence due to the liver could be felt before the operation.

"The soldier departed for his home on October 1st, 1816, completely cured. Several months later he came to Paris in good health."

Larrey was well acquainted with the fatal results of air embolism, for Sir Charles Bell (1841) tells us that: "On looking over my sketches of the wounded at Waterloo with Baron Larrey, he fixed with interest on the case of a young man who had been wounded in the lower part of the neck. 'I well know,' says this excellent surgeon, 'how that man must have died. I have seen many wounded so during my campaigns, and die from air drawn into the veins'."[12]

* * * * *

"The ancients regarded wounds of the bladder as fatal: this is expressed by the Hippocratic aphorism: *cui persecta vesica, lethale*. Although since these ancient times the causes of wounds have become more complex, yet surgery has proved by the progress it has made, and by the success obtained in the operation of cutting for stone and the treatment of wounds of this organ, that the aphorism is not always true. Nevertheless authoritative pronouncements on wounds of the bladder are as yet far from complete. One of the most up-to-date and erudite of works, the *Nosographie chirurgicale*, makes no mention of the subject, whilst those who have written on it say very little about the diagnostic side, and fail to describe all the measures necessary to deal with the immediate condition or others which may accompany it, especially the complication of foreign bodies in the viscus which has been the chief subject of my researches.

"If the bladder be empty of fluid it is very difficult for it to be wounded by a penetrating steel weapon or by a bullet crossing the pelvis in any direction, or at least this rarely happens. To be wounded it must be moderately full, which is the usual state in the course of a battle. The heat of the engagement and its duration detract attention from the need to empty the organ, so that the urine accumulates and the bladder fills the pelvis, offering so large a surface that a weapon or missile can hardly enter this bony cage without touching or wounding it. . . ."

"Wounds due to *armes blanches*, such as the sword, bayonet, lance, etc., may pierce the bladder at some part of its circumference, or may go through both of its walls. In the latter case they are usually mortal, for however prompt the contraction of the organ the urine escapes into the pelvic cavity and at once sets up a fatal inflammation. I have dressed a number of soldiers on the battlefield in whom the bladder had been so transfixed, and all perished within the first forty-eight hours from inflammation and gangrene. If, however, the weapon pierces the organ in the region of its base, or through one of the areas *not* covered by peritoneum, the patient is capable of being cured unless there has been serious internal haemorrhage.

"The most certain sign of a lesion of this sort is the issue of urine from the wound: this may be momentary, intermittent, or continuous, according to the site of the wound and the changes which supervene in the bladder. The first occurs if the bladder is very full at the time the wound is received, and is pierced in its extraperitoneal part; when the urine is evacuated the edges of the wound come together and adhere and do not re-open if the fluid continues to be passed naturally. If, however, there are obstacles to its passage along the urethral canal the bladder becomes over-distended, causing the edges of the wound to re-open and the urine to escape. The same may occur if a gum-elastic catheter has been used but withdrawn too soon; its re-introduction will direct the urine away from the wound and re-establish the normal route. Finally, the abnormal passage may be permanent and persist for a variable length of time if the wound be situated at the lower part of the bladder.

"When the track of the wound along which the urine passes is long and indirect, abscesses form at different points. We must not fail to open these and we may prevent their recurrence by passing a gum-elastic catheter into the

[12] *Practical Essays* by Sir Charles Bell, Edin. 1814. p. 11.

urethra—a procedure which is one of the principal methods used in the treatment of all wounds of the bladder. Warm baths, camphorated oily embrocations to the abdomen, antispasmodic refreshing drinks, frequent clysters, and at times bleeding or wet cups around the wound are the other measures we have used with advantage in wounds of this organ by the cold steel. I shall content myself with briefly reporting two cases which have appeared to me to be especially interesting.

"Joseph Perrier, formerly a chasseur of the Guard, was struck in the right thigh by a Cossack's lance whilst taking part in a cavalry charge. After piercing the skin and tensor muscle of the fascia lata in the upper and outer third of the limb, the point of the weapon passed obliquely beneath the crural arch at some distance from the symphysis pubis and opened the extraperitoneal part of the bladder anteriorly: the urine at once flowed out through the wound in the thigh. A few hours later the patient passed a large quantity of blood and urine by the natural passage. This haemorrhage was followed by complete tranquility; urine was no longer voided through the thigh and the patient believed himself well.

"As soon as the bladder had been emptied of its contained urine the edges of the wound came into contact and adhered. When suppuration was thoroughly established an abscess formed in the wound track which opened spontaneously and discharged a certain amount of urine and pus. For a long time a fistula persisted but by the use of a catheter in the bladder and a counter-opening in the groin, together with methodical dressing and the assiduous attention given by one of my pupils—M. Champion—he was cured.

"*Second case.* During a bull-fight which we saw at Burgos on our entry into Spain in 1808, a soldier who was slightly drunk wished to emulate the *torreros* and confront and fight the animal in the arena. The bull, which had already been made furious, charged the unfortunate man who tried to evade it by crouching: he was impaled by one of its horns and thrown backwards for a distance of several feet. A loud cry arose from all sides: one of the intrepid bull-fighters threw himself on the bull, thrust his sword into it and left it stark dead on the spot. I jumped over the barrier and running to the unhappy soldier was the first to succour him as he lay stretched senseless on the arena. I had him removed at once to the hospital and went with him to see to his immediate treatment.

"We found a ragged wound of about an inch and a half in diameter at the level of the top of the right buttock, directed from behind obliquely forwards and outwards towards the lowest part of the groin. On further investigation I discovered that the horn, which was curved and very sharp, had lacerated the subcutaneous tissue and the inguinal glands and passed beneath the crural arch into the pelvis, where it had met the lateral wall of the bladder which was full of urine. The organ was not actually perforated, but had been denuded of a part of its covering and so weakened at this point that it formed a hernial protrusion beneath the crural arch, of about the size of a hen's egg. There had been a considerable amount of haemorrhage at first, due no doubt to the severance of some branches of the femoral artery by the horn in its passage through the lowest part of the inguinal region. The injured man was cold, his face colourless and pulse very small; he was in a state of extreme anxiety and was suffering from retention of urine. I made him swallow a little pure coffee, to combat the effects of his drink and to reanimate his vital forces. He soon vomited copiously which cleared his stomach and relieved him, except for his pain and frequent desire to urinate.

"I debrided the external wound and then passed a hollow sound along its track to free the skin of the groin over the herniated bladder (cystocele), and cutting down upon the point which projected beneath the skin exposed the whole tumour. Before attempting to reduce it I took care to empty the bladder by a gum-elastic catheter which I retained in position. I then reduced the displaced part of the organ by gradually expressing the urine into its proper cavity. The patient at once became calm and from this moment we conceived great hopes of his recovery. The wound was covered with fine fenestrated linen, in such a way as to bring its edges together and keep the lint from being caught up in the flesh. A retaining bandage completed the dressing. I prescribed the customary remedies and gave instructions that the catheter should be retained until the groin wound was cicatrized, in order to prevent a fresh herniation of the bladder.

"On my return from Madrid, six months later, I saw this man again and found him perfectly well.

"Although the bladder had not been penetrated it had nevertheless been damaged; and without the prompt attention which was given it is probable that the strangulated portion in which urine was retained would have ruptured spontaneously and the patient's days would have been numbered."

*   *   *   *   *

"We now come to the question of explaining how a foreign body which has penetrated into the bladder can lodge in its cavity? It is easy to conceive that a ball can force a fragment of bone, a small coin, a button, or any other small flat body edgewise into the bladder, and that after piercing one wall it may be turned on its axis by the effect of the impulse and the volume of liquid through which it passes, and presenting its largest surface to the opposite wall be arrested, so that it falls to the bottom of the bladder. But how can balls or pellets of lead, which have retained their spherical shape, be arrested within this membranous sac and fail to pass right through it? Is not the answer that their passage through the hard and soft tissues of the pelvic wall so reduces their velocity that when they reach the bladder cavity the urine forces them to traverse a further space, depending upon its quantity?

"If these bullets or lead pellets are small they may be spontaneously passed through the urethra, or extracted through this route by certain advantageous methods employed in the Art. The case of a certain captain, related by Théophile Bonnet, is one of the most remarkable. "This officer received a pistol shot in the right side of the abdomen, the ball penetrating the bladder. The wound became closed and healed, and the patient was in all respects cured: but after a certain time he began to experience acute pains in the bladder, similar to those caused by the presence of a stone. After great efforts he passed a lead bullet the size of a pea through the urethra.

"Small lead pellets may be more easily expelled by the help of a gum-elastic catheter, which assists their passage and may be gradually increased in size up to the largest. The foreign bodies can then easily pass along the urethra or else enter the eyelet of the catheter. By this means I have saved many sufferers with gravel from a great deal of pain: quite large pebbles have been passed along the canal or removed by the catheter.

"According to Prosper Alpin, the Egyptians of his time removed urinary stones by means of a dilating instrument[13] without resorting to a cutting opera-

[13] *Medicina Aegyptiorum: de lapidis vesicae extractione absque ulla incisione apud Aegyptios.* Alpin wrote the first important work on the history of Egyptian medicine (1591). He spent three years in Egypt and afterwards was Professor of Botany at Padua.

tion. It is probable that they only used the method when the calculi were small, or in the case of women. The Egyptians of to-day do not know of it, and in any case stone must be very rare in these people since we never heard it spoken of during our stay in Egypt.

"If a musket ball remains in the bladder, either because its extraction has been neglected or its presence not known, what will happen? The results will be fatal if the foreign body is large and irregular: its presence will quickly set up irritation by its size and weight and the nature of the material of which it is made. Inflammation immediately follows and is succeeded by suppuration, and then by ulceration, with perforation of the bladder and the passage of the foreign body and urine into the cellular tissue of the pelvis, which it infiltrates and sets up gangrene leading to death. This has been the most common termination in the army. In certain favourable circumstances the bullet may reach the perinaeum and cause a gangrenous abscess, which can be opened or else opens spontaneously, allowing the ball to escape to the exterior; it may equally well pass into the rectum.

"If the foreign body is small and has a smooth surface the bladder is less affected; the urine soon deposits an earthy layer of calcareous material on the lead and these layers gradually thicken so that a stone forms which continues to increase in size. The symptoms produced are those of calculus.

"It is more difficult to interpret symptoms due to the presence in the viscus of a ball, either large or small, without any such envelope. The pains are no doubt more severe since the immediate contact of the metallic substance with the mucous membrane sets up more painful irritation than that produced by calcareous material. The almost continuous state of spasm and contraction of the bladder conceals the ball at its base so that it may fail to be found on examination; moreover, it may be covered on one surface by a layer of blood, albumin, or a portion of linen, wadding or cloth, or by a part of the mucous membrane, so that the sound may touch it without yielding a recognizable sensation. Nevertheless the expert hand should be able to detect it; it is sufficient to direct the end of the sound towards the base of the bladder and with the help of a finger passed into the rectum to push the ball up so that it can be touched by the instrument; and moreover it projects into this part of the intestine. Finally, the patient may be asked to carry out certain movements during which he can himself feel it rolling about inside him like a ball. These investigations, together with the evidence of a gunshot wound in the abdomen or pelvis with damage to the bladder and without the ball's having passed out, confirm the existence of a foreign body in the viscus.

"Assuming that such bullets are of lead should we not, before undertaking an operation, attempt to dissolve them by means of quicksilver as several writers have recommended; since when these two substances are brought into contact in correct proportions the lead is quickly dissolved and a metallic liquid results which could be passed by the urethra?

"The investigations of Ledran, the most zealous protagonist of this method[14] leave us in doubt as to their exactitude and accuracy. Experiments of this kind are in any case difficult to carry out, and those of Ledran, which were only made with the object of the removal of a small piece of lead sound weighing about two drachms, cannot be regarded as applicable to the solution of a musket ball which weighs at least an ounce. But even supposing that such a ball is capable of being dissolved within the bladder, is there any certainty that the surface of the metal will be clean, even immediately after the wound has

[14] *See* Vol. XIX of the *Bibliothèque de Planque*, p. 589.

been received? There is none. On the contrary I believe that after the first twenty-four hours it will be coated with either a layer of coagulated blood or else, perhaps, by a portion of the mucous membrane which it has detached from the bladder wall; and, finally, it may well be made of iron, copper, or some substance other than lead. The ball may also have carried with it pieces of bone or clothing which are as troublesome inside the bladder as the missile itself. In all these cases injections of quicksilver are useless and may be harmful, since its presence will increase the size and weight of the foreign body and aggravate its effects. This procedure ought to be rejected.

"We have already dealt with the method of extracting small lead shot or other small foreign bodies; when, however, these are large and incapable of passing along the urethral canal another way of exit must be made.

"Let us consider what is the most certain and advantageous route for their removal. Is it that by which the ball has entered, assuming that it has penetrated at some point on the abdominal wall opposite to the bladder? Many authors, amongst them some of the most renowned, have thought that this is so. I shall refrain from citing them, since to do so would in no wise help practitioners in considering the views which follow.

"Whatever the direction of the external wound of entry it is almost impossible for it to be in such strict alignment with that in the bladder that the surgeon is able to pass instruments through it and search for the ball at the base of the viscus: firstly, because the parallelism of the two wounds ceases from the moment the urine escapes, when the bladder diminishes in size and draws away from the external wound; and, secondly, because both the internal and external wounds retract and close almost completely, which makes the search difficult and fruitless. Moreover, where that in the bladder can be found by *débridement* of the abdominal wound, it would be necessary to enlarge it in order to pass a forceps or tenaculum. Such a *débridement* would be dangerous, especially if inflammation had set in or if vessels of any size in the walls of the organ were cut; and, furthermore, it would facilitate the escape of urine into the cellular tissue of the pelvis.

"In addition, assuming everything to have been favourable and the ball to have been removed by this route, a piece of clothing or any other soft substance might well escape the tenaculum and the surgeon's exploration and be left in the bladder to serve as the nucleus for a fresh stone, for which the operation of cutting would be required later and the patient in this way submitted to two operations. On the other hand, a counter-opening made at the base of the bladder overcomes all the difficulties we have mentioned, and has the advantages of both facilitating the extraction of all the foreign materials and of aiding the healing of the vesical wound due to the ball.

"I therefore put forward as the simplest and most certain method, the lateral form of the operation of sub-pubic lithotomy, which I perform with a single bistoury, a catheter, and calculus forceps. This procedure has been uniformly successful and has only rarely given rise to complications. It is sometimes followed by a slight haemorrhage from the transverse perineal artery, but this is readily arrested and may be prevented by ligaturing the vessel after the operation. To obtain the utmost benefit it is necessary to perform the operation before the foreign body has set up changes in the bladder, and as the wounds of this viscus are often accompanied by serious inflammation it should be carried out either before this has set in or else delayed until it has subsided.

"I do not know of any case of the immediate performance of a lithotomy for the removal of a bullet which has only just entered the bladder, or of this being done within a very few days. There are many examples in the literature of an operation being carried out for the removal of calculi, which have subsequently been found to have a nucleus of an entire bullet or else of fragments of lead.

"A single case has been recorded in Germany describing a deliberate operation, done a long time afterwards, to remove a ball lost within the bladder, whereas the one I shall describe was carried out within a few days of the injury.

"On August 3rd, 1812, as I was passing through the wards of the large hospital at Witebsk, my attention was attracted by mournful cries of a wounded officer, M. Guenow, a lieutenant of the 2nd infantry regiment of the Line. I went at once to the patient and examined him carefully. He had a bullet wound on the inner and upper part of the right groin which was directed obliquely inwards towards the pelvis. The careful introduction of a thoracic probe enabled me to make out a gap in the pubic bone and a track which appeared to lead towards the bladder, which was certainly wounded since the external wound, although surrounded with a blackish crust, was leaking a blood-stained urinous fluid and the wounded man was suffering continuous very acute pain in the bladder region with a constant desire to micturate. The urine was mixed with blood and passing intermittently in small jets, which caused him to cry out with pain. His pulse was nervous, and fever and thirst were beginning to develop, though his face was still pale his voice was hoarse and broken. Not having been able to sleep since he was wounded the officer was in a condition of extreme and distressing anxiety. Whenever he moved onto either side he said that he felt as if a ball were rolling about inside him.

"He told me that all this was the result of a bullet he had received at the battle of Witebsk on July 30th, 1812, at a range of about 70 paces, and that the ball had not come out. From these details I concluded that it had been arrested in the bladder and to make sure of this I passed a sound. I had some difficulty in locating the foreign body, but was just able to make out an indefinite and barely perceptible impulse from the instrument.

"Before undertaking the operation of lithotomy, which I looked upon as urgent and unavoidable, I thought it well to take advantage of the wisdom of a number of my confrères whom I assembled on the following morning, August 4th; amongst them my friend Dr. Ribes. The necessity for the operation was recognized and it was decided that it should be performed forthwith. Everything being in train it was completed in less than two minutes and the ball shewn to the patient (I have since placed it in the museum of the medical school). A small piece of encrusted bone was also found. One side of the ball was covered by a layer of blood and the other with earthy matter, an envelope which would have made the injection of quicksilver, proposed by one of the consultants, useless. The extraction was followed by the removal of a small sequestrum, a piece of cloth, and several dark blood clots. I gave two emollient injections into the bladder and applied a fine perforated linen dressing to the wound, with compresses and a T-bandage. The patient was placed in a suitable posture and an appropriate regimen prescribed. Except for a slight haemorrhage the same day, which I had no difficulty in arresting, there were no complications. Some fever appeared on the third day, after which the suppuration became established; the wound became clean a few days later and at the end of seven days the urine began to come *via* the urethra. The wound healed without delay and twenty-two days after the operation M. Guenow left hospital perfectly well to rejoin his regiment; from whence he wrote to me at Moscow to thank me and to ask me to solicit for him the decoration of the Legion of Honour, which he has since received."

Surgery of the Abdomen

In his Egyptian Campaign Larrey narrated a curious case which may be the earliest recorded example of umbilical endometriosis.

"A certain Pierre Bayard, a corporal in the 18th demi-brigade, suffered a periodical discharge from the umbilicus of about a litre of blood. These haemorrhages were preceded by symptoms of swelling and tension and were followed by a return to his normal health. The umbilicus had a natural appearance with no solution of continuity. At the approach of the bloody flux the umbilical tubercle swelled and took on a bluish colour, then opened and allowed the escape of a large quantity of blackish oily blood which continued to trickle for some forty-eight hours. The patient's abdomen was always rather blown up and his liver hard and engorged. There is no doubt that this discharge of blood came from the umbilical vein which had retained its calibre, which is most unusual."

*   *   *   *   *

The surgery of penetrating wounds of the abdomen involving the hollow viscera, was in Larrey's day one of the most impracticable branches of the Art, but in his great experience he met with a number of examples in which the outcome was fortunate and provided some encouragement for the future.

In 1799, at the assault on Cairo, he saw a soldier who had been struck by a bullet in the right side of the belly which divided a part of the ileum. "The two ends of the intestine were exposed outside the abdomen, swollen and separated from each other, the upper being turned inside out so that its retracted margin strangled the gut as the prepuce does in a paraphymosis. The passage of their contents was stopped and they accumulated above this structure.

"Although the man was in a desperate state from the nature of his wound, his weakness, and the condition of *cholera morbus* to which he had been reduced in the short time he had been left without assistance in the trenches, I did my best to remedy this singular state of affairs. I first divided the collar of the strangulated intestine with curved scissors, which reduced it to its ordinary state. I then passed a loop of thread through the parts of the mesentery which corresponded to the two ends of the intestine and I returned these as far as the opening in the abdomen, which I had carefully cleansed and debrided, and having done what I could I awaited developments. The first few days were stormy, but thereafter his troubles became less marked; those due to lack of nourishment improved and after two months care and treatment the ends of the ileum were in contact and ready to adhere. In this I aided the work of nature by the ingenious tampon devised by M. Desault, which was used at intervals for two months. The soldier left hospital perfectly cured.

"In a number of instances the sigmoid part of the colon has been wounded and the wounds have healed without faecal fistulae. We had three such cases at the siege of Acre and two at that of Cairo. I was careful to debride the entry and exit wounds made by the bullet. We made much use of linseed lotions and soothing drinks for these patients: their diet was restricted and the utmost rest enjoined."

At Königsberg, after the armistice of Tilsit, Larrey was shewn a small knife which a Prussian farmer had swallowed in 1613. The serious effects had caused a Polish surgeon—one Dr. Gruger—to perform the operation of gastrotomy, which the peasant survived for ten years. He goes on to say: "there is no written record of an operation performed on the viscus for the extraction of a

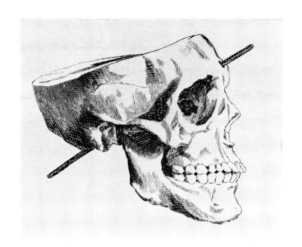

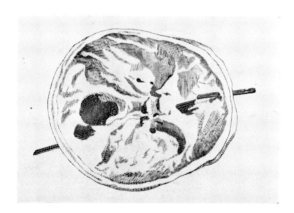

FIG. 29. Ramrod penetrating skull.

[*To face p.* 266

RELATION MÉDICALE

DE

CAMPAGNES ET VOYAGES,

DE 1815 A 1840;

SUIVIE

DE NOTICES SUR LES FRACTURES DES MEMBRES PELVIENS, SUR
LA CONSTITUTION PHYSIQUE DES ARABES, ET D'UNE STATISTIQUE
CHIRURGICALE DES OFFICIERS-GÉNÉRAUX BLESSÉS DANS LES
COMBATS ET PANSÉS SUR LES CHAMPS DE BATAILLE.

Par M. le Baron LARREY,

Membre de l'Institut de France, de l'Académie royale de Médecine, du Conseil de Santé
des Armées, Commandeur de l'ordre royal de la Légion-d'Honneur, etc., etc....

AVEC PLANCHES.

PARIS,

J.-B. BAILLIÈRE,

LIBRAIRE DE L'ACADÉMIE ROYALE DE MÉDECINE,
Rue de l'École-de-Médecine, n° 17.

LONDRES, MÊME MAISON, 219 REGENT STREET.

1841.

FIG. 30. Title page to Larrey's *Campagnes et Voyages.*

FIG. 31. Sackville Street later O'Connell Street, Dublin, in the early 19th century. (By the courtesy of the National Gallery of Ireland from a water-colour by Michael Angelo Hayes 1820–1877.)

Fig. 34. Stark's Lunatic Asylum in Glasgow. (By the kindness of Mr. A. G. Lockhead, A.R.I.B.A.)

FIG. 35. Delpech's lithograph of Larrey.

FIG. 36. Larrey's Monument at Val-de-Grâce.
(Photograph by Mrs. R. W. Spence Brown).

foreign body lodged in it and causing serious symptoms. But I recall that when I was a pupil of M. Frizac, professor at the College of Toulouse and one of the most able surgeons of the town, I saw him, in the case of a canal porter, make an incision in the epigastrium in the line of the *linea alba*, by means of which he was able to feel the point of a blade which had already perforated the walls of the stomach. He grasped this in strong forceps, and enlarging the opening with a curved bistoury, he forthwith pulled out a knife which was about 6 centimetres long. He then inserted two stitches in the lips of the incision into the viscus and a retaining suture in the abdominal wound. The patient recovered. M. Frizac extracted the threads, which were of different colours, by pulling them in opposite directions, and by the fifth day the opening had healed, no doubt by its adhesion to the peritoneum.

"I have evidence that wounds of the stomach will heal very well, even without suturing. In proof of this I shall report very briefly an observation on a guardsman who received a large wound near the cardiac end of this viscus, from the point of an extremely sharp sabre which entered his chest between the seventh and eighth ribs, wounding a small portion of the lung, incising the diaphragm, and penetrating the adjacent part of the fundus of the stomach. The local pain, the vomiting of blood, the passage of swallowed fluids through the wound, and finally its direction and depth left us in no doubt that the stomach had been opened. For the first few days the patient was extremely ill and on several occasions on the brink of the grave; nevertheless, by the help of refreshing potions, local and general bleeding, prolonged fasting, emollient clysters, and by keeping him constantly on his right side, the wound united and he left hospital to join the corps of Veterans of the Guard. He was left with a hernia of the lung beneath the scar, which was controlled with some difficulty by means of a specially contrived bandage."

All Larrey's operative interventions in the abdomen were not so successful, and after the Wagram campaign he recorded the case of a grenadier who received a sabre blow during a duel (duelling was not infrequent in the Imperial armies) which penetrated the abdomen near to the umbilicus and allowed the escape of a fairly large loop of the small intestine. The man was seen some seven hours later in a state of collapse and on debriding the wound Larrey found that there were also wounds in the mesenteric border of the gut. These he sutured and returned the intestine to the abdomen. The patient died seven days later and at post-mortem there was peritonitis and a considerable collection of blood in the peritoneal cavity from a wound in the superior mesenteric artery. Larrey, however, noted that the extruded segment of bowel had recovered, and that the damaged parts and the mesentery had become stuck together by adhesions: "a very remarkable circumstance which argues in favour of suture for wounds dividing the viscera . . . this observation may encourage surgeons to suture, with proper precautions, wounds in the intestines.

"When we are called upon to perform this operation at the time of infliction of the wound we need to use very fine, round, slightly curved, needles. These cannot cut the intestinal arterioles, and since they merely separate the fibres of the wall there is no vacant space formed and the intestinal contents cannot escape through the wound they make, as happens with the small wounds made by needles with a cutting edge."

Larrey paid a good deal of attention to herniation of the omentum through abdominal wounds; a phenomenon he must have been very familiar with. If seen before strangulation and swelling had occurred he replaced the protruded omentum, but otherwise advocated leaving the matter to nature, with the sole precaution of enveloping the herniated portion in lint impregnated with saffronated cerat, to prevent adhesion to the wound in the parieties and to give protection from contact with the air and injury from the outside.

"If the portion of omentum is strangulated by the small size of the wound which has given it passage, this must be debrided sufficiently to allow it ample space to return, when nature causes it to retract within its natural habitat. These initial steps being taken the patient is placed in a favourable position which should be maintained throughout the treatment.

"The first changes seen in an epiploic hernia devoid of a sac are an almost sudden development of swelling and turgesence of all its parts and an increase in thickness, so that in a few days it becomes dense, red, rugose and very tender. These changes gradually increase for three days, after which the tumour remains stationary until the fifteenth day. At this time it begins to diminish; the tenderness and rugosity disappear by degrees and it may be seen to shrink from the periphery towards the centre: the angles of the wound become exposed and in the absence of any foreign part between them its edges continue to heal. The rate of the further reduction depends upon the situation of the wounds and the age and constitution of the patient.

"When the wound is situated below the umbilicus the membrane returns more easily, since being at some distance from its attachments nature exercises greater traction which favours its reduction. . . ."

"I shall indicate the procedure to be followed in cases in which the herniated omentum becomes gangrenous.

"Writers advise the excision of the tumour, after first ligating its pedicle, or alternatively the separate ligation of the arteries, should they bleed after such excision. By this operation they seek by extirpating the whole of the gangrenous part to prevent the spread of contagion into the abdomen and to avoid haemorrhage into this cavity.

"Is the gangrene limited to the part of the omentum outside the abdominal cavity, or does it extend to the viscera within? In the first case it is possible to cut away the superfluous gangrenous part with curved scissors without touching the living part, thus avoiding dividing arterial branches in which blood is still circulating. The temporary adhesive inflammation which occurs between the omentum and the edges of the wound arrests the spread of the gangrene: the portion of the eschar which remains in due course sloughs, the healthy pedicle is quickly retracted spontaneously, and the patient is saved. In the case in which gangrene has already extended to the viscera in the abdominal cavity (and the signs of this are unequivocal) there is nothing that can be done; we are forced to leave the patient to nature, without of course discontinuing in the least the remedies which may assist her beneficent designs.

"Except in the above circumstances one should in no case cut off or ligate the piece of extruded omentum; for in spite of the precautions which may be taken to tie the vessels *separately* after excising the tumour, secondary haemorrhages may occur which will endanger the patient. *Total* ligature of the healthy part of the omentum is generally followed by deep and violent irritation, accompanied by inflammation, abscess, and often by gangrene and death. I have seen many examples of this. . . ."

"To return to the treatment of wounds of this sort. After all the indications mentioned above have been fulfilled, and assuming that the omentum is healthy, it should be gently and gradually encouraged as far as is possible to return to the abdomen, by wrapping the extruded part in fine fenestrated linen impregnated with cerat and soaked in hot wine, whilst waiting for nature to cause the reduction and assisting her work by methodical compression of the tumour and, if this be too slow, by applying the powerful excitation of the actual cautery, if necessary repeated on several occasions. This application is very painful, which proves that sensation develops in these adipose membranes particularly if they are exposed to the air. We have noted this several times.

"The case which follows will serve to confirm my statement on the spontaneous reduction of this membrane.

"A young officer, M. de L . . ., was brought to the Gros-Caillou Hospital in August, 1815, in an almost dying state, having received a thrust from a steel weapon in the abdomen which was followed by haemorrhage, extrusion of the omentum and injury to the stomach. The medical officer of the Guard applied a temporary dressing and vainly tried to rouse the wounded man from the dangerous state of collapse he had lapsed into shortly after receiving the blow. It was the latter condition which caused the surgeon to send for me in the middle of the night. After removing the dressing I found a wound about an inch and a half long in the middle of the lower part of the right hypochondrium and about two fingers' breadth from the rib cartilages with herniation of a considerable amount of omentum and its strangulation between the coverings of the muscles and an irregular contracted opening at the outer edge of the rectus sheath on this side. His general state, apart from the wound, was as follows: his pulse was feeble and his extremities cold; he repeatedly vomited bloodstained bilious material, his anxiety was extreme, he had hiccough, and was quite incapable of speech and in great distress: everything, in fact, pointed to his early death.

"This desperate condition forced us to postpone the necessary operation until the next day. During the night he was so gravely ill that he was expected to die at any moment. However, by the time of my morning visit he had regained some warmth and his pulse was a little better, though the local pain had increased and the hiccough and bloodstained vomit persisted. It was easy to realize the cause of these two symptoms: to remedy them I first enlarged the skin wound, without touching the omentum, and then debrided the opening in the aponeurosis I have mentioned. When the omentum was freed the serious symptoms which were the result of its strangulation disappeared almost at once. The operation also allowed the escape of a large quantity of effused blood from the abdominal cavity. (When the abdominal vessels severed by a weapon are not large the effused blood collects in their vicinity and forms a pocket, shut off by masses of lymph which develop all around and by the adhesions which form between the peritoneum and the loops of the intestines, or the folds of the omentum.) As far as I could judge from the depth and direction of the wound and the symptoms, I thought that the weapon had wounded the anterior part of the lesser curvature of the stomach, and this seemed the more likely since the first stools, which were preceded by colic and burning pain internally, were admixed with considerable quantities of black blood clot.

"The operation over, I wrapped the piece of omentum which was outside the wound (and which was as big as a large apple) in perforated linen soaked in hot wine. I put the patient into a favourable position and prescribed acidulated sweet mucilaginous drinks, emollient clysters, oily embrocations to the abdomen, and a low diet. The symptoms gradually diminished, all the functions were re-established by degrees and the patient was out of danger from the fifth day onwards.

"After the first twenty-four hours the herniated piece of omentum had become as large as a fist, forming a red mammilated and sensitive tumour. The same careful treatment and dressings were continued. Gradually, as he became better and better and recovered his strength, the omentum returned little by little and finally altogether. The wound through which it had been extruded healed step by step with its return to the abdominal cavity, and the officer was perfectly cured forty-five days after his admission to the Guards' Hospital. His only inconvenience is that he has to wear a supporting bandage to prevent a new hernia of the omentum or intestine, but I think that he will eventually be able to dispense with this. In fact I learnt some months later that he had discontinued its use and enjoyed perfect health."

Finally, Larrey gives us a case of a grave abdominal wound involving a nice problem in diagnosis.

"Etienne Belloc, aged seventeen years, a light infantryman of the Guard, received on April 1st, 1811, a sabre wound in the abdomen at a distance of about two fingers breadth above the umbilicus and to the right of the linea alba. He was brought to hospital and a simple retaining dressing was applied by the surgeon on duty. At my visit the next day I examined the wound from which a portion of omentum protruded. The right rectus muscle and its sheath were cut completely through and the blade appeared to have penetrated between the greater curvature of the stomach and the transverse colon, in a horizontal direction and to some depth.

"The patient was pale as death: he was in severe distress, with nausea and a continuous desire to vomit, hiccough, great thirst, acute pain at the bottom of the wound and extreme anxiety; his pulse was small and miserable, his extremities cold and his voice weak: in fact it seemed to us that the young man had only a short time to live. Nevertheless, I did my best for him. By displacing the omentum and inserting a finger into the wound I at once made out that the weapon had passed between the stomach and the large intestine, but I could not decide how far it had gone. I left the herniated piece of omentum, which had swelled out over the wound, outside and after wrapping it around with a piece of fine linen dipped in hot wine I put on a suitable dressing and applied some camphorated camomile oil embrocations to the abdomen, which I had covered with very hot flannel. I prescribed cooling mucilaginous drinks, emollient clysters, fasting, a suitable posture and absolute rest. The patient gained but little benefit from these measures. His prostration remained the same, his pulse small and hard, his anxiety, nausea and depression unchanged. He did not get a moment's sleep. During the second or third night vomiting came on, accompanied by violent retching and followed by cold sweats and alarming syncopal attacks: the vomitus was at first of stomach contents, but later of bilious matter mixed with some clots of dark blood. On the fourth day the bilious vomit was succeeded by thick dark blood; this was so copious that the chamber pot was filled in a few minutes. On the fifth day he had an evacuation of similar material by the bowels, which was preceded by violent colic and acute pain in the path of the wound. His abdomen, however, remained lax and shewed no sign of effusion. On the night of the 6th, following upon these evacuations, an alarming attack of fainting occurred which led Belloc's comrades to believe him to be dead. Coming to the hospital very early for my visit I found the unfortunate youth with the sheet drawn over his face and hardly able to open his eyes: he was pulseless and as cold as marble. I urgently endeavoured to make him swallow a small quantity of hot sweetened wine, and warmed him by rubbing him with very hot camphorated camomile oil and wrapping him in flannel. After a very short time he came out of this state of collapse and slowly regained his senses. The colicky pains disappeared and from this moment except for extreme weakness he felt better. I prescribed a mucilaginous tisane to which I added enough nitric alcohol to make it pleasantly acid, syrup of marshmallow and orange flower water, as well as emollient clysters and the continued use of camphorated oil embrocations to the abdomen. His vomiting ceased altogether but on the 9th the bloody stools reappeared and continued until the 12th April when they finally ceased, though the patient for a long time had a painful area in the pit of the abdomen opposite to the wound. His strength returned by degrees and after the sixteenth day I considered him out of danger. We were now able to give him a light diet; his wound healed with simple dressings and he was cured by about the thirty-fifth day. His convalescence was long and tedious.

"There was a very strange occurrence during the healing of the wound: the omentum, which to begin with formed a swelling outside the wound of the size of a pippin, gradually shrank and returned spontaneously to the abdominal cavity without contracting any adhesion with the edges of the wound which reunited as the membrane retracted from between them. I had seen this in other circumstances but had never had the opportunity of studying its spontaneous occurrence as I had in this patient. The phenomenon and the situation of the wound justify the teaching of M. Sabatier, who recommends leaving the omentum outside of wounds which are below the umbilicus. In such a case we see nature advantageously seconding our Art. What is the explanation of such a phenomenon? No doubt the vessels of the two parts do not meet with each other or establish adhesion or anastamoses although they may have a very similar structure and distribution. Likewise, in an old healed stump the vessels of a severed muscle, far from growing out into the cicatrix and joining with those of the skin and subcutaneous tissue, turn back upon themselves and heal the end of the muscle separately; this only becomes joined to the rest of the cicatrix of the stump by the vessels of the subcutaneous tissue which pass into it. No doubt the same holds for omentum which is left in an abdominal wound. After passing through the stages of inflammation and deturgescence its special vital forces cause the return of the displaced portion by a retrograde contraction and its vessels, having no sympathy with those of the skin or of the muscles of the abdomen, do not contract any adhesion with such alien parts and return to their normal situation.

"Let us now consider what part of the alimentary canal was damaged in this case. It could not be the stomach, since the patient only vomited blood a long time after he had first brought up the organ's fluid contents and bilious material, and further, the point of the weapon had passed below its greater curvature. Nor could any part of the small intestine, lying free in the abdominal cavity, have been wounded, since were this so the blood would have flowed freely and without the least resistance into the peritoneal sac, and would not have filled the intestinal tube but would have caused an abdominal effusion with all its characteristic signs; in fact there were none of these. Similarly, I do not think that any part of the large intestine could have been wounded, for if so there would have been blood in the patient's first stools which was not the case. Everything makes me believe that the second curve of the duodenum was wounded, where it is buried in the mesocolon. It seems that the point of the weapon pierced both the serous membrane and intestine, which were at full stretch when Belloc was actively defending himself. His sudden fall altered the relationship of the parts so that the opening into the gut was no longer opposite to that in the mesocolon: an adhesion no doubt quickly formed between the two serous parts and the blood from the arterioles of the duodenum was effused into its lumen where it remained for several days. The irritation due to the presence of this fluid caused both the constant local pain and the early sympathetic vomiting of the stomach's contents—a part of the blood was then expelled in the vomit and the rest passed by the bowel. Considering the direction and depth of the wound and the various symptoms which accompanied it, the reader will doubtless agree with me that this is the only part of the intestine which could have been wounded."

*   *   *   *   *

In 1821, in his *Récueil de Mémoires de Chirurgie*,[15] Larrey returns to the treatment of intestinal wounds and here we learn of his more matured opinions.

Wounds from the cold steel, he says, have a worse prognosis than gunshot wounds, which in a number of cases are recovered from. This is due to "the constriction of the wounded intestine and the inflammatory engorgement of the adjacent parts which may seal off the abdominal general cavity. In consequence the gut contents may pass to the exterior by way of the wound or accumulate in the space sealed off by the adhesions." He therefore avoided seeking the damaged gut to suture it to the abdominal wound, lest this should cause serious complications such as haemorrhage and soiling of the peritoneal cavity. The adhesions should be preserved and a simple dressing applied. A faecal fistula results which increases until the abdominal wound is free of sloughs, when healing may be encouraged by compressing the edges together by bandages, etc., the intestinal wound being already healed.

In wounds from *armes blanches* one of two procedures is indicated. The one— the easier and the best—is to fix the damaged part of the intestine to the bottom of the wound in the parieties, in order to avoid the spilling of its contents into the abdominal cavity and to give time for nature to isolate the lesion (as in the gunshot wounds just mentioned).

The second, is to bring into contact or unite the lips of such wounds immediately, by simple suture or invagination assisted and maintained by loops of thread passed through both ends of the divided intestine and sometimes with internal supports. He quotes the approval of John Bell[16] for this method of treating intestinal lesions with loss of substance and also simple wounds. Littré's[17] procedure for intestinal wounds is undoubtedly the least likely to provoke the irritation of the damaged parts but has the disadvantage of prolonging the malady and producing an artificial anus for a certain length of time. Even so it may happen that in spite of every precaution the bowel may slip back into the peritoneal cavity and allow a fatal discharge of faeces, or become herniated and strangulated with all the accompanying complications.

"All things considered I am led to believe that the method of the ancients, i.e. suture, is preferable, provided that it is done at once. It only remains to indicate the best way of doing this and the treatment to be used to assist it and minimize the inflammation which usually accompanies such a procedure.

"In suturing the intestine we must have in view:
1. To bring the edges into their exact relationship and to maintain this.
2. To include as little as possible of the intestinal tube in the sutures, in order not to diminish the lumen too much and thereby obstruct the passage of its contents.

[15] *Récueil de Mémoires de Chirurgie* (1821). Translated by John Revere, Baltimore, 1823.
[16] John Bell (1769–1820). *The Principles of Surgery.* Edinburgh, 1801.
[17] Alexis Littré (1658–1726). Suggested colostomy in intestinal obstruction.

3. The best method of stitching is over and over; for whatever writers may say the union of intestinal wounds, like that of other tissues, is by the mutual adhesion of their own vessels, and will be all the easier if the divided parts are brought into exact contact and kept there by sutures.

"The experiments on living animals mentioned in the surgical lectures I gave in Toulon and at Val-de-Grâce, which are easy to repeat, have shown me the truth of the views I have just expressed upon wounds of the intestines. . . . I prefer the upholsterer's stitch (*suture de pelletier*) to the through stitch (*à point passé*) recommended by some writers, which includes too much of the intestine and encourages undue swelling and eversion of the edges of the wound . . . mutual adhesion can only take place by the lateral portions of the lips of the wounds." This seems to show that Larrey appreciated the fundamental importance of peritoneal adhesion, which is further suggested by the remark that "adhesions may occur at the edges of the intestinal wounds, but these unnatural adhesions are only temporary and disappear in the course of time, as do the adhesions about an enterostomy which has been closed."

Larrey goes on to tell of a case of successful intestinal suture by a country practitioner in the most unlikely circumstances. A fusilier of the sixth regiment of the Guard, Jolin by name, fell by accident upon the point of his sabre. The village doctor, who was the first to see him, found a wound in the right side of the abdomen about one and a quarter inches in length, through which protruded a part of the ileum which was wounded and discharging its contents. The doctor obtained a needle and some black thread from a woman, and with this he stitched the intestinal wound and thereafter returned the bowel to the abdomen. The patient was dressed and sent to the Guard's hospital at Paris. On his arrival a loop of small intestine was again protruding which the surgeon on duty returned without much difficulty. The next day the patient was seen by Larrey who debrided the external wound, and noticing in its depths some adherent coils of intestine within the peritoneal cavity left well alone, even though the patient's symptoms at the moment suggested strangulation, limiting himself to external applications, cupping, mild purgatives, enemata, etc. Despite an attack of suppurative parotitis the patient progressed favourably. A piece of black knotted thread, three inches long, was discharged from the wound, and he left hospital at the end of ten weeks and was later shewn to the Faculty.

*   *   *   *   *

Chapter 28

Departure for Ireland. Dublin hospitals. Excision of the lower jaw. The Foundling Hospital. Political situation in Ireland and suggestions for its amelioration.

Larrey obtained three months leave from the Ministry of War for this visit, and took with him his son Hippolyte, then a youth of eighteen, believing that the experience would be of great educational value to the latter. He rather naïvely mentions that the boy had taken a course in English at college and would be able to put this to profit. In the event Hippolyte was no great success as an interpreter, and between them they made some amusing if trivial mistakes and on occasions were certainly misled; but Larrey's pertinacity and great reputation which appear to have preceded him served them well.

They left Paris on August 18th, 1826, by diligence and reached Havre at dawn three days later. This port of departure was chosen as they proposed to go first to Ireland and thence to Scotland, returning through the Midlands to London and southern England. The voyage from Havre to Portsmouth took fifteen hours in the paddle steamer *Camille* and was pretty rough, so that Hippolyte was violently sick as were most of the other passengers. Of Portsmouth Larrey says: "We visited the hospitals, the port and the vessels in the harbour or under construction in the yards; there being more than fifty of these, including both ships of the line and frigates. We were able to see the principal battleships in the greatest detail. The flagship, the only one ready to put to sea, particularly interested us since Nelson had commanded it. On this ship the famous sailor was killed at Trafalgar and since that time it has been called the *Victory*. She is a three-decker of very modern construction. The richness and admirable internal arrangements of this vessel are unequalled, and in every way she is excellently found and ordered. We were first shewn round the batteries and the parts of the ship where they are placed. We saw the place where Admiral Nelson died, after uttering the words, which are engraved in gold on the ship's quarter-deck: 'England expects that every man will do his duty today.'

"We were very agreeably surprised by their lighting up the holds to shew us the workshops and tools of the chief artificers, which we found most interesting. The ship's surgeon shewed the utmost interest and unusual kindness in explaining everything which aroused our curiosity. The Royal Naval Hospital at Portsmouth is notable for its fine construction, splendid architecture, well-arranged wards and scrupulous cleanliness, as well as for the excellence of its medical and administrative services and of whatever concerns the treatment of the patients."

From Portsmouth they travelled to Southampton—"a charming small town near the mouth of the river of the same name"—by diligence. The English diligences and horses never failed to arouse Larrey's admiration. He thought the roads excellent and the speed of the vehicles almost alarming; in fact he mentions that on his journey from Chester to Bangor a young lady of their company was so upset by this excessive speed that she alighted at a wayside cottage, although only a short distance from the posting station! He was told at Doncaster that the best horses could cover more than ten miles an hour and were worth as much as £500–£600 apiece. However, his enthusiasm was slightly tempered by the fact that the diligences were apt to depart punctually at the published time, leaving the tardy passenger behind lamenting the extra expense. On one occasion he himself narrowly escaped this vexation!

"From Southampton we went to Bath, one of the prettiest towns in England. In autumn it is a rendezvous of wealthy people who go there principally for its distractions and amusements, the mineral waters being merely an excuse for this social reunion. . . . Elegant hand-chairs on three wheels, like small tilburys, are used by ladies who have no carriage; a single man can push them at a good speed without difficulty. These three-wheelers are well sprung and have the advantage of being able to go through the narrowest streets. All of them are of the same size and the men who push them wear a similar livery."

After visiting Bristol and Gloucester they made a detour to Birmingham. None of these towns made any great impression, but Larrey was very critical of the English custom of associating cemeteries with churches, which he thought harmful to the health of the townspeople. They returned through Shrewsbury (which he calls Salisbury) and took the road through the Welsh hills to Bangor. He was full of admiration for Telford's splended roadmaking, and for his great bridge across the Menai Strait which had just been completed; this he declared to be one of the wonders of the world. He compared it with the suspension bridge over the Seine, then on the point of completion, and which he declared in a letter to his family would collapse with the first load of stone driven across it: a prophesy that came true!

They left for Dublin on August 28th, from Holyhead which was considered a safer route than that from Liverpool, and after twelve hours at sea landed at Howth.

"At daybreak the next day we set out to visit this beautiful capital. Most of the streets are perfectly straight, with splendid granite houses, five to seven stories high, of similar construction and noble and elegant architecture.

"The largest street is Royal Street[1] which has a granite column in its

---

[1] Sackville Street 1816, now named O'Connell Street. Larrey may have been confused by the Royal Arcade, which was later replaced by the old General Post Office. Nelson's figure was in stone, not bronze: it was blown up by the Irish in 1966. The other wide street was Westmorland Street and the square College Green. The "gentleman's mansion" may have been the house of the Provost of Trinity College.

centre, an imitation of Napoleon's bronze column in Paris (and of about the same size), which carries the bronze statue of Admiral Nelson.[2] This street leads to the principal bridge over the river Liffey, which flows through the city from east to west. After crossing this very large and beautiful bridge you enter another wide street which soon terminates in a large square adorned on its sides by four magnificent buildings: the University College, the Post Office, the Bank and a gentleman's mansion (Fig. 31).

"We were a little embarrassed about paying visits to the hospitals and famous buildings, as we had no letters of introduction, but by chance we met with one of the young doctors of the university, Dr. West, who had attended my surgical lectures in Paris, and with great readiness and generosity he undertook to satisfy our wishes. From that day we were visited by the leading physicians and surgeons of Dublin whom the young doctor had apprised of our arrival. Nothing could equal the kindness and attention which these estimable Irish colleagues shewed us during our short stay. Since my chief object was to visit the hospitals some of the doctors shewed me round them, whilst certain of their pupils took my son to the museum of natural history and the art collections.

"Steevens' Hospital, or the Hôtel Dieu, was the first we visited. It is a large building, solidly and regularly built, with all the resources necessary in such an establishment. The wards are well lit and sufficiently spacious and airy. All the beds are of iron, as is the custom throughout England.[3] The food is good and nourishing, and the place clean and tidy.

"The practice of internal medicine or therapeutics is based on Cullen. Surgery appeared to me no different from that in the rest of the British Isles. MM. Carmichael and Cusack[4] shewed me a number of patients on whom they had operated for aneurysm of the femoral artery, and a case of the extirpation of a considerable part of the lower jaw for osteosarcoma. We shall discuss later the English operation for aneurysm and the method used to reduce fractures of limbs.

[2] I obtained from my son, who wrote from "somewhere over France": "It seems the Irish have short memories and want to forget about pillars and things. At 01.30 hours on 8th March 1966 a dull explosion rocked the city. A taxi driver on O'Connell bridge thought a gas main had blown up as O'Connell Street was filled with dust. He ran to telephone the good news and changed his sentence in mid-word to 'Bejezus it's gone!' The 'Column' as it was always known, or 'pillar', had been lopped off 2/3rds of the way up. The job was done by suspending a bracelet of small explosive charges round the column and blowing it by remote control, causing a tangential crack and dropping the column into the street with no damage to surrounding property. Nobody has ever been charged with the offence though it was rumoured that the job was done by a French mining engineer. It was certainly very neat. The army then blew up the stump, which I witnessed from Talbot Street at 03.00 three days later, causing much damage to windows and neatly removing the corner of the G.P.O. roof!"

[3] Larrey always speaks of England for all parts of the United Kingdom.

[4] Richard Carmichael (1776–1849), surgeon to the House of Industry Hospitals and three times President of the Royal College of Surgeons in Ireland, was the first Irish Corresponding Member of the French Academy. He was drowned whilst riding across the sands near Howth at low tide.

James William Cusack (1788–1861), also three times President of the R.C.S.I., was surgeon to Steevens' Hospital and later Regius Professor at Trinity College Dublin.

"After the hospital we saw the lunatic asylum,[5] which is conveniently placed at the south of the town behind the former. It is a square building of three stories, capable of holding two hundred and fifty inmates. It is built of granite adorned by Corinthian columns, and is surrounded by spacious courts and a large garden which may be used by those able to profit by it. All the rooms have boarded floors and are airy and heated by warm pipes. They are arranged in parallel rows in the two wings of the building, which is elliptical in form with a corridor on the outside sufficiently large for their service. The wards are divided into a series of rooms of adequate size and contain such furniture as is necessary for patients of this sort. It is everywhere very clean, and each room is heated in winter by hot pipes which pass beneath the floors and are regulated by valves, which the warders and servants can open or close according to the needs of the inmates. The men and women are looked after and served by persons of their own sex with exemplary attention and humanity. The physicians base their treatment on the methods of the celebrated Pinel,[6] whose bust is in the clinical conference hall. It really seems that these lunatics are cared for with gentleness and admirable philanthropy. As far as their condition permits they are employed in various types of work which bring some financial return to the institution. This constant occupation has an effect on the disease and contributes not a little to the cure of the insane. A part of the establishment is reserved for patients who are able to pay a considerable sum for their maintenance, which is applied to the benefit of the poor lunatics and the pauper families of the town from whence they come. The two classes of patients, rich and poor, are in other respects lodged and treated in the same way without distinction. It is certainly the best ordered and most perfect establishment of its kind in Europe.

"I permitted myself to make certain observations to the doctors on the treatment used for this terrible malady, about which they are truly most solicitous. For example, instead of allowing showers of cold or iced water to be let fall from a great height onto the shaved heads of lunatics who are considered curable, a painful procedure more harmful than useful and likely to lead to hypertrophy of the cranium and engorgement of the membranes of the brain (a common cause of incurability in mental aberration), from the mechanical shock and the reaction it induces in the internal organs, I advised that a bladder filled with ice should be applied to the vertex of the skull. This sedative application should be preceded

---

[5] Swift's Asylum, or St. Patrick's Hospital, founded by Dean Swift who left his money for the purpose. He wrote in his *Verses on the Death of Dean Swift* (1731):

> "He gave the little wealth he had
> To found a house for fools and mad;
> And shewed by one satyric touch
> No nation wanted it so much."

[6] Dr. J. N. P. Moore, who has written a not inconsiderable paper on "Swift's Philanthropy", tells me that he has "no knowledge of the bust having been here at any time" ... "nor in any other Dublin hospitals or colleges in the city."

by adequate blood-letting, preferably from the jugular vein or temporal artery, and applications of wet cups to the base of the skull, between the shoulders, and to the dorsal regions. After this initial indication has been fulfilled we proceed to the use of revulsives and antispasmodics. My colleagues received these suggestions gratefully and promised to make use of them.

"I was next taken to the workhouse infirmary (general hospital).[7] This is a large building where all the sufferers from chronic diseases are treated, and where old and infirm persons of both sexes are received, including the incurably mad. This hospital contains about two thousand inmates.

"There I found the supervision, although severe and continuous, was enlightened and thus the place is a model of order and seemliness. They make everything required for the feeding, clothing, and other needs of the patients and administrative staff. There are workshops for various kinds of industries which give employment to inmates capable of working.

"The surgical department is under the direction of an able and well versed man, Professor Carmichael, who told us that he had cured a large number of patients suffering from herpetiform disease, thought to be syphilitic, without the use of mercury. He used preparations of antimony and bitters internally, and lotions of a saturated solution of silver nitrate, copper oxide, or other mildly corrosive substances externally. Mr. Carmichael, however, agreed with me that for success with real syphilitic lesions he always employed mercurials, both internally and by inunction. This rational form of treatment is usual in all English hospitals.[8]

"In the wards of the chief surgeon we saw a man who had been operated upon for an aneurysm of the popliteal artery by Hunter's method. The ligature had been passed beneath the femoral artery two or three fingers' breadth below the fold of the groin. This is the procedure in all the hospitals in England for popliteal aneurysm. The reason given by the English surgeons for this high ligation is a desire to avoid including the saphenous vein, which accompanies the artery as far as this line of demarcation, fearing inflammation of the vein and its associated complications. But experience has shewn us that this fear is unfounded: we shall refer again to this operation later.

"We were also shewn a patient in whom the same surgeon had excised a large part of the lower jaw for an osteosarcoma which had invaded the

[7] The "workhouse infirmary" was the House of Industry Hospitals. The workhouse was founded in 1772 for the accommodation of "vagabonds and sturdy beggars" who were arrested and confined there. Children were taken in later. An infirmary was opened in 1774, and later expanded into the Richmond (Surgical, 1810), Hardwicke (Fever, 1803), and Whitworth (Medical—the "Chronic Hospital"—1817). After 1840, with the establishment of the South Dublin Union, these hospitals became independent and still flourish. The 2,000 inmates Larrey speaks of would be the total population, paupers and patients.

[8] Carmichael expressed his views in "*An Essay on the Venereal Diseases which have been confounded with Syphilis*" (1814). The Dublin Lock Hospital, to which he was one of five surgeons, contained at that time between two hundred and eighty and three hundred patients.

whole of the right side of the bone.[9] The opening of the man's mouth had fallen in considerably, and through the soft parts we readily felt the gap beneath the scar due to the loss of substance; but there was no sign of regeneration of the jaw-bone, which was reduced in size by the exact amount which had been taken away.

"We also saw a number of severe head wounds in persons who had been sabred in the popular risings, so common in this town as well as throughout Ireland. The treatment of these wounds did not appear to me to be either rational or to follow any special method. In one patient a large portion of the parietal bone, denuded of pericranium and freely moveable, was still partly hidden within the cranial cavity and was compressing the brain. Surely this was a case in which a trephine should have been applied, and the piece of bone removed at once and the patient put out of danger. As it was nature was exhausting herself in vain efforts to remove the foreign body.

"The Lord Mayor, having learnt of my visit, hurried incognito to the hospital in his ordinary citizen's clothes, with the intention of according me the honours customarily given to distinguished persons visiting the establishment: in fact I received the most honourable and flattering welcome from the first magistrate and the hospital doctors.

"We were next taken to the Foundling Hospital in the doctors' carriage. This is one of the finest establishments of its kind that I had as yet seen. Like the one at Moscow it is noteworthy for its regular construction, fine architecture, large size and excellent internal plan. All the wards are heated by concealed hot pipes and kept at a constant temperature of 59°F. There are some fine courtyards ornamented with fountains and a

[9] The operation at which Carmichael removed this growth is vividly described in a letter to the *Lancet* in 1825, from a disgruntled student. I quote from Widdness' book:

"On Tuesday last (August 2), hearing that the operation of removing a portion of the lower jaw, on account of an osteosarcomatous disease, was to be performed at the Richmond Surgical Hospital, I made my way, with many others, uninvited into the operation theatre of that institution. This room, though longer than any of the theatres of the London Hospitals, was nearly filled by pupils and surgeons; the former seated on the benches, the latter standing on what may be termed the stage and obstructing and mobbishly closing up its whole area. The patient was a boy about fourteen—the operator, Mr. Carmichael. The patient was placed on the lap of an able assistant, but on the first incision the boy screamed and struggled with so much violence that it required much more than the strength, applied as it was, of the many broad-shouldered gentlemen surrounding him to keep him on his seat, but as to securing his head, the more hands that attempted it the worse they succeeded. A regular confusion now ensued; the operator supplicated for light, air and room; his privileged bretheren thronged but the more intensely about him; the pupils lost altogether a sight of the patient, the operation, and even of the operator. The patient was shifted to a table, but still remained invisible; his continued screams, however, and the repeated remonstrances of Mr. Carmichael, insisting for elbow-room, assured us that the operation was still going on, but as to a glance at the *res gesta*, we might as well have been posted at the outside of the building.

"After about half an hour, a portion of the jaw had been removed and the specimen was passed around the students. They also saw the boy 'walk stoutly out of the operating room, notwithstanding his sufferings and loss of blood, without deigning to avail himself of the assistance which was proffered to him on all sides'."

garden of about four hectaires. A part of this is reserved as a recreation ground for the children and the rest is used to grow vegetables and fruit for the house. The children's refectory, containing two rows of similar sized tables covered with very white linen and set with a thousand places, had just been thrown open for the mid-day meal. One of the children read aloud from a lectern in the middle of the room throughout the meal and was listened to in perfect silence.

"The girls occupy a half of the building, which is separated from the other by partitions or high walls, but there are communicating doors for the convenience of the internal service. A number of workshops and work rooms of every kind for both the girls and boys have been built at the ends of the lateral wings of the institution, close to the garden. The dormitories of both sexes are divided up into small rooms of a dozen beds and are prettily and excellently furnished. Each room has a male or female superintendent. Both sets of children are bare headed and wear their hair *à la Franklin*. During their recreation they drill like young soldiers. We were surprised by the elegance and precision with which a thousand girls and as many boys performed these manoeuvres. The young girls, all in the same Grecian dress, lent beauty to this tableau and for a moment I imagined myself at a ballet performance at the Paris Opera.

"The total accommodation of the establishment is for about six thousand children. Almost as soon as the infants are left at the hospital, where they are received through a turnstile without a stranger being able to observe this, they are sent out to villages near the town to be cared for by suitable nurses who are known to the local authorities as good and trustworthy mothers. They rear the children as their own until they are six or seven, when they go back to the central hospital to be suitably educated, unless the nurses adopt them, which is not uncommon. When they reach the age of eighteen to twenty they are free to follow some appropriate career. If they wish to serve in the forces they are taken as recruits in the army or navy according to their choice; if they wish to follow some art or trade they are placed under contract by the hospital administration with masters in the town who are largely responsible for their pupils' future.

"The girls likewise are placed with private persons, or mistresses of good reputation who have employment to offer. Like the boys they are provided with a set of clothes when they leave the hospital, together with a sum of money proportionate to the savings they have made. The young women are permitted to stay until they are twenty-five if they have not succeeded in finding a place or in maintaining themselves by the time they are eighteen or twenty. They are generally given preference over strangers for the posts of sub-mistresses or supervisors within the establishment. In fact of all the hospitals of this kind I have seen in the European capitals, that of Dublin is the finest, the best maintained and the most wealthy; it does honour to the generosity and philanthropy of its governors.[10]

[10] Larrey was evidently grossly deceived over the Foundling Hospital. This originated in 1704 as an asylum for aged, infirm, or lunatic persons and children over six, but in 1730 it was opened for children of all ages and called the Foundling Hospital and Work-

"From this hospital we were taken by the Lord Mayor himself to the Town Hall, one of four large buildings which surround the superb and spacious square at the end of the large street we have mentioned and close to the main bridge; in it one feels as though transported to Athens.

"The first of these palaces we visited is the Lord Mayor's house, or City Hall. It is a magnificent building surrounded by a colonnade of two rows of granite columns like the others we had already seen. Its large salons are embelished with rare pictures and all kinds of valuable artistic ornaments.

"The other three buildings, on an equally grand scale and of similar architecture, comprise the University, the Bank and the palace of the Governor-General (Fig. 31).[11] The University particularly claimed our attention: it has one of the best of the English museums of National History. We saw many rare animals, including the fossil skeleton of an unknown species of deer (the Irish Elk) of an extraordinary size discovered in a bog in the north of Ireland.[12] It is comparable in size with an elephant and is perfectly preserved and very well articulated. We also saw an enormous stuffed giraffe, much surpassing in size Levaillant's in the Paris museum. In the anatomical museum we saw some beautiful injections of the lymphatic and capillary vessels of internal organs, and some very curious pathological specimens, especially of bones. Amongst these was a growth consisting of a mass of bony spicules, set in sheaves like needles, which developed in the skull of an adult man and had caused him the most acute and terrible pain. The spicules had originated on the inner surface of the squamous portion of the temporal and right parietal bones, and were directed towards the brain which they penetrated to a depth of a centimetre and a half. A small bundle of these spines had made its way out through the squamous part of the temporal bone and had perforated the fibres of the temporal muscle, so as to produce a considerable swelling beneath the skin in this region. This singular lesion explains the pain which the unfortunate patient suffered throughout his illness, which was acknowledged to be caused by syphilis.[13] There were many other noteworthy specimens but time does not allow me to speak of them.

---

house. In 1774 the workhouse activities were transferred to the House of Industry and only children accommodated. Admissions averaged some 2,000 a year between 1790 and 1795 and the mortality was appalling. In the March quarter of 1795, 540 children were received of whom 440 died. A committee of enquiry of the Irish House of Commons in 1797 shewed dreadful conditions of dirt, overcrowding and deficient diet. During the next thirty years, in spite of "reforms," out of 52,120 children admitted 41,202 were known to have died, about a half of them "at nurse." The English House of Commons held an enquiry in 1829, and closed the Hospital. In 1826, the year of Larrey's visit, there were 1,307 children in the House and 5,200 at nurse in the country, so that his figure of 6,000 must have included the latter. The dining hall would accommodate 1,000. Larrey was probably similarly misled about certain other of the Dublin institutions he writes of. Nevertheless, he shews a remarkably shrewd penetration when it comes to assessing the state of the country generally and of the people.

[11] Dublin Castle, close beside the City Hall.

[12] This skeleton is in the museum of the Royal College of Surgeons in Ireland.

[13] More probably it was an osteosarcoma.

"We finished our visit to the hospitals with the Maternity. This is one of the finest establishments of its kind I have seen in Europe. A rotunda, encircled and sustained by Corinthian columns of grey marble, is close to the hospital, and here frequent concerts and balls are held and yield considerable profits for the benefit of the infants. Any poor woman or girl who is pregnant is admitted to this institution to be confined in privacy and to escape scandal. They are taken in under any name they wish to use and receive all the treatment and care their condition requires. Should they be unable to feed their children the best nurses in the surrounding country are obtained. When the mothers cannot provide for the children's upbringing they are sent to the Foundling Hospital, where they receive physical and intellectual education up to the age I have mentioned."

*   *   *   *   *

"In spite of the many charitable and philanthropic institutions in Dublin one is struck and greatly afflicted by the large number of poor people of both sexes and all ages to be seen in the streets of this splendid and magnificent city, and in fact throughout Ireland. It is a remarkable contrast to see at all seasons so many individuals, scantily covered by blackened tattered rags, and with heads and feet bare, searching the corners of the streets like animals for decaying remains of food, and often hustled by the carriages of the rich who in this respect shew no consideration for these unfortunates. It happened that during our brief stay in Dublin typhus, which was endemic, made great inroads amongst the common people and although care was taken to remove them as soon as they fell ill to special hospitals for this disease, these were insufficient and it became necessary to put up tents in the large courtyard of one of them,[14] beneath which camp beds were placed, or else bed frames raised about eighty centimetres above the earth. These were provided with palliasses, mattresses and other necessary bed furnishings. Women of the people, who were devoted to their service, acted as nurses under the direction and supervision of Sisters of Charity. Doctors, inspired by zeal and courage, were prodigal of their skilful assistance to these unfortunate persons, amongst whom were many shewing anthrax-like pustules or carbuncles reminiscent of those of plague such as we saw in Egypt.

"I did not wish my son to accompany me on my visit to this hospital, and I doubt if anyone less habituated than I to the morbid effluvia and the heart-rending sights could have made this with impunity. In point of fact the Irish doctors assured me that in their opinion the disease is contagious when accompanied by the kind of eruptions I have mentioned and they therefore took care to isolate the patients displaying this pernicious symptom.

"The treatment of the disease appeared to be rational and carried out

[14] This was the Meath Hospital, associated with the names of Graves and William Stokes. The latter, in his *Lectures on Fevers* (1874), describes how in the typhus epidemic of 1826–28 sheds and tents were erected in the hospital grounds, their floors covered with hay, on which the patients who arrived in cartloads were "spilled out."

with great discernment, but the mortality was considerable. A number of applications of wet cups to the neck and dorsal regions, aetherated theriac wine, and various preparations of quinine and sweet lemonade formed its basis. I advised the moxa, as a very effective method of treatment in such diseases, and applied it in their presence to a number of patients. I have since learned that great benefit resulted from the application of this local revulsive to the base of the skull and to the epigastrium.

"In one of the hospitals in the centre of the town[15] we saw a number of individuals who had been wounded in the risings which their state of profound misery had provoked. One of these, a young man of seventeen, had a remarkable head wound from a dragoon's sabre, which is a sort of damascene blade like a Mameluke's. A heavy oblique blow on the right side of the head had shorn through a part of the parietal bone and its coverings over an area of about six by eight centimetres. This oval portion of bone was embedded beneath the skull and was compressing the dura mater and brain. It should be added that the sequestrum was separated from the upper part of the wound in the bone by a space of several millimetres, which allowed the free exit of fluids effused between the foreign body and the dura. The young man was found in an artisan's house, and had had this wound for twenty days without shewing any serious consequences. I recommended my honourable colleague in charge of the surgical side of the hospital to leave the case to nature, until the sequestrum became wholly free from the membranous adhesions that were retaining it in its embedded position, for, I went on to say, the trephine, which should have been used in the beginning, is now no longer indicated. When the piece of bone becomes loose it will be easy to extract it. In fact we heard from one of the Irish students who came to Paris that the extraction was effected a few days later and that the patient recovered.

"I advised that the sympathetic or critical abscesses, which often occur in typhus cases, should be opened with the point of a knife heated to incandescence, or by caustic potash, rather than by plain incision. I also urged the doctors to excise anthrax or malignant pustules and to follow this with the actual cautery. All my recommendations were received with modest consideration and real interest.

"Time did not allow us to accept the generous invitation of the Dublin doctors to a banquet prepared in our honour.

"We shall permit ourselves to add to these short remarks some reflections on the causes which have produced and sustained the misery in this unhappy country.[16]

[15] This may well have been the Mercer's Hospital.
[16] These were Larrey's conclusions in 1826. There is nothing to shew whether they were inspired or not. The Act of Union had become operative in 1806, but Catholic Emancipation, which he so strongly urged, was only achieved after a hard struggle in 1827. The effect of the Union upon Irish industry had been unfavourable; the establishment of Free Trade between the two countries, far from providing a market for Irish goods in England, enabled English manufacturers to use Ireland as a market for their surplus products. Irish industry declined and unemployment became serious. The great move for repeal of the Union associated with the name of Daniel O'Connor had not yet made itself felt, though the bitterness engendered by the various risings encouraged by the

"The first of these appears to us to arise from the reduction in work-shops and factories which were formerly very numerous in Dublin and the other manufacturing towns, where, in spite of the absence of steam engines, large numbers of workpeople of every kind were once employed; this reduction has left them in idleness, which is all the more unfortunate as being for the most part orphans they are almost all without homes or resources.

"In the second place, it is extremely difficult if not impossible, for these unfortunate people to obtain work as there are not sufficient large land-owners in the country to employ them, and the smaller ones are self-sufficient; moreover it is forbidden to acquire more than a certain amount of land.

"The government does not appear to interest itself in the lot of these unfortunate Irish in the way it does with the people of other parts of the English countries, either because they are of a different religion or because, being generally excluded from public functions and higher offices, they often rebel against the local authorities. Nevertheless, the rich of Dublin make every sacrifice and do all they can to aid these distressed people, especially when they are ill; but their number is so great (they are esti-mated at 55–60,000) that these resources are inadequate. There is no doubt that some quite trivial causes may bring about a revolution which would be all the more formidable as these people have nothing to lose, and from the state of extreme misery in which they exist may well prefer death to their painful and unhappy mode of life.

"The only remedies of any use against this cruel disease (pauperism) would be:—

1. To give the Irish all the political rights accorded by English laws to inhabitants of the other parts of the kingdom.
2. To divide the uncultivated land, now exclusively given over to pasturage, amongst the poor people; or better, to set up on fallow land, in other respects highly cultivable, agricultural communities such as were founded in Holland by the king of the Low Countries (William), who has been called the father of the people.
3. Finally, to give prizes and rewards to such of these unfortunates who set an example of love of work and virtuous behaviour.

"I longed to get away from this great city, although we had as it were only glimpsed it: the heart-rending picture of these unfortunate people and their maladies had so depressed me that I could not have endured a longer stay. I was also anxious lest the typhus epidemic might affect the delicate and unhabituated constitution of my young Hippolyte. We therefore left suddenly in the early morning of September 1st, after receiving the farewell greetings of the doctors who had received us with

French was very recent. The Irish population was increasing prodigiously, and the potato famine of 1845 and the succeeding years was yet to come in the nineteenth century as the culminating event of the country's many misfortunes. (C. Woodham-Smith. *The Great Hunger*. Hamish Hamilton. 1962).

such kindness and generosity, and their expressions of regret that they could not have us for a fête which they had prepared at great expense for the next day. We also feared that a change in the weather might make the sea passage from Ireland difficult and dangerous, but we crossed in seven hours without mishap, in spite of several squalls which made most of the passengers sick. It was a pleasant moment for us both when we set foot ashore at Holyhead, which we left an hour later for Bangor, the chief town of Wales. We once again crossed the lonely Isle of Anglesey and the celebrated suspension bridge which unites it with the mainland."

Larrey, who rather fancied himself as an ethnologist, indulges in some reflections upon physique of the Irish, as was his habit on visiting a foreign country. He is not particularly flattering to the men and is quite devastating about the women, whom he says have a dull-brownish complexion due to long exposure to coal smoke, although the skin of the rest of the body is white, supple and elastic. Further: "the chest is rather narrow at the shoulders and generally hollow about the middle of the sternum; the back is flat and the haunches are not pronounced. The pelvis has none of the prominent and rounded contours which are seen, for example, in the women in France and Italy. The upper and lower limbs are out of proportion to the trunk and are badly shaped." One feels that he had not been fortunate!

* * * * *

Chapter 29

British hospitals. Chester. Liverpool. Carlisle. Glasgow and its Asylum. Edinburgh.

The thirty French leagues between Bangor and Chester were swallowed up in the astonishingly short time of twelve hours, and the next morning the travellers set out to explore the latter town. Here they ran into difficulty, for on presenting themselves at the Castle the sentry refused them entry as they had no passes. At this moment an elderly gentleman intervened, but as he had no French and they little English not much progress was made, until Larrey tried him in Italian, which he understood and promptly constituted himself their guide.

Larrey was chiefly impressed by the Court House and prison (he had a penchant for prisons) and thought the arrangements excellent. He noted that branding of criminals was not in use, although it was at that time in France. Later he was to be instrumental in procuring its abolition. After shewing the walls and ramparts of the city their good friend took them to the house of a leading doctor of his acquaintance, William Thackeray (Larrey spelt it Thaccary), who received them very hospitably, shewed them the hospital, and took them to lunch at his house where he arranged for them to be joined by two ladies who spoke French. The doctor and his friends all shewed themselves admirers of Napoleon, the former having an engraving of him in his reception room, with a tricolour cockade acquired in Paris in 1789.

This William Thackeray had a more distinguished brother, Joseph (1784–1832), who practised in Bedford and was on the staff of the Bedford Infirmary. He was instrumental in extending this and in establishing a museum and library. There is today, in the library of Bedford Hospital, a set of the first four volumes of Larrey's *Mémoires* inscribed: "*Offert à Monsieur Thackeray par l'Auteur comme un témoinage de son estime particulière.*" No doubt these were a gift to William who presented them to his brother's library.

They journeyed from Chester to Liverpool by diligence, crossing the Mersey by the ancient Birkenhead route which had been established by the monks of Birkenhead Priory in the Middle Ages. They esteemed the crossing rather perilous, but eventually landed safely and found a warm welcome and good accommodation at the Hôtel de Paris, and after a good dinner and a few hours rest set out to visit Dr. Brandet to whom they had letters of introduction from Thackeray.

"Dr. Brandet[1] received us in the most friendly manner and with

[1] Probably Joseph Pilkington Brandet, M.D., although he does not appear to have had a brother, a physician, alive at this date.

evidence of great interest. We were invited to dine at his house the next day, Saturday, and at that of his brother, a leading physician, on the Sunday (a rare event in England since this day is set aside for prayer and repose). The latter did us the great kindness of shewing us the principal buildings and monuments of the town; beginning with the Institute[2] where the meetings of a number of learned societies are held. This presents a very fine portion of the Tuscan order and contains a large and well-provided museum of natural history and physics, as well as magnificent assembly halls. In the museum we saw perfect specimens of stuffed animals, in particular cetaceans and reptiles, as well as a great variety of interesting objects belonging to the peoples of the south polar regions, chiefly from the icy recesses of Baffin's sea, brought back by Captain Parry[3] such as canoes, various weapons, clothing and implements.

"I saw in the library a copy of our large work on Egypt as well as one of my *Campaigns*. There are in addition many rare ancient manuscripts and a large collection of medallions of every description, dating from the most remote times.

"From the museum we visited the public market.[4] This is the most curious building of any of the English towns. It consists of a large salon or gallery, which may be compared to the Gallery of Apollo at the Louvre, and is lighted by its vaulted roof and from both sides, like the Paris Museum. Inside there are two rows of high stalls on which goods of every kind are displayed for sale in the most perfect order, with their names and prices marked on tickets.

"All the ladies of the city come to this market at certain times in the morning with their cooks to make their purchases. The price of the goods is fixed in advance by the municipal authorities and displayed on notices on the doors. This custom appears to me to have the double advantage of ensuring the honesty of the cook and of accustoming the mistress of the house to take regular and healthy exercise, and at the same time to learn about the quality and prices of articles of food or whatever serves to nourish the human race. Moreover, it is a way of obtaining mutual information of value and is very instructive. It would be a good thing if there were establishments of this kind in all the cities of civilized nations.

"We had some difficulty in getting through the market because of the crowd, and were then taken to the port which may be considered one of the finest achievements of art and nature. It consists of four principal docks in the form of elongated squares or parallelograms communicating with each other by locks; each is a mile in length and has on one side the necessary sheds to hold and protect the merchandise. The docks are

[2] The Royal Institution in Colquitt Street, which was opened in 1817, "for the promotion of literature, science and the arts." Larrey's description of the building is a very good one. It was the house of the first Liverpool School of Medicine (1834) and accommodated a number of learned societies for many years. The building was some time ago taken over by the University of Liverpool.
[3] Sir Edward Parry (1790–1855); the famous English arctic explorer. See also p. 295.
[4] St. John's Market is still in use as a public retail market supervised by the Liverpool Corporation.

filled with merchant vessels of different sizes from all parts of the world, carrying the important trade of the city which is one of the richest in Europe.

"The first of this series of docks communicates with the roadstead, which was full of ships ready to sail; some of them, destined for the other hemisphere, left whilst we were watching. Others entering the port were crossing with those leaving, forming a constantly changing picture. Amongst these splendid ships was a steamer, blackened with smoke and dark paint, bringing to Liverpool Irish immigrant families, clad in rags and seeking to escape from that ungrateful country with its horrors and misery, and to find a livelihood in this hospitable town. It was with difficulty that I dragged myself away from this remarkable port, but we were pressed for time if we were to see the principal buildings in the town as our intention was. One of the finest and richest of these is the residence of the Lord Mayor; it is noteworthy for its size, fine architecture and magnificent apartments.[5]

"On the following day I was invited to visit the Hôtel Dieu which is near to the Cathedral and the only hospital in the town.[6] It has an elegant portico with granite columns in a single piece. The wards are spacious, light and airy, the beds of iron, and the routine and methods of medical treatment much the same as in the other hospitals in England. I found the practice of surgery in many ways unsatisfactory, especially in the treatment of fractures, and hence the surgeons were grateful for some suggestions I was able to make on this as well as on other subjects. I readily accepted the opportunity offered me of demonstrating the application of my fixed appliance in such cases, as well as my improved moxa and wet cups. We have, in fact, nothing but praise for the kindness and attention of the doctors and surgeons of this town.

"Being in a hurry to continue our journey, we left Liverpool at five o'clock on a Monday morning. We had not been warned of the exact hour of departure of the diligence, though our luggage had already been taken, and only learned that it was on the point of leaving by a chance meeting with another traveller, so that it was not without some difficulty that we arrived just as it was about to depart without us, which it would have done. This is a warning for those who travel in this way in England; you cannot be a minute late for these vehicles, unless you wish to have your journey broken and incur more expense. However our alarm at what might have happened was soon forgotten at the sight of the many interesting objects between Liverpool and Lancaster.

[5] The Town Hall in Castle Street had been rebuilt and opened in 1811, and would certainly be a show-place at the time of Larrey's visit. The Mayors of Liverpool never lived there, although it was often popularly referred to as the Mayor's residence. Neither was there a "Lord Mayor" at that time: this dignity dating from 1893.
[6] The Hôtel Dieu—the term Larrey uses for all general civil hospitals—would be the Infirmary in Brownlow Street, which was opened in 1824 to replace the first Infirmary at Shaw's Brow which had been pulled down to make way for St. George's Hall. The present Royal Infirmary occupies the same site. The Cathedral would be the Roman Catholic church of St. Nicholas in Copperas Hill, which for many years was the pro-cathedral of that community.

"One travels for a long time along the western slopes of a chain of mountains which inland is prolonged eastwards to join with the Scottish mountains. The sea lies on the left and is only lost sight of after Lancaster has been passed. This is a small irregularly-built town which has an old castle and fortress of gothic design at the top of a hill at the entrance to the town. We quickly reached Karlisle (Carlisle) and from thence Glasgow. The road, though good as is the case throughout England, is difficult and wearysome; it passes between two chains of almost arid and uninhabited mountains which only end at Glasgow which we thought never to reach, the more so since we were travelling at night and could see from a great distance the beacon lighting the entry gate to this great city.

"We were fortunate in finding a good inn in which to recover from our fatigue, and there we alighted in the middle of the night of September 4th, 1826. We brought letters of introduction to one of the principal doctors of the town and hastened to present ourselves to him early the next morning, and were received, I venture to think, with sincere cordiality. Together with one of his sons, who was his pupil, we paid a visit to the University and the hospitals.

"The first consists of two square buildings in Saxon style separated by a large quadrangle. The exterior is ornamented by a superb and rich façade, with cylindrical towers at the angles containing fine staircases leading up to more or less spacious rooms for teaching or other forms of the student's work.

"The second and more modern of these buildings has, in addition to a splendid amphitheatre for anatomical lectures, a rich museum of natural history and art.[7] I was very pleased to see original portraits of the immortals—Harvey, Newton, Vesale and William Hunter—as well as

[7] The old University buildings in High Street, erected between 1632 and 1656, consisted of two quadrangles named the Outer and the Inner, the latter being the larger. Beyond was the Museum Square, to which Larrey refers, which separated the College building from the Museum of Natural Curiosities which housed William Hunter's private collection, bequeathed by him on his death in 1783 to the Principal and Faculty of the College of Glasgow as trustees, together with the sum of £8,000 to provide for its preservation. The museum building was erected in 1804 to the design of William Stark, the architect of St. George's church and the Lunatic Asylum in Parliamentary Road. Hunter's famous collection soon grew by the accession of numerous gifts from outside. On the removal of the University to Gilmorehill, in 1870, it was housed in a part of the new building. In 1878 strong pressure developed for the sale of many of the valuable objects, such as the collection of coins, only rivalled by that in the British Museum, and many of the early books and manuscripts to defray the growing expenses of the University, but fortunately wiser counsels prevailed and the suggestion came to nought.

Larrey's description of the Hunterian Collection is not particularly accurate, which is understandable in view of the shortness of his visit, whilst some of the opinions about the pictures have been revised by experts in later years. The "Vesalius" portrait, (Fig. 33), which once belonged to Dr. Richard Mead and was for many years ascribed to Titian, is now believed to be that of an unknown sitter and is catalogued as "After Tintoret." It seems that it is a copy of a portrait attributed to Tintoretto in the collection of the Duke of Bedford at Woburn. "The Birth of Vesalius" is the picture now called "The Birth of John the Baptist" by Lo Scarsellino; in Hunter's day it was thought to be by Véronèse. There are no Titians in the collection. The "Head of St. Francis" was formerly

those of benefactors and donors. In addition to the portrait of Vesalius, the museum, which has a number of paintings from the celebrated Italian schools, also possesses one of the most beautiful and rarest of Titien's, representing the birth of this great Evangelist. One is also able to see and admire many fine pictures of other evangelists at different epochs in their lives by the same painter; an admirable head of St. Francois de Salles by the Dominician; many extremely fine paintings by Tintoret and Paul Véronèse; a collection of rare Arabic manuscripts and Egyptian papyri, and a complete collection of medals struck during the reign of the Emperor Napoleon. There are also every kind of stuffed animal, some of them very rare, including two polar dogs from the antarctic;[8] as well as the clothes of the mountain savages with their arms and armour, and a number of heads of men and women which have been either embalmed or preserved in the most perfect state by the doctor accompanying Captain Parry's expedition—to say nothing of a large collection of shells and minerals. The library, which is very fine, includes the large work on the Expedition to Egypt,[9] as well as my *Campaigns*.

"We were invited to sign our names in the register of visitors to the museum. As soon as mine became known it was told to the director who hurried to offer his services and help us in our enquiries. He was at great pains to take us wherever our desire for information led and we were thus conducted from the University to the hospital (The Royal Infirmary), where the whole of the medical staff assembled to meet us and gave us the most cordial and honourable welcome. Whilst I concerned myself in matters of detail my son visited the Cathedral and other interesting monuments in the company of a medical student. At the summit of a promontory near this church an immense granite column has been erected surmounted by the statue of the religious reformer (John Knox's monument, in what is now part of the Necropolis of Glasgow).

"At the hospital I made suggestions similar to those I had made in the others I had already visited. The surgeons, all of them men of intelligence and some with well-deserved reputations, heard my remarks on certain questions of surgical practice with appreciation. I especially

---

attributed to Domenico Fefi but is now catalogued as "Italian, Early 17th Century." Larrey does not mention the pictures by Rembrandt, Chardin, Rubens and Philip Koninck, which were all present in his day, and are the gems of the collection. Hunter's interest in pictures was no doubt stimulated by his being the first Professor of Anatomy to the Royal Academy. Amongst his friends were Alan Ramsay, Reynolds and Sir Robert Strange, who supervised the illustration of his brother's superb book on the gravid uterus. Strange was an amateur dealer in pictures and it was from his sales that Hunter obtained a large proportion of his collection.

Mrs. Christine M. Davies, assistant curator of the pictures at Woburn Abbey, has written to me that "the portrait from the Hunterian Collection does indeed appear to be a copy of the portrait which is at Woburn Abbey". George Scharf in his catalogue of these (1890) attributed it to Tintoret though questioning that it was of Vesalius. It is unlike the well known picture of Vesalius, holding a small torso, in the Belvedere Gallery, at Vienna, and contemporary wood engravings of him.

[8] Mistake for arctic: the same occurs elsewhere and may be a printer's error.
[9] *Description de l'Egypte*, 20 vols. Paris 1809–28.

urged them to modify the complicated apparatus they used, as every-where else in England, for the treatment of fractures, and to substitute my simple appliance which I offered to demonstrate in detail, and did so on one of their patients who had a fractured leg.

"Glasgow is a large city and one of the richest in England: it is traversed in different directions by canals (probably the Clyde) which communicate with the basin of a seaport close to the city, which brings the water to its walls. The rapid current in these channels works the machines for a variety of factories which provide the wealth of this almost entirely manufacturing town. We were shewn certain of these of a remarkable size, including works for the manufacture of sulphuric acid and soaps, the latter covering about a hundred acres (1,000 sq. metres, or 1,200 sq. yards). We also saw spinning mills and cloth factories employing from a hundred to five hundred looms and a similar number of girls, mostly orphans, to attend and feed the machines. Cotton cloth of an excellent quality only cost 25 to 30 centimes a metre (about 2½d. a yard).

"We finished with a visit to the Asylum, of which we made a drawing (Fig. 34). This building might well serve as a model since it is the most suitable we have seen for the treatment of diseases of the brain. It is constructed in the form of a star with five branches; the ground floor of one of these has a façade ornamented with large columns, and above it is a cupola within which is a magnificent staircase leading to a circular corridor from which all the different apartments open off. These consist of as many sets of rooms as there are branches to the star I have mentioned, all of them opening onto a common corridor.

"All the apartments have parqueted or boarded floors and are warmed by hot pipes from a large furnace on the ground floor which is constantly in use. The outside air comes into a reservoir immediately above the furnace and being heated and quickly expanded passes into a double sheet-iron pipe from which other smaller pipes come off, which ramify infinitely to supply each room in the building with the warm air necessary to protect against the winter frosts. The heat of the rooms can be regulated at will. Overseers and keepers are accommodated in each division to watch the patients and give the attention their condition demands.

"As at Dublin there are two classes of lunatics, pauper and paying patients. No distinction is made between them as regards their food, lodging, exercise and the attention they receive; all are treated alike. Each division has its yard and garden.[10]

---

[10] Until the year 1814 cases of mental disorder were received in the old Town's Hospital in Clyde Street, which was in effect Glasgow's Poorhouse. In 1804 a committee of the Town Council reported that "the ward in the Hospital was totally inadequate for its object and could never be made a fit place for the accommodation, relief or comfort of the unhappy persons under consideration"; and some time later a site adjacent to the modern Parliamentary road was purchased. The architect for the new building was William Stark. The Asylum was opened in 1814 and became at once an object of interest from its distinguished architecture and internal arrangements for the accommodation and treatment of patients. It was not a free hospital, except to those whose treatment and maintenance were paid for by the towns or parishes to which they belonged. Those in a position to pay were charged from 15/- to 63/- a week. The rooms of the higher

"The paying patients have a billiards room and a variety of mechanical games. All are employed according to their abilities or desires. I permitted myself to make the same suggestions to the Medical Director for the treatment of the insane as I had made in Dublin, basing these upon bleeding from the jugular vein or temporal arteries, cupping the lower part of the cranium and the sides of the spine, mustard foot-baths and the continuous application of ice to the head.

"Eventually we said goodbye to our colleagues and left for Edinburgh which we reached very late the same day.

"The following morning we were anxious to go to the hospital both to visit it and to find out the addresses of a number of doctors in the town to whom I had letters of introduction. But before doing so we paid a rapid visit to the city which has the appearance of a truly great capital and is divided into the Old and New towns. These are situated upon two flat-topped hills between which a small sloping valley[11] runs from north to south, appearing at first sight like the bed of a river, but instead of the expected water it is filled with two parallel rows of houses of the old town, almost all of them very aged and irregularly built with narrow winding and ill-paved streets.

"On the western plateau is an ancient castle, or rather a citadel, which formerly defended the old town; it is still maintained as a stronghold and is provided with a considerable number of pieces of artillery. On our way there we chanced to meet a young doctor who had attended my lessons on Clinical Surgery in Paris and who spoke French. He very generously offered to accompany us wherever we wished to go. We began by visiting the fortress, in the middle of which is a square building[12] flanked at each corner by conical turrets furnished with guns of small calibre. This is the Governor's residence. On the east side is a tower, remarkable for its height and the staircase inside, which slopes so gently that a carriage could easily be driven up it. Here are kept under careful guard the crown, sceptre and sword of the last kings of Scotland; these trophies, displayed on a cloth of red velvet, are surrounded by an iron grille, and the room, from which daylight has been shut out, is lit by a sepulchral lamp of antique form. The crown is a large one of solid gold, covered with diamonds and other splendid and very valuable stones. The sword, of a Roman pattern, is also adorned with brilliants and was a gift from the

---

class patients were 11 feet 6 inches long, 8 feet wide, and 10 feet 6 inches high; those of the paupers 18 inches narrower. The method of heating was described by a contemporary Scottish writer as by "rarefied air" which, adds another, was generated in "two coccles on Sylvester's Plan," in the sunk storey. In 1843 the Glasgow Royal Asylum for Lunatics was opened at Gartnavel in Great Western Road and the City Parish of Glasgow took over the Parliamentary Road building as the Poorhouse. It was used for this purpose until about 1904, when it came into the hands of the Caledonian Railway Company for use as offices in connection with the Buchanan Street Station. It continued to be used for this purpose, but has been greatly diminished and adapted so that little seems now left, except for the buildings on the street front, of Stark's original structure.

[11] The present Princess Street Gardens; it actually runs from East to West.

[12] An open square, formerly called the Police Yard. The Governor's House is at a lower level.

Pope; it once belonged to one of the Byzantine Emperors. The sceptre is very heavy and also of solid gold. All of these had been lost for a matter of eight hundred years and were discovered by chance in a deep vault in the castle in a massive chest which we were also shewn.[13]

"We passed through a large part of the old town on our way to the hospital.[14] The latter is a superb building with a front ornamented with a very large peristyle of joined columns; its interior is in no way different from other English hospitals but Edinburgh has a superb amphitheatre for the teaching of anatomy and clinical surgery, and for operations upon patients.[15] Amongst the rarer cases shewn us was an enormous false aneurysm, the result of a knife wound in the middle of the thigh in the line of the femoral artery. The trunk of the injured vessel had been tied below the common muscular branch. The patient was in good condition and the operation promised to be successful. I was not so satisfied with the treatment of a woman of fifty-five who had a large contused wound on the forehead, and a fracture of the frontal bone with the depression of a large fragment onto the dura-mater and probably into the brain as well, the result of a fall from a height. Moreover the wound had been received as long as seven days previously and was associated with all the signs of cerebral compression. A single trephine opening would have sufficed to free and extract this fragment and have allowed the escape of the effused fluids and have saved the life of the unfortunate patient; but it appeared to me that the doctors were unwilling to perform this operation which in common with most of the French doctors, they deem useless, and in general they rely upon expectant treatment. It seems probable that this woman died unless nature caused the speedy exfoliation of the sequestrum which was the source of danger.

"The young surgeon, Mr. Fox, took us from the hospital to the houses of the doctors to whom we had letters of introduction but we were unable to see them until the morrow. We used the remainder of the day to see the modern part of the city, which is on a plateau to the east (north) of the old town and parallel to it. This is certainly one of the most beautiful of the important European cities I have visited. A very large and perfectly straight street runs its whole length, and has on each side a row of houses or mansions all of the same height (four stories) and type of architecture.[16] At both ends are squares surrounded by monuments. In one of these is an immense white marble column surmounted by a statue of the celebrated sailor, Nelson. In the other there is a superb church (the cathedral), the bell tower of which is the fellow of this column.

[13] The regalia (the *Honours of Scotland*) were never actually lost, far less for eight hundred years, but hidden in 1607, at the time of the union, and "discovered" by Sir Walter Scott in 1817. The sword had been given by the Pope to King James IV.
[14] The old Infirmary, built in 1741: the present Infirmary was not opened until 1879.
[15] It seems doubtful that the same theatre was ever used for teaching anatomy and for operations on patients.
[16] Possibly George Street. The column in St. Andrew Square had nothing to do with Nelson, but is a monument to Viscount Melville and dates from 1821, so that it would be fairly new when Larrey saw it. The church in Charlotte Square is St. George's, opened in 1814.

"The modern town communicates with the old, which as we have said is built upon a similar hill, by a number of wide bridges[17] flanked with small houses of a like size. Below these bridges is a large street (in fact the valley I have previously described) entirely filled with houses, so that these places overtop one another in a way which appeared to us very curious. At the southern end of the new town is a conical hill[18] on which has been built another monument to Nelson in the form of a round tower which can be seen from a great distance. There is also a camera obscura which gives a panoramic view of both the towns.

"Opposite to this hill and at the extremity of the second is the palace of the ancient kings of Scotland, Holyrood. In the left wing is the room belonging to Mary Stuart, where the furniture and tapestry have been kept as they were in her time; the bed is especially noteworthy for its antique design and is furnished with curtains and coverings. In the same room are portraits of the Queen, her husband and his mistress. We also saw the recess in the ante-room where Rizzio, the unfortunate Queen Mary's music master, was murdered.

"From this apartment we were taken down to the ruined chapel[19] containing the tombs of the ancient kings of Scotland. It was here that the Queen used to pray. We ended our interesting visit with the port of Yff (Leith) which may be looked upon as the Port of Edinburgh, although about three English miles from it. This port, which is at the mouth of the river of the same name, has immense docks containing ships of every size and every nation. To facilitate the disembarkation of travellers, and the landing of merchandise from large ships which could not enter without danger, a suspension bridge has been built well out in the roadstead at about two thousand metres from the shore, but it is only wide enough to permit two porters to pass one another without difficulty. This bridge, which certainly is the most daring ever seen, has only five points of support in its whole length. Although its construction is light and elegant it is, we were told, very strong and has often been crowded with passengers without the slightest sign of trouble: all its supports are of iron wire.[20]

"We used the last two days of our stay in this ancient capital of Scotland to visit the general museum, the prison, the orphans, schools, the college of surgery and some special anatomical collections.[21] In the latter we saw some beautiful injections of blood and lymphatic vessels; some remarkable pathological specimens, especially of the heart and large arteries, the hydrocephalic head of an adolescent with a circumference of more than

[17] This is rather obscure. The North Bridge was built in 1772, but there is no other bridge.
[18] The Calton Hill.
[19] Holyrood Abbey Church, dating from the 12th century.
[20] The bridge between North and South Leith was a wonder of its time.
[21] The College of Surgeons was presented with a museum by Dr. John Barclay in 1821, and it is probable that it is to this that Larrey refers, as it was originally for Natural History as well as anatomy and surgery. The famous Dr. Robert Knox, the anatomist, and patron of Burke and Hare, was its Conservator in 1825, so that it is possible that Larrey met this notorious if somewhat unfortunate character. The present Royal Scottish Museum was not built until 1875.

70 centimetres, and a number of healed intracapsular fractures of the femur. One of these had been injected and it was possible to see the vessels of the callus pass from the diaphysis towards the head of the bone. I asked the Edinburgh surgeons to send such a specimen to Sir Astley Cooper of London, to prove to him that such fractures are capable of healing, which is contrary to the view he has expressed, and I was gratified to find that these preparations confirmed the truth of what I have stated in my writings.

"The general museum is in a superb elliptical building of elegant design, built especially for the purpose. The entrance gate is supported by large Corinthian columns of grey granite. One of the wings is reserved for meetings of professors and for instruction in the sciences. The side with the façade is the museum proper: it is very splendid and of great beauty and contains the rarest stuffed animals of the Three Kingdoms. I was surprised and very pleased to see a white bear that had been killed by Captain Parry during his voyage in the polar seas. This huge animal was placed beside an African elephant which it equalled in height. I measured the length of one of its fore feet, from the end of the middle claw, with my stick and found it to be eighteen inches (about 45 centimetres). It was exactly similar in size and appearance to the one I saw on a mountain in Newfoundland when I was out shooting game in the interior (see my Campaign of North America).

"Captain Cook saw one of these bears in the Southern (sic) polar region at the time of his last voyage round the world, and described it as one of the most ferocious carnivorous animals and remarkable for its great size. The famous traveller was right in saying that one of its feet, as judged from imprints in the snow, was over two feet in length. The animal we saw is more than a metre and a half high and nearly three metres from muzzle to the tail, which is very short and buried between the buttocks. It is to Captain Parry's keen interest in science during his polar expeditions that we are indebted for this enormous animal, doubtless the only example of the species in the European museums.

"In the same gallery are two huge male and female walrus, the female has no defensive weapon but the male has two tusks as large as those of a full-grown elephant but curved in an opposite direction. There are also many other rare mammals, as well as Chinese and New Holland pheasants of extraordinary beauty, birds of paradise of an unknown species, and bats from Canada and Louisiana as big as the squirrels of the Russian forests. We also saw a number of prepared heads of savages from the icy mountains of the polar seas: their jaws are furnished with fine teeth of a brilliant whiteness and the hair is well preserved; they are fitted with enamel eyes and the whole appearance perfectly reproduces the living subject. What a number of other interesting objects enrich this museum!

"We did not fail to visit the town prison; its orderliness and the philanthropic sentiments which appeared to animate the governor filled us with admiration. Detention there, far from hardening the hearts of the prisoners as is the case in the majority of prisons on the continent, tends to lead to a change for the better and to a real reformation. Each Sunday ministers of religion preach sermons directed towards their encouragement, and each year a large number of those discharged re-enter society with new talents and fresh industry and continue to give evidence of the best intentions. They are able to take full advantage of their opportunities since they carry away with them no marks of degradation.[22]

"We spent Sunday, our third day in Edinburgh, in visiting the schools for orphans of the shopkeeper class.[23] The Lord Mayor, the Governor, the Director of the schools, and the leading doctors, having heard that we wished to pay this visit were anxious to receive us ceremoniously and consequently prepared a splendid repast for us in the boys' school, which is the largest and finest, where with other magistrates they assembled to meet us. We were completely unaware that we should be invited to this banquet. The Lord Mayor did us the honour of greeting us and invited us to this luncheon in the name of his compatriots. At the end of the meal a cup was brought in made from a mother-of-pearl nautilus, mounted on a golden pedestal and filled with excellent Constance wine. The Lord Mayor, beside whom I was seated, drank from it first, after which he offered it to me; having tasted this nectar I followed suit and passed it on and in this way it made the round of all the guests. With this cup in hand each gave a toast, first to the founder of the schools and then to Napoleon's surgeon, Larrey, and to other of the leading men in the company. It will be easily understood how sensible I was of this honour and delicate attention. This was surely one of the most pleasant days of my life!

"After the meal the Lord Mayor and the school doctors took us over the building. It is an old square mansion, with turrets at the four corners, within which staircases have been built leading to the rooms occupied by the children. The regimen is based on sound hygienic principles, and good order and remarkable cleanliness were found everywhere. All the children receive a primary education and they can also learn all kinds of trades and useful crafts depending upon their wishes and intelligence. They are regularly exercised in military drill and gymnastics.

"We next visited the girls orphanage which is similarly constituted. Like the boys, these maidens are dressed in a uniform of cotton or other fine material; their food is the same. These two schools, which are directed by the most enlightened philanthropy, are certainly the best of their kind in England. When the time arrives for the children to leave, their future is assured from the training they have acquired and the sum of money which each of them receives, for these establishments are extremely rich.

"After being overwhelmed with kindness and attention by all the doctors and magistrates of this remarkable town we said goodbye to its noble and generous inhabitants and parted from them with sincere regret, and in particular from the doctors who had received us so graciously. We

---

[22] This may have been the Calton Jail, built in 1817, see note on branding p. 309.
[23] George Heriot's School. The *Nautilus Cup* is illustrated on p. 175 of Vol. 1 of *Old and New Edinburgh* by J. Grant. 1882. The girls' school was the Trades Maiden Hospital.

shall always remember Drs. Thomson, Belingal, Monro and Cullen,[24] the last two being the sons of famous surgeons of the same name. All these honoured colleagues gave us singular proofs of a real brotherly friendship.

Our journey from Edinburgh to London was quickly accomplished. In passing through Northumberland we were astonished by the remarkable appearance of the antique castle, which was formerly the residence of the Viceroy of this province. The top of its high walls is interrupted at regular intervals by battlements or embrasures, designed no doubt for archers, and the intervals between are surmounted by numerous bronze statues of natural size representing various warriors, some armed with lances and others with swords or scimitars, as if to defend this ancient fortress against a threatened assault.

"We stayed some hours at York to see the cathedral which is one of the finest Gothic edifices in Europe. Of a prodigious height and grandeur its architecture is particularly splendid. The interior columns, which carry the vault and all the bas-reliefs are in white marble or alabaster: it is adorned with a number of pictures and contains many tombs or mausoleums of great beauty. That of Sterne was particularly pointed out to us, as well as those of the first Kings and Queens of England, represented by life-sized wooden statues dressed in the costumes of their times, and from this and their features suggesting a true likeness.[25] This singular form of sculpture, which is in a way almost living, is to be found in other English churches.

"After passing through the Duchy we reached Doncaster, which is notable for an immense arena (or racecourse) for horse and vehicle racing. In fact the finest horses in Europe are bred here. They combine beauty and lightness which makes them much sought after for racing.

"We made a slight detour from our route to London to pass through the town of Cambridge, celebrated for its University, which I was anxious to see. The College of the Physicians on which it is based is most remark-

[24] John Thomson, 1765–1824, was Regius Professor of Military Surgery from 1806 to 1822, and subsequently the first Professor of Pathology in Edinburgh. Sir George Ballingall succeeded Thomson: on his death in 1855 the chair was abolished. Alexander Monro (Tertius), 1773–1859, was the least distinguished of this famous family. He held the Chair of Anatomy from 1808–1846. William Cullen, the anatomist, was grand-nephew of the famous Glasgow physician.

[25] I am indebted to Mr. C. B. L. Barr, the Assistant Librarian to York Minster, for the following note. The series of statues are of stone, not wood, and they comprise only kings and no queens. The series is on the organ screen or choir screens of the Minster, carved in stone under the supervision of the master mason, William Hyndley of Norwich, between 1475 and 1505. The figures, like the screen as a whole, are of stone, lifesize, and were once painted and gilded. They depict the fifteen monarchs from William I to Henry VI, each named, dressed in royal robes, with crown and sword and/or orb or sceptre. The figure of Henry VI was removed, after 1476, and in 1617 replaced by one of James I. In 1810 this was taken to Ripon Minster, and a new statue of Henry VI, carved by Michael Taylor of York was inserted. Other smaller repairs and restorations to the screen were carried out at the same time and this is the condition in which it will have been in 1826. The screen suffered little damage in the fire of 1829, which completely destroyed the organ above it.

able.[26] It possesses a fine library containing many valuable manuscripts, numerous medallions from the Roman Empire and of all the great men of the period, including Napoleon 1st, my illustrious friend and colleague Bichat etc. We were asked to write our names in the register and received a most honourable welcome from the Director. There are many other remarkable buildings in the town; the Senate House is interesting in many ways and one of the finest edifices we had so far seen.

"Time did not allow us to carry our explorations further, and as we wished to take advantage of the diligence for London we were forced to leave the same evening and arrived at our destination on September 14th, 1826. We were amazed and almost intimidated by the size of this city and thought it well to have a few days' rest before commencing our visit in earnest."

*　　*　　*　　*　　*

[26] Professor Ronald Greaves thinks that the "College of Physicians" probably refers to the Faculty of Medicine: the Director to have been the Regius Professor of Medicine. The library would be the Medical School Library, now housed in the Department of Pathology. There is a copy of Larrey's book in the Fitzwilliam Museum but nothing is known of the manuscripts, medallions nor the register.

Chapter 30

London. Greenwich Hospital. The Rosetta Stone. A comparison of English and French Surgery.

"After we had settled ourselves in lodgings in Piccadilly which had been recommended to us from Paris, we were early abroad the next morning. Although I had no letters of introduction to any of the London doctors I had no hesitation in presenting myself to those whom I knew by reputation, beginning with Sir Ashley Cooper,[1] one of the most widely known, who received us very courteously and with all the signs of sincere fraternity. He took us with him to the hospital (Guy's) of which he was the director.

"This presented the same order and cleanliness as other English hospitals, so that there is no need to speak of it especially. We saw a number of interesting surgical cases and shall refer to them when we come to compare English surgery with that in our armies and the Paris hospitals. One of Sir Ashley Cooper's pupils took us to the other London hospitals. We were especially interested in that for the army pensioners (Chelsey) where we were welcomed with great kindness by the celebrated Everard Home, Hunter's brother-in-law, who made me a present of his splendid work on comparative anatomy. No doubt the English army veterans are well treated in this hospital, but comparing them with those in the Invalides at Paris their lot is different from the latter whom we believe to be better clothed and fed. In London they are lodged in small separate rooms, like monk's cells. We were agreeably surprised to see over the door of a number of these rooms the plaster bust of Napoleon. In other respects everything has been done to satisfy the needs of the pensioners. During this visit we were also received with the greatest respect by Mr. de Sommerville, the chief medical officer of the hospital and Mrs. de Sommerville, well known for her profound knowledge of astronomy. As we were leaving the commandant pointed out three pensioners of over a hundred who headed the first rank of a line of this venerable corps which was parading at the moment of our departure.

"The pensioners hospital for sailors (Greenwich) is a splendid building, as magnificent as a Royal Palace, and indeed had at one time been the King's residence.[2] The sailors' children are brought up with the same care as is bestowed on the old sailors; they lack for nothing. It would be difficult

---

[1] Here, as elsewhere, I have followed Larrey's spelling of proper names.

[2] Greenwich Palace, now the Royal Naval College, was acquired by the Navy in 1694 as a Royal charity; in the first instance as a home for old and disabled seamen. In 1790–1807 there were six pensioners of over 100 years old. The school for orphans was begun in 1717 with twenty boys; by 1821 the number had risen to six hundred.

Keevil, Lloyd and Coulter, *Medical History of the Navy*, 1200–1900.

to find more solicitude anywhere in the civilized world, or a more suitable education than these young pupils receive, nor better hygienic conditions for all.

"In these establishments we saw only a few individuals who had suffered amputation. One of the main causes, as we noted during the war, being the poor results of this operation as performed by the English doctors in their armies. This, we think, is due to their mode of operating which consists in making a single division through the flesh, and tightly closing the wound by first intention. I have pointed out the drawbacks of these procedures in my Memoirs and long experience has confirmed this.

"After seeing the five or six principal London hospitals, in all of which the surgical practice is very similar, we visited a number of anatomical museums and picture galleries, of which the King's was the most important. In the Museum of Arts I was chagrined to see the rare and valuable antiquities we had collected in Egypt, and which are illustrated and described in the great work on our memorable expedition to this ancient world at the end of the eighteenth century. The most remarkable are the famous Rosetta Stone[3] which is a cube with its four sides engraved with a long inscription in hieroglyphics, cuneiform, arabic and Greek characters (it was from this that our illustrious Champollion appears to have found the key to the translation of the hieroglyphic writing), and the red granite hand of the Colossus of Memphis, which we discovered buried deep in the soil of the former Egyptian capital on the left bank of the river about a league from the Pyramids. I was a witness of this discovery which was due to the excavations which General Duga, the commandant of Cairo, made in one of our caravans a few days after the departure of General Bonaparte. The first phalange of the large finger, which I measured at the time we found it, is three feet long by our old scale of measurement, from which it is easy to calculate what was the height of the colossus. In this museum we also saw many other Egyptian curiosities which the Commission of Arts had collected at great expense and with much difficulty during our stay in that country, and which the English took from us at Alexandria at the time of our return to France.

"The museum which interested me the most was Hunter's where I

---

[3] The Rosetta Stone, believed to date from about 195 B.C., was discovered by a French officer. Its smooth and admirably preserved surface (not sides) is engraved extremely legibly with closely written inscriptions in Egyptian hieroglyphics, a cursive form of these, and Greek. All commemorate the same event. Napoleon appreciated the possible importance of the discovery and copies of the inscriptions were sent to various oriental scholars. The solution was partially arrived at by Thomas Young but the final achievement was Champollion's. At the capitulation of Alexandria it is sometimes said that the stone was serving as a threshold to Menou's tent, but it seems more likely that it was deliberately hidden. There was a dispute about the ownership of the various trophies gathered in Egypt between the British and the French, the former claiming that they were the spoils of war and by custom belonged to the victors, the latter that they were the personal acquisitions of Napoleon's savants. A compromise was reached by which the savants kept most of their specimens, but the major trophies, including the Rosetta Stone, were taken by the British, who deserve some credit for their perspicacity in rescuing it and bringing it safely to the British Museum.

was accompanied by Sir Astley Cooper himself. Here I saw and greatly admired the fine injections of all the organs, made with the same success as those of Prochaska, Soemmering and other great German anatomists."

"As for a number of reasons it was urgently necessary for me to return to France, I was unable to devote the necessary time to taking notes on all the anatomical and pathological specimens in this important museum, most of which were of great interest. To study it profitably would have required about eight days. As it was we were fortunate to have seen all the hospitals and to have been able to follow the work of the leading surgeons for a short time, and we shall make bold to give a brief comparison between various aspects of their work and the corresponding French practice."

A Comparison of English and French Surgery.

"I noticed with pleasure that the English surgeons operate with calm deliberation, confidence, and complete mastery. They do not hurry the work of the knife in the way I have seen done in France by certain of our well-known surgeons.

"I cannot equally approve their method of treating their operation wounds. Their principal aim is the complete obliteration of the solution of continuity. In consequence they effect an exact union of both the edges of fresh wounds and they treat old wounds and ulcers in the same way.

"Generally speaking it is a mistake to believe that we minimize nature's work of healing by bringing all the surfaces of a wound into close and mutual contact when these are the result of an amputation; no matter by what method this may be practised. The structures here are all divided perpendicularly to the bone or the axis of the limb, and however exact the union there is always a space at the bottom of the wound for the collection of the fluids which escape in some quantity from the open vessels (I assume that the visible arteries have been tied); the resulting effusion persists in this space and exercises a harmful effect, both by its physical presence and from the rapid and more or less noxious alterations which occur in it, the speed of these depending upon the idiosyncrasy of the subject. (1) These fluid collections distend the flaps or closed edges of the wounds in proportion to their size, and this is at once accompanied by severe and widespread pain and with heat and reddening of the parts. Swelling begins, and if the means of union, such as sutures or closely applied adhesive bandages, offer too strong a resistance to this spontaneous expansion, devitalization develops and gangrene shews itself and spreads with great rapidity. At the same time a part of the effused fluids is absorbed by the veins in the depths of the wound and passes from them into the general system; and since we have overburdened nature in the work of transference or re-absorbtion, so that the purulent matter is absorbed or pumped from the crannies of the wound into the veins of the amputated limb and may be found to extend as far as their openings in the vena cava, or even to the heart, it has been concluded that the disease has become complicated by *phlebitis*, and the failure of the operation and the death of the patient is attributed to this new condition; whereas if these veins remain in their normal state they only carry away such of the morbid material as develops in the incision. This is a matter we have verified on many occasions. The divided nerves are also penetrated by the carbonic acid or special miasmas which a kind of fermentation produces in these purulent foci. Such absorption attacks the organs of internal life and

302

affects the whole nervous system. (2) When the injured parts are inflamed they are unable to unite and only by the process of suppuration can they become disengorged: it is therefore a waste of effort to employ measures for their direct union. (3) It is well known that no sooner have the fluids coming from the several vessels and lymphatics—or those derived from the fatty and medullary fluids, the areolar spaces, or from the cells of the spongy tissue of the divided bone—accumulated in the spaces or cavities we have mentioned, a sort of putrid fermentation commences in them which causes their decomposition and gives them harmful and irritant properties. A portion of these fluids undergoes absorption by the veins and is thus carried by the circulation into the whole economy and affects the function of the organs essential to life, more especially those with a parenchymatous structure, such as the liver, spleen, etc. We have many times detected these abnormalities of nature; so that in opening the bodies of those who have died shortly after having undergone an amputation, where the wound in the stump had been closed by first intention and with a certain amount of force, we have seen severed veins with their openings plunged in the septic focus and filled with ichorous or purulent matter. The abnormal fluids were carried by these vessels to the centre of the circulation; and having reached the viscera concerned with nutrition the morbid material at once set up irritation, which brought on a pathological exudation and disease, which could be regarded as traumatic in origin, and endangered the patient's life. Hence, at the opening of the bodies of those who succumbed to the effect of these secondary, metastatic, or traumatic conditions, we find abscesses in the liver and foci of suppuration in the lungs and even in the brain, especially on the side of the amputation.

"These facts allow of no doubt about a true metastasis, the signs of which can be followed by careful dissection along the course of the veins which have drawn upon or imbibed the purulent fluid from the focus in the wound, and we can equally well follow their passage and discharge into the vena cava and the organs affected.[4]

"The inner coat of these veins is often inflamed from the presence of this septic material in their lumen, which is the reason for certain medical men saying that these secondary complications are the effect of a phlebitis (a disease much less common than is thought).

"It is not unusual for all these phenomena, or at any rate most of them, to be seen after an amputation in which the wound has been treated in the fashion I have just mentioned; more especially where this has been performed for some form of chronic disease, such as caries or necrosis of the bones with ulceration of the soft parts, or for cancerous ulcers or *tumor albus*. In these cases experience has shewn the truth of our assertion, but without needing to draw upon this it is easily understood that whatever may be the appearance of the limb at the point where the operation is performed, the tissues which are cut through are, like the rest of the member, saturated with the morbid materials of which I have spoken; and in spite of this seeming integrity we should find, if we were to analyse the fluids which flow from the cut surface, the same abnormal materials as are present in the focus of disease for which the operation was required. In fact a few hours after the amputation a seropurulent effusion may already be seen soaking the dressings, and it becomes so copious that by the next day it will have come through these.

[4] Larrey's clear recognition of thrombophlebitis and pyaemia is in advance of his time. His English contemporary Guthrie observed the changes but failed to interpret them correctly.

"It would be difficult to explain this phenomenon were we not to accept the presence of this morbid secretion in the tissues at the seat of amputation, brought thither by the passage of purulent fluids from the ulcer or the caries in the bones (an effect of capillarity). It is therefore imperative, if we are to obviate this local inflammation and a proportionate metastatic absorption, not to close the wound in the stump so early, so that the fluids may not be retained but rather may flow away freely.

"We have likewise found that when a limb requires to be amputated for a recent wound, even though the operation is through apparently healthy tissue, these complications almost always appear if the parts are united by first intention; their severity depending upon the irritability of the subject and the rigours of the climate. One of the first effects of the tension resulting from this method of union is the immediate production, together with some nervous spasm, of local turgidity soon followed by passive haemorrhage, for we assume that all the visible vessels were tied during the operation, and this haemorrhage is mainly from the venous system. The effusion of this venous blood into the interior of the wound is a fresh source of irritation and is soon accompanied by inflammation and erythrism, so that surgeons who use such a method of treatment are obliged to take off their dressings prematurely to relieve this restrictive and painful compression. On the other hand the haemorrhage ceases and the other complications diminish when the wound is set free. If the operator responds quickly to this natural need the situation is restored and the patient may be saved, although the wound is in the same state as it was before the primary closure: even so the partisans of the method give it the credit for the patient's recovery. This we have generally found, and it is what happened to the soldiers who underwent amputation at the capture of the citadel of Antwerp.

"In almost all these patients immediate closure of the wound had been carried out at the time of operation, but after the first twelve to twenty-four hours at most the reaction was so violent that, on the admission of the surgeons who had performed the operations, it was necessary to remove the dressings and adhesive bandages. The wounds being allowed freedom the storm was dissipated, but in none of them was the cicatrix formed before the fifty-first or fifty-fifth day.[5] It was, however, maintained that this success was due to the English method of treatment, that is to say to immediate union, the results of which had been only momentarily interrupted, as the adhesive bandages were reapplied as soon as the turgidity of the wounds had diminished.

"To sum up: Nature should be allowed to heal these wounds gradually and without disturbance, irrespective of whether they have been performed for acute conditions or necessitated by chronic disease. This aspect of English surgery lacks the perfection one would expect from such well informed practitioners.

Fractures of the lower limbs.

"English doctors, following the teaching of one of their most famous men, P. Pott, put fractured legs on an inclined plane and maintained them in this flexed position by an ingenious hinged mechanical device which allows for extension or flexion at will.

[5] Many amputations of the arm and forearm which were performed according to my method by my son, who was in charge of the siege trench, promptly recovered. The cicatrices were complete between the twenty-fifth and the thirty-first days and healing was uncomplicated.

"The limb is placed bare on a small board, or part of the apparatus, and kept in position by a number of ties or bandages at each end. The result is that the power of the muscles is never overcome, since nothing less suffices for this but careful and exact peripheral compression by the direct application of compresses and an eighteen-tailed bandage soaked in the tonic and gummy liquid we have described in our Memoirs. Moreover the apparatus (assuming the fracture to have been reduced) has no mechanism for keeping the fragments in position and preventing their subsequent displacement. The union is delayed, the callus is irregular, and the limb often deformed, painful and difficult to use.

"I have seen a number of fractured legs treated by means of these mechanical devices, and I can say with confidence that this branch of surgery has by no means reached the state of perfection in England that it has in France today. There was a total ignorance of my rigid appliance, which I have constantly used with complete success. I was given the opportunity of demonstrating this in the great cities of Liverpool and London, when the English doctors who had invited me to treat two cases appeared to be well satisfied with its simplicity and rigidity. But they were no less agreeably surprised by its efficacy, when on its being removed at the indicated time they found the wounds healed and the fractures firmly united in perfect position. (I have letters on this subject from the chief surgeons of the hospitals.)

"For fractures of the neck of the femur they use various appliances giving permanent extension and consequently they rarely obtain union: this no doubt is the reason for Sir Astley Cooper's statement that union never takes place when the fracture is intracapsular. However, I have learnt that since the publication of the fifth volume of my *Clinical Surgery*,[6] this famous surgeon now accepts the truth of my teaching.

"Certain London surgeons, who advocate resection of the two fragments of a bone when a false joint has formed as a consequence of an ununited fracture, have nevertheless told me that they have not obtained all the success desired from this procedure; and agree that it is better to resort to some form of splinting rather than to undertake so painful and difficult an operation in which the outcome is uncertain. I therefore maintain the views I have stated in my *Clinical Surgery* with regard to this operation. Nor, in my opinion, is there any greater indication for this, nor is it permissible, in caries or chronic disintegration of the articular ends of the bones of either the upper or the lower limb, except in some very unusual cases and when nature has completely isolated these articular parts by necrosis, or when, in a complete dislocation, the articular ends have been extruded through the fibrous capsule and the skin; as, for example, in a complete dislocation of the astragalus, or of the heads of the metatarsal, metacarpal, or phalangeal bones. In such a case these should be removed or resected."

Obstinate retention of Urine.

"In cases of complete retention in which it is impossible to pass a catheter, the English perform the operation of perineal section; that is to say, they penetrate into the membranous part of the urethra by an incision behind the bulb in the line of the canal, carrying the bistoury a little to the right, and then prolong the incision as far as the neck of the bladder, which they avoid, and thus give free issue to the urine. Following this they treat the stricture by gradual dilatation and only rarely by catheterization. They continue in the use of elastic bougies until the patient is well. I have seen many patients in the hospitals

[6] *Clinique Chirurgicale*, J.-B. Ballière, Paris 1829–1836.

of a number of English towns who had been operated on in this way with complete success for total or extremely serious urinary obstruction. This method is certainly preferable to those in use in France; such as perforation of the canal with Boyer's conical bougies, which is favoured by a number of practitioners, or other useless procedures. Many patients die as a result of these operations who could be saved if we employed perineal section in the English fashion."

Cutting for Stone.

"Lithotomy is almost always successful in the hands of English surgeons. This appears to me to be due: 1st. To the complete confidence the English have in their doctors, and their entire *resignation*.[7] 2nd. To the lymphatic and little irritable constitution of the English, whose blood appears to me to be more plastic than that of the nations of southern Europe; which perhaps is due to their great consumption of the flesh of fully grown animals, such as oxen and sheep, which may provide the blood with more fibrin. 3rd. To the method of operating. It is clear, that apart from the precision and dexterity of their lithotomy, they know how to arrest severe haemorrhage, which in any case seldom occurs. These successes mean that the English surgeons do not readily accept or practice lithotrity.

"With a few modifications I approve their method of operating, for like them I use a knife very similar to Cheselden's, and stop the incision well below the limit reached by *frère* Come's instrument, which most French surgeons employ.[8] I have pointed out in my *Mémoirs* the modifications we have introduced into the lateral lithotomy operation to render it as perfect as possible. When we have seen a sufficient number of cases of lithotomy and lithotrity it will be possible to make a comparison between them."

Aneurysms.

"With the perfect candour which characterizes us, we declare that the English surgeons have carried the operation for aneurysm to the highest stage of perfection. It is also true to say that this desease, and especially traumatic aneurysm, is much more frequent amongst the English than any other nation of the continent. This appears to me to be due to their greater exposure to mechanical injuries, since the majority of them are employed in factories or workshops of various kinds, and frequently suffer from accidents which damage the main arteries of the limbs giving rise to traumatic aneurysm; hence their doctors have many opportunities of studying it. In consequence they have perfected the

[7] It is to be remembered that this operation was done without an anaesthetic. Samuel Pepys underwent it on March 26th, 1658, and ever afterwards celebrated its anniversary with high festival.

[8] The operation of "Cutting for the Stone" goes back to the "cutting on the gripe" of Celsus. Median perineal lithotomy was described by Marianus (1524). John Douglas had much success with the supra-pubic operation about 1719–21, and this attracted the interest of Cheselden who practised it and in 1723 wrote a "Treatise on the High Operation for Stone." Frère Jacques (Come) had great vogue as a lithotomist in Paris at the end of the 17th century. He practised a rough and ready form of lateral lithotomy in which he directed his incision upon a staff passed into the bladder. He was ignorant of anatomy and though some of his results were highly successful others were the reverse. Cheselden later abandoned the supra-pubic operation and, influenced by Raw of Leiden who introduced the grooved staff, he experimented with various forms of the lateral approach, finally evolving a technique which held the field for one hundred and fifty years. (See Zachary Cope's *William Cheselden*. Livingstone, Edinburgh and London, 1953.)

operation for this disease and have been the first to perform it on the deepest vessels and those to all appearances least accessible to surgical Art, such as the common carotid, the sub-clavian, the external iliac arteries, and even the abdominal aorta.

"Usually they employ Hunter's method, that is to say they apply the ligature at some considerable distance above the aneurysm, though in my opinion they carry this too high when tying the femoral artery for popliteal aneurysm.

"It is right to say that these estimable doctors received my observations on this point with great interest, as well as those concerning the reproduction of arteries in the substance of parts when the principal trunks are for some reason obliterated. Nevertheless Sir Astley Cooper expressed surprise at the possibility of this phenomenon, and appeared to doubt the reality or the exactitude of the facts supporting my assertions, which gave the proof of this discovery I made in 1811 in the case of a grenadier of the Imperial Guard.

Diseases of the Eyes.

"All the delicate operations which diseases of the eyes call for have had their origin in England. In particular we owe to Cheselden the idea of making a window in the opaque curtain which in certain cases obstructs the passage of light between the cornea and the lens, the pupil being closed by adhesions at its edges or by the pupillary membrane which sometimes persists in the child after birth. The formation of an artificial pupil is carried out in England today with as much success as in Cheselden's time, and in general all operations for diseases of the eyes are performed there with equal dexterity and success. They have adopted almost exclusively Scarpa's method of couching for cataract. They do not believe in the contagiousness of ophthalmia at a distance, whatever its type, which is contrary to the view of certain French and many Belgian and Dutch doctors. In point of fact contagion only occurs when the purulent matter from the ulcerated eyelids of a sufferer is placed on the mucous or inner surface of the lids of a healthy subject.[9] To sum up, we may say that all diseases of the eye are very well treated by the English. We shall have more to say about ophthalmia in speaking of our journey through Belgium.

"As I have neither the time nor the intention of making a full comparison between English surgery and our own, I have limited my remarks to the more salient facts I have been able to observe. To make a profitable study of all branches of English surgery it would be necessary to spend six months there and to follow in detail the practice of the leading surgeons in their hospitals."

*   *   *   *   *

"We ended our visit to the remarkable establishments and buildings of London with the wonderful subterranean road which our compatriot Brunel[10] was building under the Thames. Finally, we said good-bye to our kind confrères and left for France at the end of September 1826.

[9] He is speaking here of gonorrhoeal ophthalmia which he did not clearly differentiate from trachoma.

[10] Marc Isambard Brunel was born near Rouen. He served in the French Navy and at the Revolution escaped to America where he lived for six years. He returned to Europe in 1799 and built the Thames Tunnel between 1825 and 1843. The difficulties were immense, the project became bankrupt and for a time the tunnel was used for holding annual fares. In 1865 it was sold for a third of its cost to the East London Railway Company and is still in use on the line between Whitechapel and New Cross. (See Isambard Kingdom Brunel by L. T. C. Rolt, Longmans, Green & Co., London, 1957.)

"Instead of taking the sea route, from the Tower of London to Calais, as we had been advised, we left by diligence which allowed us to stop at various places of special interest. In particular we were invited to break our journey at Chatham, one of the finest of the English Royal Navy ports. A number of ships of the line were under construction, and there were many others in the docks or roads ready to put to sea. Although foreigners were forbidden to enter without a permit from the Minister of War or the Admiralty, the Governor, of whom M. Mac-Gregor (Mcgrigor) the Inspector-General of Military Hospitals had previously requested this favour, received us with great civility and unexpected kindness. After putting on his general's uniform the worthy governor took us in his carriage over the whole of this immense port. Orders had hurriedly been sent to all the workshops to have the machines working when we arrived. Afterwards he took us on board the principal vessels in the roadstead, where various manoeuvres were carried out and the holds lit up to show us everything of interest. Finally we were taken to the Military Hospital, for the use of men of both army and navy, where the Inspector-General was awaiting us with his staff of surgeons of all grades and the principal officers of the garrison. As we re-entered the outer gate of the fortifications we were received with the military honours accorded to generals, which much surprised me and affected me not a little, so that this visit is one of those which will ever remain in my memory.

"On my visit to the hospital I was accompanied by the whole corps of army surgeons in full uniform, all wearing the epaulettes of their respective grades like army officers. We saw the barracks of the garrison troops, which like the hospital we found in excellent order and admirably clean. I was glad to see that the beds (all of iron) were folded up during the day so that the soldiers could not lie on them. The military discipline appeared to us severe and perhaps a little harsh, but every soldier was well nourished, well clad, and had a bed to himself.

"The work of the hospital was in no way unusual; the surgery being similar to that in other hospitals and the operative procedures the same. Whilst we were there a splendid banquet had been prepared on our account, and to this we repaired at night with the chief officers of the land and naval forces and all the surgeons of these services. The Governor should have presided but was indisposed. It can well be imagined that most of the toasts were to the surgeon to Napoleon, for that great man's name had become an object of public veneration. We found his picture in the barracks and at the bed of almost every patient in the hospital, and earlier we had seen a plaster bust of him at the Pensioner's Hospital at Chelsey.[11]

"At length we had to part, and to continue on our journey by diligence. We were glad we had chosen this means of travel, for the ship we should have embarked on at the Tower of London sank in the Thames during the night after being in collision with another vessel in a thick fog. However the passengers were all saved and a number of them joined our diligence.

[11] This seems a little unusual, when we think of the detestation of "Bony" so widespread in England at the time.

"For the whole of my life I shall preserve the memory of the honourable and generous welcome we received everywhere from the doctors and a host of other people.

"We crossed the Channel quickly and reached Calais in good health. My son returned to Paris to resume his studies, whilst I had to go to lower Picardy to see General Caulaincourt, Duke of Vicenza, who was dangerously ill and about whom I had had letters whilst in England. This, to my great regret, prevented my travelling to Holland and Sweden, both of which I had intended to visit before returning home."

*   *   *   *   *

Chapter 31

Abolition of branding of prisoners. The July Revolution.
Inspection of the Belgian Medical Service. Ophthalmia.
Larrey's recommendations. Return to Paris. Reforms at
Les Invalides. *Italy.* Mme Mère. *Cardinal Fesch.*
Criticism of Roman administration.

On his return that December Larrey was elected to the Institute in place of his teacher, Pelletan. But for his kindness for Percy, against whom he had refused to stand, he might have been elected at an earlier date, and although on the latter's death in 1825 Larrey received a nomination, the vacancy went to Dupuytren.

The year 1830 came in pregnant with possibilities which were soon to be realized. For the surgeon, who was to find it full of new difficulties and dangers, it opened with a period of relative tranquility in which he busied himself with the editing and publishing of his work on *Clinical Surgery*, fortified by the experience of his visit across the channel and occupied with his duties at the Guard's Hospital. Early that April he was involved in an incident that illustrates his humanity and courage, and which might have had political repercussions. Being called to an assize ury, he ventured to oppose the sentence of branding on the left shoulder passed upon a young man found guilty of forgery and condemned to ten years' forced labour. He was supported in this by his fellow jurors, and with the help of an advocate obtained an Act of Clemency in the particular instance, which ultimately led to the suppression by the Chamber of the article in the Criminal Code relative to branding. Such political activity in the pursuit of liberal ideas might have brought him into unfavourable notice under Charles X and Polignac, but to some extent Larrey's position protected him, since his post at the Guard's Hospital also carried with it the responsibility for the care of the Royal Household.

The swift crisis of the July Revolution brought dangers of a different sort, and his hospital was soon to receive casualties from the three days fighting in which the troops under the luckless Marmont were employed to oppose the popular rising. As a surgeon to the army Larrey's duty was to the soldiers without heed to political changes, however sudden and revolutionary and of whatever kind these might be.

"The duties of a Surgeon-in-Chief of the army," he wrote, "are not simply confined to giving assistance and succour to the wounded and in this way preserving their lives. He cannot decline his responsibility for other means of protecting them against hostile aggression and of ensuring their survival, even though this often involves facing great dangers and great obstacles. It was to carry out the second of these tasks that on the third day of the fighting I threw myself unhesitatingly into the midst of five or six thousand assailants, who were threatening to burst into the asylum of our wounded and were menacing them with death. A short firm harangue halted this frenzied mob, who dispersed after simply possessing themselves of our soldiers' weapons."

The topsy-turvy backwash of all this was that before long the rôles were reversed, and under the new government Larrey found himself a member of a board set up for the medical examination of the insurrectionist wounded—now become patriotic heroes—to advise on the compensation they were to receive as a reward for their injuries and their bravery. The wheel had, indeed, come full circle, when Louis-Philippe decorated him with the order of the July Revolution!

Hardly had the Citizen King settled himself uneasily in the saddle when crises arose in both Belgium and Poland. The Belgians, who had grown increasingly resentful of the union with Holland imposed upon them by the Congress of Vienna—a union with a country differing in its people, religion and language—rose in October 1830 and proclaimed their independence. Whilst the powers hesitated and debated the Belgians offered their crown to the Duc de Nemours, the second son of Louis-Philippe. But although French sentiment was strongly sympathetic to Belgium, Louis-Philippe had the good sense to realize that Britain would never countenance a French prince on the throne of one of the Low Countries, and vetoed the proposal. After various diplomatic exchanges the crown finally went to Leopold of Saxe-Coburg who was acceptable to both France and Britain. The Dutch, however, refused to ratify the treaty contrived in London, and in August 1831 invaded Belgium, putting an end to an armistice that had maintained the peace since the previous autumn. The French sent troops into Belgium, and under military and diplomatic pressure the Dutch retired behind their own frontier. A treaty for the separation of the two countries was drawn up and accepted by the Belgians, but repudiated by the Dutch who refused to give up Antwerp. Under the pressure of a British fleet blockading the Scheldt, and a renewed French invasion culminating in the bombardment of the town between December 4th and the 23rd, Antwerp surrendered.[1] The French thereafter evacuated Belgium, but six years were to elapse before the separation of the two countries was fully agreed. The British government throughout was very averse from seeing the French and Belgians fighting side by side, and used its influence to prevent this, to the extent of allowing the French to enter the country and fight the Dutch whilst keeping the Belgians on the side lines. This led to a good deal of ill-feeling from the latter, whose pride was hurt by this minor rôle. Larrey's mission to Belgium in October 1831, of which we are about to speak, took place in the lull between the two French incursions.

[1] Hippolyte Larrey served as a surgeon with the French army during this siege.

The fact that this whole troublesome business was in effect settled by Britain and France was due to the preoccupation of the other interested powers—Prussia and Russia—with Poland. The Polish diet had proclaimed their country's independence on January 25th, 1831, and in spite of violent popular agitation France did not intervene, and the insurrection ran its course leading to the annexation of Poland in 1832. This is how these events touched Larrey.

"Following the lead of France, Belgium threw off the yoke of her sovereign, although his actions were wholly paternal and dictated by pure philanthropy. But the Belgians aspired to return to the breast of the Great Nation, considering themselves a part of the same family. The policy of the King of the French decided otherwise, and the country was formed into a separate kingdom under the direct protection of France. This was not achieved without difficulty, since the country was menaced by a coalition and Holland, in particular, made great preparations to seize the ports and principal fortresses.

"Belgium, for her part, took her own precautions and pressed forward her preparations. To ensure success King Leopold sent a despatch by special envoy to the Minister of War, Marshal the Duke of Dalmatia (Soult), asking me to organize the ambulances in his army and to inspect the military hospitals at the camp at Diest, as well as the fortresses on the Dutch frontier."

Larrey left Paris on October 7th, 1831, for Brussels, where he met the Minister of War, Wlamink, the Inspector-General of the Health Services, and the Surgeon-in-Chief, M. Seutin, one of his former pupils. He had brought with him cases of instruments and a model of his light ambulance to shew the Belgians, and was soon giving lectures and demonstrations of his methods to the army surgeons. On the 12th he was presented to the King, who asked him to inspect the medical arrangements of the fortifications of the eastern frontier and the camp at Diest, especially stressing the problem of ophthalmia. Armed with this authority he set out on the 17th, visiting Antwerp first. The conditions in the hospitals and camps are best described in his own language.

"The hospital which attracted most of my solicitude is unfavourably situated near to the eastern rampart and close beside the port. Its construction is bad and ventilation inadequate. We were sorry to find it filled with soldiers who for the most part were suffering from chronic diseases, such as ophthalmia, old-standing wounds or ulcers, ulcerated syphilitic buboes, and chronic skin eruptions. The cases of ophthalmia were together in a ward at ground level, with inadequate windows hermetically sealed to prevent the passage of light: it therefore lacked air or any form of ventilation. All the patients had become blanched, and the pallor was associated with extreme weakness which kept them all confined to their beds. They hardly had the strength to rise and satisfy their natural needs on the commode chairs which were placed here and there in the various recesses of the ward, and added not a little to the general insalubriousness. I could hardly stand the effect of these noisome effluvia. Out of fifty cases of ophthalmia in this ward we found more than thirty who had become

completely blind. There must be an apathy and fecklessness in the character of these Belgians that they shewed no signs of discontent or despair.

"And here I must allow myself a short digression. In the difficult and
arduous campaigns we made with the Dutch, Belgians, and other peoples
of northern Germany, I studied the physique and character of these
nations, and I have actually published a comparison between their
soldiers and the French. The result of my observations has been that a
French soldier, subject to the same laws and similarly educated to these
people, is infinitely superior, not only in his physical strength but also in
his intelligence, moral energy, alertness and activity.

"But to return to our subject: in contrast with the indifference of the
blind Belgians, I recall that I saw in Egypt many of our grenadiers who
had lost their sight from severe ophthalmia, take their lives with their own
weapons, or throw themselves into the river.

"After examining the treatment books of the Antwerp hospital and
obtaining information from the chief doctor, we came to the conclusion
that the method of treatment and the other causes of ill health we have
just mentioned served to aggravate the disease and to lead to blindness.
It would certainly be difficult to prescribe a form of therapy so irrational
and illogical. Thus, after the application of leeches to the temples—a
procedure more harmful than useful—they prescribed, as is the custom
of the Dutch doctors, a lotion composed of a solution of corrosive sub-
limate and extract of belladonna. I have noted two effects from this liquid:
one is to blunt the nervous sensibility of the eye, or paralyse the contractility or elasticity of its vessels and membranes, and to maintain the stasis
of fluids in the engorged or inflamed deep tissues, and thereby maintain
the ophthalmia. The other is to shrivel and contract the tissue of the
cornea and quickly render it more or less opaque: the passage of light is
thus intercepted and blindness almost immediately ensues.

"We found in fact that in all the blind in this ward the cornea had
become opaque and insensitive, with an appearance like mother-of-pearl.
The lack of fresh air and light aggravated the pernicious effects of such
medication. This profound alteration of the visual organ which had
affected in varying degrees all the patients confined within this ward,
was attributed to contagion, and this erroneous idea was widespread
throughout the country: I shall deal with it later.

"My first care was to inform Inspector Wlamink of the state of the
hospital and of these particular patients. This was done by a letter written
at my request by the chief doctor, who was present at my inspection. The
object was: (1) To desire the competent authority to evacuate all these
patients immediately to the hospitals farthest removed from the army
and towards the southern frontier. This measure was urgent, both in the
interest of the health and of the eyes of these unfortunate men, and to
clear the place for casualties should war break out, as seemed probable.
(2) To clean and whitewash all the wards and to effect such urgent repairs
as I pointed out. I also took it upon myself to leave detailed written
instructions with the chief surgeon at this hospital on what I considered
to be the most effective treatment for this cruel malady; as well as for a

number of other severe afflictions which we saw during the course of the day I spent in this inspection.

"From the hospital we went to the garrison's barracks. These are built under the ramparts near the docks and are damp and ill-ventilated; the ground-floor rooms in particular provide all the factors liable to cause symptomatic ophthalmia of the kind we encountered in Egypt. To these are to be added the effect of tobacco smoke (for the men of these northern nations all smoke pipes) and the soldiers' indolence, for we found most of them lying half dressed on their beds. Their diet is not particularly healthy; they receive a great deal of salted and farinaceous food and poor quality beer.

"We asked the General-Officer-Commanding to keep as few men as possible in the ground-floor rooms and to have these whitewashed at once. We also pointed out certain important hygienic measures to the soldiers: that they should pull down their forage caps over their eyes and ears at night and be well covered whilst asleep; that they should not walk bare-footed on the cobbled streets and, above all, should not drink the local brandy neat, which is very harmful, nor should they smoke in the barrack rooms which should always be kept extremely clean.

"From Antwerp, we retraced out steps to visit the camp at Diest, where we attended the review to which H.M. had invited me at the time of my departure from Brussels. I was present at all the manoeuvres, in company with my honourable friend General Belliard, the French ambassador.

"After the review I visited the camp and ambulances which had been set up in an adjacent farm; all the equipment having been made ready and put in proper order. The transport wagons for the wounded were of themselves in some respects unsuitable as I pointed out to the officer in charge, and to enable him to improve them I made him a present of a model of one of our mobile ambulances. I also made some suggestions on a number of matters concerning surgical instruments and dressing materials. In the camp itself some most grievous faults awaited correction.

"1. The soldiers' bedding was bad: it consisted of a mass of straw retained in place by four small boards, which never succeeded in keeping it dry. The heavy rains soaked under the straw and into the huts, which no one had taken care to protect by a circular ditch. I requested the Chief-of-Staff to provide each tent or hut with a simple bed frame on four legs, eighteen centimetres high, and in place of strewn straw to furnish a thick and inexpensive straw mattress.

"2. The ditches, which had been dug to the north of the camp as latrines, were full of dejecta and disseminated infected emanations afar. I advised that they should be filled in and others made with one side cut obliquely, and provided with a supply of the clayish sand which forms the base of the hill on which the camp is situated. Also that they should place a number of wooden shovels at regular intervals, so that each soldier could throw sand on the excreta when he went to relieve himself. This is the simplest and most effective way of preventing infection. We had praise for the soldiers food and clothes; in these there was nothing to be desired.

"We left for Louvain, which is some 12 or 15 miles distant, the same night. The next morning we visited the military hospital and barracks. The hospital was full of sick, with a small number of old French wounded from the battle of Waterloo who recognized me and on whom I performed some delicate operations which their wounds required, although they were of long standing. Here also we found many cases of ophthalmia, of whom at least a quarter had lost their sight. They had been treated in the same way as the Antwerp patients. I urgently requested the evacuation of our own wounded to France, and I gave the chief surgeon instructions, similar to those I had left at Antwerp, for the treatment of the cases of ophthalmia and certain others of special interest. I also inspected the barracks and took the same steps as at Antwerp."

From Louvain Larrey proceeded to Liége where he found "a large number of cases of ophthalmia amongst the garrison troops, who were lodged in insanitary barrack rooms where the soldiers smoked their pipes and which they maintained in a repulsive state of filth." On his return to Brussels he sent the King a final comprehensive report on the state of the hospitals and the ambulance service, full of practical details relevant to the hygiene of barracks, the pressing problem of ophthalmia, and the reception, treatment and speedy evacuation of the wounded should war break out. He tells us that his report resulted in immediate action being taken and his proposals adopted.

On his departure he received a very flattering reply from the King accompanied by a gold snuff-box ornamented with the royal cypher in diamonds.

Where are all these snuff-boxes, cameos and swords of honour today?

* * * * *

On his return to Paris Larrey resumed his duties as Surgeon-Inspector to the Army Health Council, but almost at once, at the request of Jourdan,[2] now Governor at the Invalides, was appointed Surgeon-in-Chief to its hospital, where he commenced his duties on April 1st, 1832.

He was far from satisfied with the conditions at the Invalides and exerted himself to change them for the better.

"I was concerned with the proper application of the rules of hygiene to ensure the well-being of the veterans, and the employment of more rational surgical treatment than heretofore in the institution's infirmary. All these old soldiers, at least three-quarters of whom had been cared for by me at one or other of the many engagements the French army had fought in all parts of the globe, had not forgotten this and it gave them confidence and a readiness to conform to any measures which might be taken on their behalf. I was not fortunate in persuading the administration to adopt some of those concerned with the regimen and occupation of these veterans, but I had my way over the rules of hygiene for the hospital wards. I had difficulty in abolishing the washing of the floors—an old

[2] "Un bon français, un brave soldat et un excellent père de famille" on Jourdan's monument at the Invalides.

custom pleasing the visitors eyes, but very harmful to the patients—and had this replaced by waxing and polishing and the provision of imitation brickwork.

"My other main proposals were: That during meals, which should last at least forty minutes to give time for the old soldiers to masticate their food, one of the under-officers who was sufficiently capable should give a reading on a chosen subject from the *History of Wars and Conquests*, from a simple lectern in the middle of the refectory. Such a reading would have been of great interest in recalling their own heroism, and by prolonging the meal would have made it more profitable and nourishing. That the band granted by the Emperor, but suppressed at the Restoration, should be restored. That some mechanical games and simple workshops should be provided, to give distraction and pave the way for the abolition of strong liquors, pipe smoking, etc. . . . ."

"We also met with difficulties in having the bed curtains kept close against the posts, to encourage free ventilation which these multiple partitions obstructed. There were many others, which I shall not mention, that we succeeded in overcoming.

"It was easier to simplify the surgical treatment, and to attack many of the cases of chronic disease by little-used means, with success that surpassed my hopes. These formed the subjects for the clinical lessons I gave each Thursday to a large gathering of foreign doctors and surgeons who attended my visits."

*   *   *   *   *

"This first part of my task accomplished, I made up my mind to visit the Italian Mediterranean coast which I wished my son to see, and by so doing I also hoped to shake off a state of severe depression into which I had fallen owing to a variety of unfortunate circumstances, more especially the death of my protector, the Emperor Napoleon. This agreeable voyage might also give me the happiness of seeing once again the respected mother of that great man.

"After receiving authorization from the Minister of War to be absent for two months to inspect the French military hospitals on the Mediterranean and being granted the necessary passports, my son and I set out on September 2nd, 1834, at six in the evening."

After a visit to his sister at Baudéan, where he was received with great honour, and also had the pleasure of visiting the Abbé de Grasset, formerly *curé* of Baudéan, who had taught him as schoolboy and chorister in his childhood, Larrey and his son took the steamer from Marseilles to Genoa (where he was extremely critical about the surgery at the hospital), and so on by diligence to Pisa, Civita-Vecchia and Rome, arriving at the latter on the evening of October 30th.

"The thought of being in this city, whose monuments attest to the glory and splendour of antiquity, prevented me from sleeping on the first night, and as soon as I saw the sun's early rays I wakened my son so that we could go out at once. I was careful to take a guide for our first visits, which were to Cardinal Bernetti, the Pope's Secretary of State, Cardinal Fesch, and the reverend father Don Raphael, the Greek Patriarch, to whom I had letters of introduction.

"The formal reception accorded us by Cardinal Bernetti, an enemy of Napoleon's, caused me to refuse his offer to present me to His Holiness, whom we saw later at the pontifical ceremonies. Cardinal Fesch on the other hand welcomed us as though we had been members of his family. After shewing us his valuable and superb gallery of pictures, he gave each of us a cornelian cameo, a perfect reproduction of his nephew the Emperor, and a snuff-box ornamented by another exquisite cameo of the head of Minerva, and at once took us to visit his august sister, Mme Letitia, the Emperor's mother. This illustrious woman of eighty-eight, who had become blind as the result of a double cataract, recognized my voice and held out her arms to embrace me. Learning that my son was with me, she exclaimed: "Come, my child, let me embrace you also." It would be difficult for me to convey the heartfelt kindness with which this honoured princess received us, and her tenderness and friendship towards us. For me it was a moment of happiness such as one rarely meets with in a lifetime.[3]

"Early the next morning the Cardinal's carriage, bearing his livery, was at our door to take us to see the monuments of Rome. I shall dispense with an account of these since they are described by so many travellers and historians. Moreover it would be impossible from any descriptions, however expert, to appreciate the grandeur, beauty, and richness of these buildings. They must be seen. I shall therefore limit myself to some reflections of a physiological kind which my visits to the Capitol and Vatican museums have suggested. I was particularly impressed by the head of Nero; the able artist who sculptured this has perfectly portrayed his cruel and bloodthirsty character, giving his orbital arches the great prominence we noticed in Gasparoni. The thick eyebrows above these are separated at the root of the nose by deep vertical furrows; the forehead is partially covered by thick frizzled hair, the eyes hidden deep in their orbits: in fact the head of this ruler arouses both repulsion and a kind of terror.

"After we had visited the famous Capitol, the Church of St. Peter, the Vatican with its museum and rich library where there are many rare and interesting manuscripts and had seen many other monuments worthy of the greatest admiration, I turned my particular attention to the hospitals of this great city, which I examined with the most scrupulous care. They are all large well constructed buildings, airy and well kept, but their medical and surgical practice did not appear to me to have made the progress attained by these sciences in France and England. The physicians, both here and elsewhere, use leeches if they can get them, but these aquatic worms had all died as a result of the great heat of the summer and a number of storms which were followed by the sulphurous emana-

[3] My son has written a biographical note on this visit which he proposes to publish. (*Mme Mère* by Hippolyte Larrey, 2 vols., Paris 1892.)

tions which are usual in this district. I was astonished to find that neither in this hospital nor in any of the others we saw in Italy do they use wet cups, once so much employed both here and in Greece and Egypt, and moreover so useful and efficacious. Our colleagues, however, received my advice on the matter with evident appreciation, and I was very glad to be able to shew them how to use this mode of abstracting blood as well as my method of applying the moxa.

"Syphilis is the commonest disease in the hospitals in Rome. It is less severe than formerly and is methodically treated by mercury, both by inunction to the soles of the feet and by various internal preparations; the same procedure as I have recommended in the fourth volume of this work. I was surprised and grieved to see in the female wards many little girls, of not more than seven, eight, nine or ten years of age, suffering from the malady, which indicates great moral laxity in the population, of which we shall say more later. There were similar numbers of young boys also affected, which is less surprising. Urinary stones, I was told, are rare: treatment is exclusively by lithotomy which is very successful. The methods of the Roman surgeons are rational; they operate with a dexterity and precision which indicate that they are perfectly informed in the science although we saw nothing out of the way in their anatomical museums.

"From the general hygienic point of view, Rome is well constructed and well ventilated. Sculptured fountains play in all the public squares, but as soon as their pure limpid water falls into the basins it becomes lost in subterranean pipes which run through aqueducts to empty into the Tiber, and none of it flows in the streets which in consequence are very dirty. Most of the crossroads are stinking localities: it would be easy to let the water from the fountains periodically run in the streets to wash and freshen them and render them less insanitary as is done in Paris. As these are all paved they reflect the sun very strongly especially in summer, and this causes the decomposition of the fermentable materials which are everywhere thrown in large quantities at the sides of the pavements, below which are numerous openings into the aqueducts.

"It is disturbing to see the almost uncountable numbers of priests and monks of all classes in this city. Including nuns, there are more than twenty-five thousand of them; that is, more than a sixth of the population. These religious persons are generally well-built, of good physique, and possess a ruddiness and rotundity which indicates that they live well. Every convent possesses a nursery for children who are also dressed like monks. These individuals are to be seen in the streets mingling cheek by jowl with an equal number of beggars of both sexes and all ages who importune travellers. This striking contrast is humiliating to the free man who supports himself by his labours.

"Time did not allow me to pursue my investigations further but a humanist doctor could make many observations on the Roman people of today. The women, for example, shew none of the fine physique and beautiful features with which historians have endowed the Roman women of antiquity. The features of those we saw are far from regular, their bodies are not shapely, and generally speaking they lack grace. I noted a certain similarity between the populaces of Rome and Dublin; for, except for the religious orders which are not found in the latter city, the contrast between the opulent class in Dublin and the many unfortunates who trail their misery in her streets is much what one sees in Rome. Similarly the country around the latter, like that of the Isle of Anglesey which leads to Dublin, is uncultivated although excellent as pasture land. Immense herds of cattle, sheep and goats fill the fields between Civita-vecchia and Rome, and as in England they remain in the open day and night whatever the season, the oxen being particularly notable as they have horns as much as a metre long. If these fields were thrown open to cultivation it would remove the pauperism which so degrades both of these great cities. It would also be possible to provide the unfortunate people with a comfortable existence by establishing agricultural colleges. In Rome such measures could be supplemented by employing some of the indigent population in sweeping the streets, instead of using convicts who always scamp their work and trail their heavy jangling chains before the eyes of the inhabitants and passing strangers. It would be easy to employ them in the ports, on repair or constructional works or in clearing the canals as is done at Toulon. But everything languished in this ancient city. The papal government does almost nothing to remove abuses or to stay the ruin of the classical monuments which are the glory of the country, or to remove the causes of ill health; neither does it do anything to develop industry, to improve the towns, or ameliorate the lot of the inhabitants."[4]

[4] When the Emperor Napoleon designated this as the second city of the French Empire, and gave its name to his son, he intended to carry out the badly needed reforms and renovations and to make improvements such as he had already done in the metropolis. His reign was too short for him to put these large and generous ideas into practice.

Chapter 32

Cholera in the Midi. Fear of burial alive. Views on nature of cholera and its treatment.

In March 1832 Indian Cholera which had already decimated the Russian and Polish armies appeared in France. Its spread in an unusually hot spring was rapid, and on April 11th 1,200 deaths were recorded. Altogether over 20,000 people perished, amongst them the enlightened and courageous Casimir Périer, who perhaps might have saved the July Monarchy from collapse.

Larrey was nominated a member of a medical commission to observe the epidemic in Poland, but the Minister of War vetoed this on political grounds: "They expected," he said, "to see one of the Chiefs of Napoleon's Old Guard appear in Warsaw. He shall not go!" His duties at the Invalides, however, soon made up for any loss of this experience, for the disease early invaded that institution and in his view was more serious than plague, though he was insistent about its non-contagious character.

Cholera rumbled on during the next two years, diminishing in winter and reappearing in summer, but in 1835 there was a major recrudescence in the Midi, and once more the authorities turned for assistance to the old surgeon—now in his seventieth year. On July 18th the Minister of War wrote:

"Monsieur,

Cholera rages at Toulon with an ever increasing intensity and without any hope of an end to these misfortunes. The flight of the inhabitants continues and adds to the difficulties of an unfortunate situation. The latest reports I have received are even more disturbing and suggest that the disease may break out afresh at Marseilles, which would greatly aggravate the recent demoralization.

"In these circumstances I believe it to be urgent to send a Medical Officer of high reputation to this area, and my choice at once fell on you, Monsieur, believing as I do that your presence will of itself have the best possible effect on those whom fear has demoralized.

"I therefore beg you to post as quickly as possible to Toulon, the centre of the epidemic, from whence the invasion of Antibes and Cette is threatened, with the further possibility of spread to Marseilles and Montpellier.

"You will be accompanied by M. Périer, sub-assistant surgeon to the Hospital of the Invalides. Nine francs will be allowed you and this medical officer for your posting.

"As soon as you reach either Toulon or Marseilles you will get in touch with the Lieutenant-General and with the Military Intendant of the 8th Division, to inform them of any urgent steps you consider should be taken.

"Your first consideration should be to send me a detailed report of the state of affairs, the progress of the epidemic, and the measures you have required of the military authorities for its arrest. You will correspond directly with me.

"Your activities should cover all the places where the epidemic may have broken out, and for this purpose you should follow the line of its spread and go wherever your presence may be necessary.

"I am instructing the Military Intendant of the 8th Division to co-operate with his colleague of the 10th Division, and to draw from the military hospital of this division and from that of the Western Pyrenees the Medical Officers required for the treatment of the cholera cases. I am advising my colleagues, the Ministers of the Interior and of the Navy, so that the officials of these departments may do whatever is required in their respective spheres to ensure the success of this mission, which will include the general interests of the localities you are to cover.

"Your customary zeal and great experience are my guarantees of the way you will discharge this important duty.

Accept, Monsieur, the assurance of my highest regard.

(*Signed*) MAISON.
Marshal, Minister of War."

"I reached Marseilles about mid-day on the 25th of the month, and without losing an instant presented myself to the civil and military authorities of the Department to inform them of my mission and to request them in the name of the Government to use their authority to assist me to discharge the task entrusted to me. Early the next day I began my visits to the hospitals and barracks, as well as to the principal officers of the Commission of Public Health whose duty it was to render immediate assistance to the cholera victims. My first care was to give assurance regarding the contagiousness of the disease, which was firmly believed by the common people and by the majority of the local doctors. At the same time I instructed the members of the commission and the doctors in the hospitals on the methods to be used at the onset of the disease, and the precautions to be taken to ensure that this treatment was administered as early as possible and continued without intermission until it was clear that the patient had been either saved or would die. The example I set of handling the cases of cholera myself, and performing autopsies with my own hands on those which had especially interested me (an operation which no one had so far dared to undertake), effectively disposed of the idea of contagion, and from this moment I had no difficulty in getting the young doctors to put their hands to this work in the way I myself did, and to treat these patients with the same confidence that we brought to the treatment of our wounded on the battlefield. The remarkable success we at once obtained, even with some of the most severe cases of cholera, encouraged our colleagues and inspired confidence amongst the inhabitants. So much so that the Commander-in-Chief, Count Danrémont, had no hesitation in joining me at dinner three days later, together with the town authorities.

"I spent the whole of the 27th in attending to the patients and in instructing the young doctors at the hospital. A further group of these young men sent by the Minister of Education to the centre of the epidemic area to assist the local doctors arrived on this day from Lyon. Having been informed by the Minister himself of the reason for my presence at Marseilles they came to ask my instructions and how they might be most useful. In reply I gave them a lecture in the theatre at the hospital, tracing the symptoms of the disease, its progress, effects and termination, and the next day it was easy enough to show them its anatomical results in the cadaver. From the lecture room I took them to the cholera wards and ended my demonstration with a clinical conference. They were afterwards allocated to the service of these wards or to the sanitary offices of the town, and throughout showed great zeal and exemplary devotion. I regret that I did not record their names and inscribe them in this book.[1]

"Our method of treatment which was at once adopted by the doctors of the town produced a visible diminution in the mortality and raised the spirits of the people (we shall go into this in more detail later). But it was not long before the disease took on a kind of recrudescence, and we do not flinch from recording what we consider to have been its cause.

"The Catholic priests, who had done not a little in spreading alarm and who thought to profit by the grievous state of affairs to impose a religious terrorism, asked permission from the civil authorities to go in procession to the image of the Virgin of Nôtre-Dame-de-la-Garde and to carry it to the cathedral; in order, they said, to appease the wrath of God and to obtain of his pity a downfall of rain to moderate the great heat which had lasted so long. Consent being given the translation took place on July 29th. The 31st was a Sunday, and after the celebration of a solemn mass a general procession was formed to tour the town. This was made up of persons of both sexes and all ages belonging to all classes of society together with very many clergy. The image of the Madonna and all the relics of the saints possessed by the churches were borne along in this great concourse. Fraternities of penitents, denominated by their distinctive colours, led and ended the procession which took more than six hours to pass through certain designated streets which had previously been beflagged. The temperature throughout the day remained as high as 99.5°F, and in the days following there was an increase in the cases of cholera and consequently in the number of deaths. This especially affected the townspeople, for fortunately the soldiers were not invited to participate in the

---

[1] The fact that we lost none of these young doctors is an irrefutable demonstration of the non-contagious nature of this disease; neither did we lose any of the sisters or orderlies in our hospitals.

procession. The young girls who, from their delicacy and the conventions of their sex, had suffered the most from heat, thirst, and fatigue during this long march, furnished most of the victims. When to such potent physical causes is added the excitement engendered in weak minds by religious fanaticism, it is easy to understand how powerful an impetus is given to a disease which will decimate a population. The facts demonstrate beyond dispute the abuses and danger of the exercise of the outward forms of religion in such circumstances. They emphasize the necessity, so wisely appreciated by Napoleon, of seeing that the article of the Concordat, forbidding the ceremonies and pomps of religious observance to pass beyond the thresholds of their temples, should be respected.

"When I found that the cholera had almost entirely disappeared from Toulon, but was making great progress at Aix and Avignon, I made arrangements to go to these towns and did this all the more readily as the epidemic had sensibly diminished at Marseilles. According to my original itinerary and the Minister's instructions I should have gone to Toulon from Marseilles, but for the reasons I have just given, and after taking the advice of the military intendant, Baron Rey, I set out for Aix on August 2nd. Early in the morning of the day after my arrival I hurried to visit the barracks and the civil hospital where our soldiers were treated. I found about forty of them suffering in varying degrees from the epidemic and gave instructions to the young doctors for their treatment, whilst I myself set to work on some who seemed to be in the greatest danger. I also pointed out to the local engineer officer certain necessary alterations and improvements in the barracks.

"On the 3rd I left for Avignon which I reached the same day. Here I had a larger and more important task to perform and for this I stayed until the 6th. The great necessity was to reassure the populace, whom the idea that cholera was contagious had reduced by emigration to a half of its number. This mistaken belief not only struck terror into the inhabitants but it caused the priests to bury the dead with improper haste, and on the very day of my arrival a riot had broken out amongst some women who accused the Curé of having interred a young woman a few hours after her supposed death, at a time at which it was alleged she was still living. To quieten these people and to prevent such mishaps, in case the event which so excited them should have actually occurred, I asked the Mayor to order the covering of the corpses of cholera victims with a sheet soaked in sodium chloride[2] (taking care to protect the face with a hoop) and so to delay burial until the customary twenty-four hours had elapsed. This produced an excellent effect and did away with these fears. I also sent a copy of the instructions I left at the hospital for the treatment of cholera patients to the chief medical officers of the branch establishment of the Invalides.

"I had barely completed my work at Avignon and taken these essential measures, when the sub-prefect and the mayor of Arles wrote to the mili-

[2] This presumably is a misprint for *Chloride of Lime* which is the substance mentioned in his report to the Minister of War.

tary sub-intendant asking that I should go to their town as soon as possible, since the disease was making alarming progress there. The same news was told me by a group of six young doctors who had been sent to assist the local physicians, but had been unable to fulfil their mission. In fact, such was the prejudice of the people of Arles, in common with those of the rest of Provence, that they actually believed the doctors brought the contagion with them from Avignon, and they had been assaulted and only saved themselves by hurried flight. In spite of this incident, and the danger with which the young men said they had been menaced, I went to Arles on the seventh of the month, arriving in the evening. I was taken to the house of the sub-prefect, M. Prat, who gave me hospitality and received me with real friendship and evidence of the greatest satisfaction. The mayor and doctors of the town were told of my arrival, and invited to be at the hospital early the next morning where M. Prat himself accompanied me. He remained during my visit and witnessed everything that I did in treating a number of severe cases of cholera whose lives I had the satisfaction of saving. Up to the time of my arrival no one had dared to touch the victims of this disease. My presence reassured the doctors and in due course dissipated the fear which possessed most of the inhabitants. M. Prat and the mayor were also present at a clinical lecture I gave in the Council Chamber to all the doctors and pupils at the hospitals.

"The sub-prefect was diligent in seeing that all the measures I proposed for the improvement of the various services at the hospital and of the public health were carried out. It would be difficult to find greater zeal and devotion than were shewn by this worthy public servant in these critical moments.

From Arles, Larrey proceeded to Beaucaire, Tarascon, Nîmes, Montpellier, Cette (which he thought little likely to favour the disease from its healthy position and good water supply), Balaruc, Bézieres, Castelnaudary, Carcassonne, Narbonne and Toulouse, encouraging the populace, stimulating the authorities, pouring contempt on the dread of contagion, and by his reputation and moderate methods of treatment and his insistence on hygiene, possibly contributing not inconsiderably to the defeat of the epidemic. The Minister of War had written on August 19th:

"Monsieur, Paris. August 19, 1835.

I am in receipt of the direct reports you have sent me, as well as those you have regularly transmitted to the Intendant of the 8th Division, giving an account of the result of your mission to Marseilles, Aix, Avignon, Arles, Beaucaire and Nîmes.

I have nothing but praise for the sanitary and hygienic measures you have recommended in these towns. I have noted with especial interest that your efforts through your many acts of personal devotion have constantly tended to raise the morale of the population, and by the evidence of facts to destroy morbid prejudices. By these means you have fulfilled the mission confided to you.

You are at liberty to decide yourself on the date of your return to Paris. You are the best judge of the favourable influence your presence exercises in the areas where cholera is present, and you will no doubt realize that a humanitarian mission like yours is only terminated when the disaster which has evoked it has ceased its ravages.

Accept, Monsieur, the assurance of my highest regard.

(*Signed*) MAISON.
Marshal; Minister of War."

And thus did the old Surgeon, who had served his King, Country and Empire from Newfoundland to Moscow and back again, at the age of 69 step forward to proffer a shield for the Civic Power in its hour of necessity!

Feeling that his duty was now accomplished, Larrey left Toulouse on August 27th, after visiting the Glave Hospital where he had worked as a student forty-five years earlier. *En route* he visited General Bertrand, now returned from St. Helena and living with his family at Châteauroux, and reached Paris on September 1st after an absence of six weeks.

It is interesting to know something of Larrey's views on the nature of cholera and of his methods of treatment, as well as of the other forms of therapy then in use for a disease that through the whole period covered by medical history has been attacked by every conceivable, and many almost inconceivable, methods. In his report to the Minister he wrote:

Paris. September 15th, 1835.

"Monsieur le Maréchal,

The Director of the War Office having desired that a general report on the mission I have just completed should be presented to you, I undertook this and have the honour to offer you a *précis* of the observations I have made, and of the measures I have taken or advised in the different places I visited, as well as of the rational treatment of epidemic cholera which I instituted in all the military or civil hospitals of the towns invaded by this disease.

"M. le Maréchal, it is clear that a number of important causes in the areas in question have combined to produce Indian cholera, whose morbific principle appears to have been actually transmitted from India where it is endemic, either as an air-borne effluvium or as a sort of cloud of imperceptible animalcules which certain winds have carried in succession from country to country as far as this zone. In its advance it has received sufficient of the emanations for its alimentation from the surfaces it has passed over, so that its effects on men are more or less deadly according to the moral state of the individual, and his idiosyncrasy or lack of physical fitness.

"The passage of this noxious air-borne vapour over the southern Mediterranean ports and nearby areas, where the cholera has raged so violently, together with the unhealthy gases and other sources of miasma which constantly arise from the docks of these ports, have augmented the harmful properties of this vapour and infected the susceptible members of the populace with a poisonous substance, the immediate cause of the nervous or ataxic condition which characterizes the disease which has decimated the country through which it has passed. Thus the basin at Toulon, like that at Marseilles, receives the town's sewage from the drains which empty into it, and in certain circumstances is the source of harmful emanations. It has only required a summer as hot as July and August have been in Provence and along the Mediterranean coast this year (where the thermometer has been continuously between 100–104°F), for the sea water to fail to neutralize entirely the noxious gases coming from human excrement and other putrefying animal material which is carried into the harbour by the heavy rains or from the sewers.

"To these insanitary effluvia, which are almost negligible at other seasons, there is added in these towns, and especially in Toulon which I know extremely well, the infected emanations from the excretions I have mentioned, stagnating in private closets, varieties of latrines, or the open pots in use in every house; and also the effect of the crowding together of the people whose numbers are disproportionate to the capacity of the houses, and finally the terror which had taken a hold in these parts from the dreadful effects of the disease, and the idea which certain doctors spread of its supposed contagious nature, produce a sudden and very extensive exodus. This emigration has nevertheless been beneficial to those who remained behind, by increasing their living space and removing the refugees from the epidemic area. The ill-effects of overcrowding are also seen in the prisons and barracks, which in other respects are properly kept and well ventilated. The convicts, who are continuously employed in the workshops alongside the harbour and its infected water, have of necessity been the first to be affected by the emanations I have spoken of. It is obvious that no great success could have been obtained from the treatment, however rational, of patients brought to the mud hospital, since this lacked every quality of a good institution.

To sum up: large and very costly improvements are necessary in this fortress town (Toulon) to remove the local causes of ill-health. No doubt the question will some day engage the attention of the government."

* * * * *

"During my journey from Avignon to Marseilles on July 24th and 25th, I was struck by the scene presented by the population of these towns and the places between. Carriages, wagons, horses, pack donkeys and entire families mingled in endless confusion along my route, so that I had the greatest difficulty in reaching my destination. Terror and consternation were imprinted on the faces of most of the men and women of these itinerant convoys.

"M. le Maréchal, I had the honour in an earlier report I addressed
to you from the latter town of giving an account of the result of my
visit to the hospitals, barracks, and other places especially involved
in this epidemic.

"I introduced certain hygienic measures into the barracks, some
of which should be applied throughout the army. One of these,
which concerns the soldiers' bedding, is that this should be turned
back from the head of the bed from the time of rising until bedtime.
This keeps the bed furnishings in good condition and prevents the
soldier from lying on his bed during the day, which is bad for his
health especially when he spends eight hours out of the twenty-four
in repose.

"A mildly tonic and agreeable drink has been prescribed in all
the corps, consisting of a weak infusion of camomile, sweetened with
liquorice and mixed with a twentieth of its volume of good red wine.
Daily cleansing lotions were recommended, bathing in the sea forbidden, and other sanitary measures taken wherever these appeared
necessary. To calm fears and to prevent the dispersion of unhealthy
miasmas which may come from bodies after death from cholera,
particularly when putrefaction sets in as is often the case in this
warm climate, and to ensure that the bodies are not buried too soon,
as may perhaps have occurred at Avignon, I recommended that they
should be at once covered or wrapped in an old sheet soaked in
chloride of lime, care being taken to protect the face by a hoop. By
the use of this disinfective wrap the period of twenty-four hours can
safely be allowed to pass, and if necessary exceeded."

*   *   *   *   *

"I shall first recapitulate the chief symptoms in the various stages
of the disease and thereafter briefly recall the lesions we have found
in the cadaver.

"At the onset there are malaise, vertigo, weakness, nausea or
vomiting, with increased mucous and serous secretions: later, more
or less painful or violent involuntary contractions of the limbs and
cramps: the tongue, the surface of the body, and in particular the
extremities become cold and a blue tint spreads over them and
around the eyes, nose and ears. Finally the patient grows weaker;
the algid state deepens, he falls into coma, and death supervenes
often after a sort of agony of some hours duration."

*   *   *   *   *

"These findings, which are constant and hardly vary, have led
me to institute a rational form of treatment which except in minor
ways should not be changed. It consists (1) In giving the patient a
filtered infusion of ipecacuanha (to relieve embarrassment of the
stomach). (2) In reanimating by all possible means the latent heat

and the circulation in the capillaries of the skin and membranes of the organs of internal life. Thus substances which contain an abundance of oxygen, or which most stimulate organic contractility, may be used to rub the surface of the body and especially the limbs, since they are best able to develop the vital properties of the chilled parts and those affected by stupor or paralysis. Such are snow or ice rubbed on the surface by the hand encased in a woollen glove; or, in default of ice, the tonic and mildly camphorated oils of camomile or St. John's Wort, or alcoholic frictions applied with the naked hand. (3) During the algid period small pieces of ice taken internally, or small doses of mild sweetened aromatic infusions taken at atmospheric temperature are equally suitable to restore the circulation in the capillary vessels of the internal membranes. (4) These methods of treatment should be immediately followed by the application of dry, or wet cups to the slightly scarified hypochondria, the epigastric, dorsal or lumbar regions, and the periphery of the abdomen; the effect of these revulsive bleedings can be modified at will. (5) We pass on to other revulsive topics such as the moxa, applied to the base of the skull, the sides of the spine and the epigastrium, and warm sinaptic cataplasms to the limbs and abdomen. (6) Finally, warmth being in some measure restored, the body and all four limbs are wrapped in wool and the parts compressed by bandages and a body binder; these are supplemented by sources of artificial heat which may be gradually increased as desired, such as hot bricks or stone bottles filled with hot water. Internal treatment should be restricted to sweetened mucilaginous drinks, slightly acidulated with vegetable acids."

Larry goes on to say that the various specific internal remedies that have from time to time been recommended—camphor, quinine, morphia, bismuth and Oil of Cajuput—are useless and frequently harmful. He likewise rejects artificially applied external heat, hot baths, blisters, caustic pomades, hot water enemata, and the injection of hot water into the veins, the latter being "already rejected by humane doctors." He adds: "Everyone knows the fate of the unfortunate individuals who believed in the transfusion of blood, so greatly advocated in the 17th Century for the rejuvenation of old men." The aim, he says, of those favouring internal injections is the restoration of the lost serum or fluidity necessary to the blood for its free circulation; but the function of organs can only be restored by supplying "vital qualities perfectly identical or homogeneous, which physics and chemistry cannot transmit from the interior to the exterior,[3] but which can be made to develop by those means capable of reanimating the individual's own latent powers."

Unlike his contemporary, Dr. Hamilton Bell, of the Indian Army, a nephew of Sir Charles Bell, to whom venesection produced "magical

---

[3] I think this should read: "Exterior to the interior," and to be one of the many errors of transcription. Otherwise a very penetrating remark becomes meaningless.

effects" in cholera, he rejects bleeding as impracticable and leeches as useless; but as soon as the jugular vein becomes obvious he opens it, believing that one of the most profound effects of the disease is congestion of the brain. He finishes "The cholera patients are to be looked upon in the same way as the wounded in a battle. If surgeons, who so often are mindless of their own survival to save the lives of their fellows, did not give their unremitting attention to the wounded many would perish in the first few hours. A cholera hospital is in truth a battlefield."

He concludes his report:

"The epidemic, after raging in the cities I have mentioned with extreme violence for about forty days, gradually declined and had finally ceased by the time of my departure from many of them. We have reason to believe this due to a change in the prevailing wind from the south and south-west quarter, in which it was during the month of July and for the greater part of August, to the north and north-west which produced a drop in temperature. At the end of August this was accompanied by a good fall of rain without storms, and had a salutary effect on the health of the populace in the endemic areas.

"To these main causes of the evaporation or neutralization of the deleterious principle, should be added: (1) The measures we took everywhere to remove the local causes of disease and to improve the hygiene of the troops and civil population in the towns where cholera had broken out. (2) The tranquilization we were able to bring to the population who were alarmed by fear of contagion. (3) Finally, the introduction of a simple, rational and easily administered method of treatment, the results of which gave confidence to the patients and encouragement to the doctors.

"Such, M. le Maréchal, is the result of the mission which you did me the honour of entrusting to me. I venture to say that on the one hand it has restored confidence to the alarmed population, and on the other that it has simplified the treatment of cholera.

"It is my hope that this last report, like my earlier ones, will have deserved the approval of Your Excellency.

"In this persuasion,

I am, with respect,
Monsieur le Maréchal,
Your humble and devoted servant,
(*Signed*) B^{on}. LARREY."

Chapter 33

Something of the man, and the last phase.

The time has come to look upon another page of Larrey's life; one very different from the smoke and glory of the campaign, with its hardships, its demand for swift decisions, its great rewards in triumphs over disease and death, and, alas, its tragedies. What of the man without these trappings? What of his domestic life?

He married in 1794, during a short furlough between his first campaign with the revolutionary army on the Rhine and the invasion of Andalusia. His wife was Elizabeth, the younger daughter of Leroux de Laville, Louis XVI's last finance minister who survived the Terror to become a senator under Napoleon. *Ma douce Laville* he called her in his letters, and there is no doubt that he loved her dearly. The marriage was celebrated "sous les auspices de l'Etre suprème et devant le feu sacré de la liberté." Elizabeth Laville was a young woman of spirit and culture, a member of a gifted family and with her sister not an unknown figure in Parisian polite society. Moreover she was an artist of some ability, a pupil of David and a friend of Gros and Giraudet. The marriage must have been something of an adventure for them both; the linkage of this devoted strong man of blood with the *spirituelle* and, as it would seem at this distance, rather detached and unpractical young woman of the lesser aristocracy. Convent educated and bred in the customs of the old monarchy, one wonders what were her feelings about the republican altar and the benediction of the Supreme Being, bestowed a mere four months after the enthronement on the altar of Nôtre Dame of the Goddess of Reason (temporarily detached from the Opera!). Good republican though he was, Larrey's stern realism must have girded against this flummery, and after his return from Austerlitz the union was solemnized by a priest at their joint desire.

The early years of the marriage would seem to have been tranquil and happy for them both, to judge from his letters: but how frustrating must this correspondence have been, for it was not until just before the siege of Alexandria that he received in Cairo the one letter that reached him from his wife during the whole Egyptian campaign—although he himself had written more than forty! From this he learnt of the birth of a daughter, Isaure, so named by Mme Larrey after an earlier child who had not survived. It was a disappointment he did not conceal, for he had longed for a son. When he left for Spain in February 1808 his wife was again pregnant, and to his enormous and boyish delight he received in Vittoria a letter from Isaure (now become his cherished and intimate correspondent) announcing the birth of a boy on September 18th. His cup was full, despite the dangers and hardships of the Spanish war. This long hoped-for son, Hippolyte, his education and his future, became one of Larrey's main pre-occupations; so that at the nadir of his fortunes, when the Empire had collapsed in ruins and he himself was rebuffed, suspect, deprived of his honours and means of livelihood, he could write that his solace would be to devote himself to his son's career. But a world of events was to pass before the proud moment of 1841, when in his seventy-fifth year he was to witness the induction of Hippolyte Larrey to the Chair of Pathology at Val-de-Grâce, where he himself as a young man in his full vigour had professed Surgery. Much of Larrey's life in this period of thirty years or so has been told here in his own words, but there is a good deal more to tell, not all of it easy to discern.

What type of a man was this Larrey? In person he was below middle height. The portrait from Val-de-Grâce (by Mme Benoist) (frontispiece) shews an attractive-looking young man with a rather thin and strong face, humorous and arrestingly intelligent. The better known portrait by Delpec (Fig. 35), when he was just under forty, is less interesting. It is of a man who has arrived and has run to fat. In his later years the American surgeon Collins Warren, who attended his Clinique at the Invalides in 1832, described him as short and corpulent with a pleasant face, his long grey hair falling in curls over the collar of the uniform coat he always wore at his visits. Clearly he must have been unusually robust to have withstood the continuous hardships of his many campaigns and the retreat from Moscow, as well as to have survived two attacks of typhus. He never seems to have been wounded until Waterloo, and although then left for dead by the Prussians he recovered from his wounds without much difficulty.

He exposes himself in his diaries as a zealous and efficient army surgeon devoted to his Art, unquestionably courageous in both physical and moral senses, eager to follow every advance in his subject but healthily sceptical about unproven doctrines. One moreover who thought, reasoned, and wrote; not in the seclusion of the study but in brief hours snatched from the duties of active campaigning. His more leisurely discussions upon the causes and development of the processes of disease reveal a thinker of a depth unusual for his period. This is well seen in his views upon infection, on the transmission of epidemic diseases, on aneurysms, the arrest of haemorrhage, the fatal complications of infected wounds, and on the spurious nature of the so-called Plica. In many of these matters and especially on the treatment of battle wounds he was well in advance of the generality of the leading surgeons of his time, not excepting John Hunter, and with the changes which later discoveries have added these views are for the most part as sound today as when he enunciated them.

To appreciate his moral fibre we need to go no further than the im-mortal dictum of Napoleon, to be told that we have to deal with a man of uncompromising honesty. Furthermore, he was unyielding when he felt a stand for the right was required. He faced the Emperor's cold anger after Lutzen and braved the wrath of a general whose horses he had killed to feed the wounded at Libau, with the same firmness he shewed in protecting his patients from the Cossacks at Eylau, or the wounded and royal troops against the mob during the July Revolution. His humanity reveals itself in a hundred ways, not least in his stand against the branding of convicts under Charles X, whilst a protest against the cruelties of military punishments was one of the last acts of his life.

In this connection it is to be remembered that the position of a surgeon in the French armies was at the time a lowly one. Even the senior surgeons did not hold a commission, and were separated by this distinction in rank from the officers with whom they had to deal. This was a grievance that peeps out time and again in Larrey's writings and he worked hard for its removal but without success. We have seen his satisfaction at Menou's organization of the surgeon's grades during the latter's brief command in Egypt, and his enthusiasm about the combatant rank and epaulettes of his British hosts on his visit to Chatham. His obvious satisfaction at the friendship accorded him by some famous soldiers, such as Desaix, may have been tinged with appreciation for an equality not conferred by rank.

At the back of his many responsibilities and dangers he was chronically plagued by some degree of financial anxiety, for the surgeon did not profit from the opportunities so eagerly seized by many of Napoleon's generals to enrich themselves; nor, when the Emperor dispensed largesse to finance his new aristocracy, or as a reward for successful battles, did he ever receive anything approaching the sums that fell to their lot. At Napoleon's request the Directory made a grant of 1,200 *livres* to Mme Larrey for his services at the Battle of the Pyramids, and he received an annuity of 5,000 francs when created a Baron at Wagram. This, however, was secured in Swedish Pomerania, and after 1813 was seized by Bernadotte, and was never paid despite Larrey's requests and the promises of this ci-devant Marshal of France. After Lutzen he was granted 6,000 francs and a pension of 3,000 francs, and he also received an annuity as a Commander of the Legion of Honour; but all this was very small beer compared with Berthier's amassment of forty millions, and Massena's annual income of nine hundred thousand francs from his appointments, to mention only two senior officers and to say nothing of the many other sources of income open to them. Successful generals could expect an income of 50,000–100,000 francs, as well as a similar capital sum.

Larrey generally ended each campaign in debt[1] and Mme Larrey had to fall back on her painting to supplement the family income from time to time. After Austerlitz he had found himself with insufficient money to post back to Paris, and was forced to make the journey by short stages, and hard put to replace the two horses he had lost in the campaign. He was constrained to write to his wife to suggest that she might through Rapp obtain an audience with the Emperor and present him with a portrait she was painting of him, using the occasion to request the grant of a small property, "which I have well deserved." In the event, Napoleon received Mme Larrey very charmingly, and although he did not give the hoped-for estate he readily granted a sufficient sum to compensate Larrey for his losses.

[1] M. Hassenforder. *Société de Médecine Militaire*, 1957: 6; 242.

It is against this background that we have to view a financial disaster which overtook husband and wife, and with it in mind it is not difficult to comprehend in some way the mental aggrievement they both suffered. Our sympathy must be greater for the woman, who so much alone and helping in hard times to maintain the home, often in periods of racking anxiety, had the misfortune to bring down disaster. The facts are that before Larrey left for the Russian campaign he put into his wife's hands his slowly accumulated fortune of thirty thousand francs, relying upon her for its employment. Mme Larrey entrusted the whole sum to an old friend who embezzled it and subsequently denied the transaction. Larrey, surely, endured the depths of frustration, when after two years disastrous campaigning he returned to his home for a few weeks in the early part of 1814 to face this outrageous loss, to which within the space of a few months was added the menace of the Bourbon restoration. From this situation he was to hurry forth again in mid-1815 to the battlefields of Ligny and Mont St. Jean and—after being reported amongst the killed—to return at last to a Paris occupied by the enemy: his world in ruins, his money gone, and his life in danger. He was forty-nine years old.

Resentment must have been inevitable. He was a man brought up close to the land and tinged with the French peasant's thriftiness in money matters, so that it is not hard to see how for the future his domestic life was to bear the permanent scar of this wound. Moreover, the events coincided with a deterioration in his wife's health, and for the rest of her life she suffered from neurasthenia and terrible headaches, in addition to the cardiac malady of which she died.

Nevertheless he weathered the storms of the restoration, the reign of Charles X, and the disturbances which ushered in the July Monarchy, and maintained his position as surgeon to the Guard, now become the Royal Guard, and to the hospitals of Gros-Caillou and the Invalides. He worked hard and unsparingly amongst the veterans, attending the hospital at seven in the morning, teaching, operating, and spending more than three hours a day in the wards in the practice and improvement of his Art. As the fires of the legitimists' resentment died down, he moved freely in society and more especially under Louis-Philippe engaged in practice amongst the Napoleonic circle and his old companions in arms, many of them become sadly decrepit. Amongst his female patients were such well known women as the Duchesse d'Abrantès, the Princesse de Salm and Mme de Staël. Like many another he stifled old resentments but his toleration was not unlimited, and he refused to countenance the worst turncoats and traitors, such as Talleyrand, Fouché and Marmont. It is related by Triaire that at a certain *salon*, where the old imperialists were accustomed to gather, he was addressed by an officer who had been on Bourmont's staff and had deserted with him to the Prussians on the eve of Waterloo. Stopping before Larrey he held out his hand. The old surgeon regarded him coldly.

"What, don't you remember me? I'm d'Y. . . ."

"The officer of that name I once knew died at Waterloo." And he turned away.

But through these years of peaceful employment, with his clinical work and attendances at the Institute and Academy, there ran in the mind of Larrey his preoccupation with the education and career of his son. The boy, Hippolyte, was from his birth destined by his father to follow the career of a surgeon, and it must be said that in his ambition for him the older man shewed himself a domineering and oppressive influence. In his pride and consciousness of achievement, and his jealousy for a like achievement for the fruit of his loins, he did injustice to both son and daughter. In the outcome his paternal domination prevented the marriage of the latter—the Isaure whose sight he had saved as a child by his cool nerve and steady hand—with the celebrated Clot Bey, and in like manner he vetoed the union of Hippolyte with the woman of his choice. Hippolyte for whose career he sacrificed so much—and by these acts he caused the extinction of his line.

The son inherited a good share of his mother's charm to soften a considerable measure of his father's stern rectitude. Slim, well mannered, pleasing, with more than a young man's share of good looks, he failed one feels to supply that intimacy between father and son the elder Larrey had so desired. Doubtless the parent pressed too hard and failed to realize— as many another man of great qualities has failed to realize—that his son was of a different metal. How much, if at all, the son felt his ability to soar limited by the overpowering personality of the father we do not know. What we do know is that his devotion and loyalty were real as well as exemplary. Ever a step behind the great man he became his amanuensis, and as bodily power declined his physical prop. It was upon Hippolyte's arm that he leaned on that bitter December day of 1840, when wearing the uniform of Wagram he followed Napoleon's coffin from Corbevoie to the Invalides, and it was on Hippolyte's face that he looked as his sight faded out for ever.

Yet Hippolyte Larrey, although overshadowed, was not an inconsiderable man. He saw service at the siege of Antwerp, and as surgeon to Napoleon III he was present at Magenta and Solferino. He became a Grand Officer of the Legion of Honour and was Surgeon-in-Chief during the siege of Paris in 1860. He was President of the Academy of Medicine and entered the Chamber as deputy for Bagnères. Here he assisted in the passage of the law giving the autonomy and status to the medical service so much desired by his father. Hippolyte left a permanent monument to his filial piety by purchasing and endowing as a home for children the parental house at Beaudéan, to which he applied the balance of Napoleon I's legacy; this having fallen short of the amount bequeathed by 57,000 francs, owing to the Emperor's overestimate of his assets, and being made good by Napoleon III from his civil list. The son of his father to the last he declined on his death bed the ministrations of a priest, saying: "All my life I have followed the straight course set by my father, and his image has been my guide."

The Last Phase

In 1838 Larrey was retired from his post at the Invalides by Maison, the Minister of War, who three years earlier had been glad to lean on the reputation of this old servant of the Empire to combat the formidable epidemic of cholera in the Midi, but who now decided to terminate his employment, at the same time as Desgenette's, the latter, indeed, being no longer employable. Although he was seventy-two, Larrey took the blow ill, for it meant the severance of a link with the army which was a part of his life. The empty years would be hard to fill, even though time contracts as we become older. But fate was not unkind to him and an opportunity to pay a quasi-official visit of inspection to the French forces in Algeria enabled him to end his days in the atmosphere of camps and field hospitals he knew so well.

In March, 1842, he set out for North Africa in the company of Hippo-lyte, to join the army then in its ten-year old struggle against Abd-el-Kader, and to tread again the soil of that continent where in his Egyptian days he had dreamed such dreams of the creation of a great French colonial empire. His visit was a minor triumph, for by now his fame was almost legendary and the new generation of medical officers were eager to do him honour. With them he re-lived much of the past—the battles of the Empire, with their heroism and their suffering—and to them he preached the lessons of humanity and humility so indispensable to the good doctor. He chided the suggestion of impetuous youngsters that all was glory, and exerted himself to bring about the mitigation of the humiliating and severe military punishments then in use.

But four months in the field took their toll of a man of seventy-six, and it became clear to those about him, and especially to Hippolyte, that his body could not continue to sustain the strain. Wearied, he turned home-wards on July 5th, for a journey made the more anxious and urgent by the news that his wife was dangerously ill. He reached Toulon on the 9th, and struggled on to Avignon by the 18th where his forces seemed expended. But the old dominant will remained, and after a few days rest and against all advice he embarked by the Rhône canal for Lyon. Refusing to stop at Valence he reached Lyon on the 24th and died the following morning: the day that a letter came to Hippolyte giving the news of his mother's death.

*   *   *   *   *

Larrey had wished to be interred in the Invalides amongst the shades of his old soldiers whom he had served so well: and it was his right. But grudging Soult, who had not forgiven his forthright defence of the young conscripts accused of self-mutilation at the battles in Saxony, refused. His heart is in the vault of the chapel of the military hospital of Val-de-Grâce, where forty-five years earlier he had been Professor of Surgery, and in its forecourt is a monument to his memory (Fig. 36). He stands on a plinth, on the four sides of which are scenes from famous battles in which he served: The Pyramids, Summa Sierra, Austerlitz, and the Beresina. In his hand he holds a document—Napoleon's will.

"*C'est l'homme le plus vertueux que j'aie connu.*"

Vertue is a difficult word for us to translate. Better than to attempt this I would use Newbolt's noble lines:

> "A fairer name no Roman ever gave
> To stand sole monument on Valour's grave."

Napoleon's Military Aristocracy

(1)	Arrighi	Duke of Padua
(2)	Augereau	Duke of Castiglione
(3)	Bernadotte	Prince of Ponte Corvo (Betrayed France to become Crown Prince of Sweden)
(4)	Berthier	Prince of Wagram and Neuchatel
(5)	Bessières	Duke of Istria
(6)	Caulaincourt	Duke of Vicenza
(7)	Champagny	Duke of Cadore
(8)	Clarke	Duke of Feltre
(9)	Davout	Duke of Auerstadt and Prince of Eckmühl
(10)	Duroc	Duke of Friuli
(11)	Junot	Duc d'Abrantes
(12)	Kellermann	Duke of Valmy
(13)	Lefebre	Duke of Dantzic
(14)	Lannes	Duke of Montebello
(15)	Marmont	Duke of Ragusa
(16)	Moncey	Duke of Conegliano
(17)	Maret	Duke of Bassano
(18)	Mortier	Duke of Treviso
(19)	Masséna	Duke of Rivoli (Prince of Essling after retreat to Lobau)
(20)	Ney	Duke of Elchingen and Prince of the Moskova
(21)	Soult	Duke of Dalmatia
(22)	Savary	Duke of Rovigo
(23)	Oudinot	Duke of Reggio
(24)	Victor	Duke of Bellune

Kings, etc.

Louis Bonaparte	King of Holland
Joseph Bonaparte	(1) Naples (2) Spain
Jerome Bonaparte	King of Westphalia
Joachim Murat	King of Naples
Eugène Beauharnais	Viceroy of Italy

Joseph Bonaparte called himself Count of Survilliers, when in America after the Hundred Days.

The Republican Calendar

On the 24th of November 1793 the National Convention, in its perfervid desire to have done with everything that smacked of the *Ancien Régime*, altered the calendar to accord with republican ideas and divided the year into twelve months of thirty days, plus five complementary days to correspond with Republican fêtes. All the old names disappeared. The year was divided into twelve months each of thirty days, viz. Autumn became *Vendémiare; Brumaire* and *Frimaire;* Winter: *Nivose, Pluviôse* and *Ventose;* Spring: *Germinal, Floreal* and *Floveal;* Summer: *Messidor, Thermidor* and *Fructidor.*

The months were divided in three *dizaines* or decades and the names of the week now called *primidi, doudi, tridi,* etc.

This was all very well for the law-makers in Paris, but it had a poor reception from the common and country people who prefered the old calendar or the much frowned upon Saints' days.

Larrey's letter (p. 324) shews his use of the Conventional Calendar.

Appendix C

Authorities Consulted

Amongst others:—
(In the National History of France)
The History of the French Revolution by Louis Madelin
The History of the Consulate and the Empire by Louis Madelin
The Memoirs of Baron Marbot
The Memoirs of Bourienne
The Memoirs of Caulaincourt
The Life of Napoleon Bonaparte by Sloane
Napoleon, The Last Phase by Lord Rosebery
Bonaparte in Egypt by Christopher Herold (Hamish Hamilton, 1963)
Corunna by Christopher Hibbert (Batsford, 1961)
The Memoirs of General Bertrand (Cassell, 1953)
Sir John Moore by Carola Oman (An excellent book)
The Hundred Days by Philip Guedella
The French Revolution by Georges Lefèbre
The French Revolution by J. M. Thompson (Blackwell, 1947)
Waterloo by John Naylor (An excellent book. London, B. T. Batsford)
Napoleon Immortal by James Kemble
Napoleon's Russian Campaign by de Ségur
Life of Napoleon Bonaparte by W. M. Strane
Bonaparte by André Castelot (Paris, Librairie Académique Perrin, 1967)
Napoleon by André Castelot (Paris, Librairie Académique Perrin, 1967)
Napoleon and Waterloo by A. F. Becker (Kegan Paul, 1914)
Napoleon and the Invasion of England by H. F. B. Wheeler and A. M. Bradley
The Fall of Napoleon by Oscar Browning
The French Revolution by Georges Lefèbre (2 Vols.)
The Trial of Marshal Ney by Harold Kurtz (Hamish Hamilton, 1957)
The Duke by Philip Guedalla
The Empress Josephine by E. J. Knoptron (1964)
Britain Against Napoleon by Carola Oman (Faber, 1962)
Thiers: The History of the Consulate and the Empire of France. Translated by
    D. Forbes Campbell and John Stebbing (Chatto and Windus, 1893)
Eloge du Baron Hippolyte Larrey by Paul Reclus (Paris, Masson et Cie, 1898)

Index

Abdominal surgery, L's views on, 266
Abercrombie, Sir George, landing at Aboukir, 48
Abernethy, 142
Aboukir
  battle, 26, 41
  capture by Turks, 41
  English landing, 48
Alexandria
  capture, 23
  siege and capture by English, 48
  evacuation, 54
Almeras, General, wounding, 45
Alpin, Prosper, 262
Amaurosis, 107
Ambulances, field, 5, 9, 16
Amiens, Treaty of, collapse, 58
Amputation, L's views on, 120
Anel, Dominique, 252
Aneurysm needle designed by L., 4
Aneurysms
  comparison of English and French practice, 305
  L's views on, 137
Anthrax
  in Italy, 21
  L's work on, 15
Antwerp, 311
Appareil inamovible, 136
Arcis, French capture of, 231
Arles, cholera outbreak, 323
Army School of Medicine, L. appointed Professor, 15
Arrighi, wounded at Acre, 32
Arteries
  canalization, L's views, 143
  surgery, L's views, 137
  translator's views on, 143
Aspern, battle, 110
Asphyxia, L's work on, 69
Assalini, 178
Augsberg, capture of, 59
Auklappen, 72
Austerlitz, battle, 62
Avignon, cholera outbreak, 322

Bâle, treaty, 8, 14
Belingal, Sir George, 297
Bancel, 163, 165

Barbnègre, Colonel, embalmed by L., 64
Barre, Antoine, 94
Baste, Rear-Admiral, 116
Bath, 275
Baudéan, 1
Baudot, General, death at Alexandria, 50
Bautzen, 205
Bayard, Pierre, 266
Bayonne, Joseph Bonaparte crowned King of Spain, 86
Béarnais' soldier, 10
Beauharnais, Alexandre, 7
Beauharnais, Eugène, wounded at Acre, 32
Beaumarchef, 108
Belgian medical services, L's report on, 311
Bell, Sir Charles, 259
Belliard
  wounding of, 45
  surrender of Cairo, 48
Belloc, Etienne, 270
Benchenkowiski, battle, 152
Benevente, battle, 105
Benningsen, 70
Beresina, crossing, 184
Berg, Grand Duke see Murat
Berlin, capture of, 68
Bernadotte, 71
Bernetti, Cardinal, 316
Berthier, appreciation of L's work in Egypt, 56
Bessières, defeats Spanish, 100
Bianca, Casa, 23
Bilbao, capture of, 101
Bilguer, views on amputations, 51
Biron, 4
Bladder wounds, L's views on, 260
Blanchard, Mme, 195
Bleeding, L's views on, 244
Bon, General, death at Acre, 32
Bonaparte, Joseph, ascends Spanish throne, 100
Borrisow, battle, 186
Boudet, General, 113
Boulaq, capture of, 45
Bourgeois, Dr., 194
Bourienne, 25, 26
Brandet, Joseph Pilkington, 286
Brienne, battle, 221, 227

Brisnot, Jacques, 252
Britain, preparation for invasion of, 58
Brodie, 130
Brueys, Admiral, 23
Brün
    capture of, 61
    epidemics at, 64
Brunel, Marc Isambard, 306
Brunswick, 5
Brussels, 311
Bruyères, death at Bautzen, 206
Bullfighting, 87
    wounds resulting from, 261
Burgos, 87
    advance on, 103
Burns, L's views on treatment of, 10

Caffarelli, death at Acre, 32
Caillot, Professor, 141
Cairo
    march on, 24
    capture, 25
    revolt in, 26
Caizergues, 248
Cambridge, 297
Cammas, General, wounded at Dresden, 215
Campo Formio, peace of, 22
Carmichael, Richard, 276, 278, 279
Caulaincourt, General, death, 162
Cerebral hernia, L's views on, 250
Champaubert, battle, 222
Chateau, General, wounded at Craönne, 228
Château-Thierry, battle, 222
Chatham, 307
Chatillon conference, 222
Chaumont, Treaty of, 222
Chébreisse, 25
Chemineau, General, wounded at Lutzen, 203
Chenaps, abuse of, 149
Cheselden, William, 305, 306
Chest wounds, L's views on, 253
Chester, 286
Cholera, L's work on, 319
Claparède, General, 177
Circulation, collateral, L's views on, 140
Claye, Louis, 256
Clot-Bey, A. B., 38
Cognats, 182
Cold, effects, 194
Colditz, 203
Colic, Madrid, 98
Cooper, Sir Astley, 295, 300, 304, 306
Corfu, expedition to, 18

Corsica, Army of, L. appointed Surgeon in Chief, 9
Corunna, battle, 106
Corvisart, views on aneurysms, 137
Cossacks, L. meets, 84
Cothenet, 113
Craönne, battle, 223, 228
Cretin, death at Aboukir, 41
Cretinism, 16
Cross, Christophe, 248
Cullen, William, 297
Cusack, James William, 276
Custine, 5
Czarnova, battle, 70

Dagiaut, 61
Damankhour, capture of, 24
Danton, Georges-Jacques, 221
Davout, at Eylau 72
Débridement, 4
Delmas, General, death at Dresden, 215
Delzons, General, death, 178
Denzel, Baron, 107
Desault, 4, 266
Desgenettes, Baron, 23, 146
    refuses Bonaparte's order to poison wounded at Jaffa, 34
    inoculated against plague, 38
Dessaix, 22
    advance to Cairo, 24
    pursuit of Mourad Bey, 25, 26
    death, 46
Destrès, Brigadier-General, wounded at Sâléhyeh, 25
Dido, 55
Dillon, 4
Djezzar Pasha, 26
Doncaster, 297
Dorogobouje, 158, 180
Dresden, 208
    battle, 213
Dublin, 275
Dubois, Antoine, 13
Duga, General, 24, 35, 300
Dugommier, General, 10, 12
Dumbrona, 183
Dumoriez, 5, 7
Dupont, surrenders at Baylen, 100
Dupuy, General, killed during revolt in Cairo, 26
Duroc, Marshal
    wounded at Acre, 32
    death, 206
Duvilars, Captain, death at Alexandria, 50

Elbing, 194
Eckmühl, battle, 110

Edinburgh, 292
Egerton, Lord, embalmed by L., 64
Egypt, expedition to, 23
el-A'rych, 30
   capture by Syrians, 43
Elba, Napoleon's escape from, 233
el-Hhaleby, Soleyman, assassin of Kléber, execution, 45
Emangard, 252
Embabeh, 25
Embalming, 63
Embolism, air, L's views on, 259
Empyema, L's operation for, 253
Enzerdorf, 110
   capture of, 115
Eole, 18, 19
Essling, battle, 110
Eye disease, comparison of English and French practice, 306
Eylau, battle, 71

Fabar, 89
Fabre, 205
Faubourg St. Antoine, 15
Faure, on amputation, 120
Femur, wounds of, near knee, 164
Fesch, Cardinal, 316
Figueras, battle, 9
Finkeinsten, 80
Fractures, comparison of English and French practice, 303
Framberg, 194
Franche-Comté, invasion by Schwarzenberg, 220
Franck, Dr., 114
Frankfort, recapture by Prussians, 7
Friderich, General, killed at Dresden, 215
Friedland, Battle, 83
Frioul, Duke of *see* Duroc
Frizac, Professor, 85, 89, 267
Frostbite, L's views on, 198
Fugières, General, mortally wounded at Aboukir, 42

Galvanic stimulation of nerves, L's work on, 6
Gangrene, 91
   hospital, 65
Ghjat, 159, 161
Giad *see* Ghjat
Gilbert, 194
Gimelle, 142
Giza, chateau of, 25
Glasgow, 289
Gloire, 18
Godoy, 86
Goercke, 147

Goitre, 16
Goldmin, battle, 70
Groeffe, 147
Gruger, Dr., 266
Gruyer, General, wounded at Méry, 229
Guadarrama mountains, 105
Guenow, 265
Guerricke, Othon, 147
Gubert, 107
Guibert, death at Aboukir, 41
Gumbinen, 191
Gunshot wounds, 4
Guthrie, J. G., 129
Guyton-Morveau process, 20

Haemorrhage, L's views on, 138
Hainaut, 206
Hair, Polish plica, 78
Halle, 68
d'Hautpoul, General, death at Eylau, 71
Head wounds, L's views on, 245
Heilsberg
   action at, 81
   battle, 83
Heliopolis, battle, 44
d'Héralde, 61
Hip joint, amputation through, 129
Hoff, battle, 71
Hoffman's mineral liquor, 24
Home, Everard, 299
Horse flesh, use as food, 53, 113
Hospital infection, 75
Houchard, 7
Hounaud, Dr., 100
Houneau, Dr., 89
Hufeland, 147
Humboldt, 68

Ibrahim Bey, 25
Immobilization, L's use of, 136
Intestinal wounds, L's views on, 272
Invalides, reorganized by L., 314
Ireland, 274

Jaffa, 34
   capture of, 31
Jeannin, Colonel, wounded at Heilsberg, 82
Jena, 85
   battle, 67
Jolin, 273
Jouan, 77
Jourda, 113
Junquière, La, 9
Juville, 81

Kalmucks, L. meets, 84
Kalouga, 175, 177

Keith, Admiral, 55
Kellermann, 5
Kirchener, General, death at Bautzen, 206
Kléber, 23, 24, 32, 43
   assassination, 45
Knee wounds, 164
Koloskoi, 179
Königsberg, 193
Königstein, 7
Kowno, 149, 190
Krasnoë, 156, 182
Kutusoff, General, 175, 177

Laboissirère, General, wounded at Bautzen, 205
Lagrésie, 13
Lanfranc, 114
Lannes
   wounded at Acre, 32
   wounded at Aboukir, 41
   battle of Czarnova, 70
   death, 111
   embalmed by L., 115
Lansnaberg, General, death, 162
Lanusse, death at Alexandria, 49
Laon, French retreat from, 223, 230
Larrey, Alexis, 1, 108
Larrey, Auguste, 88
Larrey, Dominique Jean
   education, 1
   voyage on Vigilante, 1
   work at Hotel Dieu, 3
   joins Marshal Luckner, 5
   battle of Spire, 5
   ideas on field ambulances, 5
   work on electrical stimulation of nerves, 6
   battle of Limbourg, 6
   mentioned in dispatches by Beauharnais, 7
   marriage, 9, 329
   appointed Surgeon-in-Chief to Army of Corsica, 9
   appointed Director of Surgical Services to Army of Eastern Spain, 9
   battle of Figueras, 9
   views on treatment of burns, 10
   siege of Rosas, 12
   returns to Toulon, 15
   appointed Professor at Army School of Medicine, 15
   joins Army of Italy, 16
   organizes medical services for capture of Corfu, 18
   appointed Surgeon-in-Chief to Army of England, 22
   organizes medical services in Italy, 20
   expedition to Egypt, 23

Larrey, Dominique Jean—contd.
   work on ophthalmia, 26
   visit to Suez, 29
   devises camel panniers, 30
   Syrian campaign, 30
   returns to Egypt, 34
   work on plague, 36
   leeches, 39
   cuts name on pyramid, 41
   battle of Aboukir, 41
   battle of Heliopolis, 44
   recapture of Cairo, 45
   siege and capture of Alexandria by British, 48
   views on amputation, 51
   work on scurvy, 52
   appointed Surgeon-in-Chief to Consular Guard, 58
   receives Doctorate in Surgery, 58
   Officer of Legion of Honour, 58
   criticizes Bonaparte's coronation, 58
   capture of Ulm, 59
   battle of Austerlitz, 62
   embalming activities, 63
   epidemic at Brün, 64
   work on hospital wound infection, 65
   battle of Jena, 67
   Berlin, 68
   views on asphyxia, 69
   battle of Eylau, 71
   Commandant of Legion of Honour, 77
   Polish plica, 78
   Reysembourg, 80
   battle of Heilsberg, 81
   battle of Friedland, 83
   peace of Tilsit, 83
   return to Berlin, 84
   Doctorate of Medicine from Jena, 85
   returns to Paris, 85
   Chevalier de la Couronne de Fer, 85
   joins Murat at Burgos, 86
   views on bull fighting, 87
   arrives in Madrid, 88
   work on gangrene, 91
   work on Madrid colic, 98
   advance on Burgos, 103
   battle of Corunna, 106
   returns to Paris, 110
   battle of Essling, 110
   battle of Wagram, 116
   created Baron, 118
   views on amputations, 120
   appareil inamovible, 136
   aneurysms, arterial surgery etc., 137
   preparations for Russian campaign, 146
   capture of Wilna, 150

Larrey, Dominique Jean—*contd.*
 battle of Benchenkowiski, 152
 battle of Witebsk, 153
 battle of Smolensk, 156
 capture of Moscow, 161
 work on wounds of femur, 164
 retreat from Moscow, 175
 arrival at Königsberg, 193
 contracts typhus, 197
 views on frostbite, 198
 Saxony campaign, 201
 battle of Lutzen, 202
 battle of Bautzen, 205
 views on self-inflicted wounds, 209
 battle of Dresden, 213
 battle of Leipsic, 215
 reaches Mayence, 220
 reports on conditions between Mayence
  and Sarrebruck, 225
 returns to Paris on defeat of Bonaparte,
  235
 meets Bonaparte after his escape from
  Elba, 236
 battle of Waterloo, 238
 captured by Prussians, 240
 released by Blücher and sent to Louvain,
  241
 time in Brussels, 242
 offered employment outside France, 242
 views on
  bleeding, 244
  head wounds and trephining, 245
  throat wounds, 252
  thorax wounds, 253
  bladder wounds, 260
  abdominal surgery, 266
 visits
  Portsmouth, 274
  Southampton, 275
  Bath, 275
  Dublin, 275
  Chester, 286
  Liverpool, 286
  Glasgow, 289
  Edinburgh, 292
  York, 297
  Doncaster, 297
  Cambridge, 297
  London, 299
  Chatham, 307
 comparison of English and French surgery, 301
 opposition to branding of prisoners, 309
 July revolution, 309
 inspects Belgian medical services, 311
 appointed Surgeon-in-Chief to Invalides,
  314

Larrey, Dominique Jean—*contd.*
 visits Rome, 315
 cholera epidemic, 319
 domestic life, 329
 character, 330
 financial difficulties, 331
 retirement, 334
 visits North Africa, 334
 death, 334
Larrey, Elizabeth, 9, 329, 332
Larrey, Hippolyte, 274, 329, 333
Larrey, Isaure, 329, 333
Lasalle, death, 116
Latour-Maubourg, General, 39
 wounded at Dresden, 215
Laubert, 163
Laurancé, General, wounded at Bautzen,
 205
Lawless, Colonel, 135
Leclerc, 55
Ledran, 263
Leeches, in nose and throat, 39
Leipsic, 214
 battle, 215
 L. visits, 85
Leture, General, death at Aboukir, 41
Leibnitz, 85
Limbourg, battle, 6
Lisbon, capture of, 86
Lithotomy, comparison of English and
 French practice, 305
Liverpool, 286
Lobau, 113, 115
 capture of, 110
London, 299
Longwy, capture of, 5
Louvain, 242, 314
Lovemberg, 212
Loxa quinine, 96
Luckner, Marshal, 5
Lutzen, battle, 202

Macdonald, defeated at Kutzbach, 212
McGrigor, James, 48
Mack, trapped at Ulm, 59
Madrid, 88
 colic, 98
Ma'dyeh, Lake, 48
Magdeburg, 146, 201
Maisonade, Dr., 108
Malajaroslaw, 175
Malaria, 17
Malta, capture of, 23
Marabout, 23
Marbot, Baron, 64, 72
Marseilles, cholera outbreak, 319

Masclet, 24
death from plague, 38
Mauban, 49
Maugras, 113
Mayence
annexation, 6
meeting place for Russian campaign, 146
Meckel, P. F. T., 201
Menou, General, 23, 48
appointed to command of Army of Egypt, 46
contracts plague, 55
Mentianoni, 152
Mersbourg, 202
Meteor observed by L., 185
Michel, wounded at Aboukir, 42
Miedneski, 188
Miranda, 100
Mongin, killed during revolt in Cairo, 26
Monro, Alexander (Tertius), 297
Mons, occupation by Bülow, 220
Montbrun, General, death, 163
Montebello, Duke of see Lannes
Montereau, battle, 222
Montmirail, battle, 222
Morand, General, wounded, 162
Moreau, General, surrender of Soissons, 223
Morlan, embalmed by L., 63
Moro, Faure, wounded at Alexandria, 54
Moscow
campaign, 148
battle, 161
capture of, 167
architecture, 168
hospitals, 169
burning, 171
evacuation, 172
retreat, 175
Moskova, battle, 161
Mourad Bey, 25, 26
Mouton, 113
Mozaisk, 166
capture of, 175
Multon, 214
Murat, General, 86
wounded at Aboukir, 41
battle at Wittemberg, 71
occupies Madrid, 86
affected by Madrid colic, 98
desertion during retreat from Moscow, 194

Nangis, battle, 222
Nasouty, General, wounding, 163
Nazareth, visited by Bonaparte, 32
Needle
aneurysm, designed by L., 4

Needle—contd.
suture, designed by L., 4
Nelson, Admiral, 59
Nerves, electrical stimulation, L's work on, 6
Neumarck, 207
Newfoundland, voyage to, 1
Ney, 71, 72
defeated at Juterbock, 212
Niel, death from plague, 38
Niemen, pursuit of Russians to, 83
Nuremburg, 68

Oberuchel mountains, 7
Oedema, unilateral, 107
Omentum, hernia, L's views on, 267
Ophthalmia, L's work on, 26
Orcha, 183
Orient, 23
Osmiana, 187
Oudinot, defeated at Grossbeeren, 212

Padua, L. founds School of Surgery for Army officers, 18
Palau, 13
Paper, use as bandage, 157
Paré, Ambroise, 257
Paris, battle, 224, 232
Parry, Sir Edward, 287, 295
Paulet, Dr., 63, 74, 112, 114, 146
Pelchet, 84, 113
at battle of Eylau, 74
Percy, Baron, 16, 61, 78, 83, 101, 160, 236
Commandant of Legion of Honour, 77
Polish campaign, 71
Pérignon, General, 12
Perrée, Rear-Admiral, 24
Perrier, Joseph, 261
Phélippeaux, 32
Pincon, 178
Plague, 36
in Cairo, 29
in el-A'rych, 30
Pläswitz, armistice of, 207
Plica, Polish, 78
Poland, campaign, 70
Portsmouth, 274
Posen, 147
Potsdam, 68
Pott, Percival, 130, 303
Presburg, Treaty, 63, 66, 67
Pultusk, battle, 70
Pyramids, battle, 25

Quinine, 96

Rahhmanieh, 24, 48
Rampon, Lt-General, 54

Ratisbon, capture of, 110
Rayfer, 113
Reynier, 30
Reysembourg, 80
Rheims, capture of, 231
Ribes, Dr., 77, 141, 142, 190, 265
Riou, Captain, 2
Robsomen, wounded at Leipsic, 218
Roize, General, death at Alexandria, 49
Rome, 315
Romeuf, General, wounded, 163
Rosas, siege of, 12
Rosel, 103
Rosemberg, 80
Rosetta, capture of, 24
Rosetta stone, 300
Roussel, General, death, 81
Roussel (Surgeon), killed during revolt in
    Cairo, 26
Royer, 34
Rudolphi, 147
Russian campaign, 144

Sabatier, 141, 271
Sackoveninsk, Count, wounds, 165
Sainte-Croix, 115
Sâléhyeh, 25, 35
Salisbury, 2
Saragossa, siege, 101
Sartelon, 49
Saxony campaign, 201
Scarpa, views on aneurysms, 137
Schleitz, engagement at, 67
Schloditten, 72
Schönbrun
    Imperial headquarters, 60
    Treaty of, 67
Scurvy, 2, 3
    during siege of Alexandria, 52
Seasickness, 1
Sedment, battle, 26
de Segur, Louis-Philippe, wounded at
    Heilsberg, 81
Serpalten, 72
Shoulder joint, amputation, 123
Smallpox, 3
Smith, Sir Sidney, 32
    rôle during el-A'rych campaign, 43
Smolensk, 181
    battle, 156
Smorgonie, 187
Soemmering, Dr., 110
Soissons, surrender by General Moreau, 223
Sotira, Dr., 48
Soult, 71
    refuses L's wish to be buried in Invalides,
        334

Sourd, Colonel, wounded at Waterloo, 239
Southampton, 275
Spanish campaigns, 86, 103
Spire, battle, 5
Stewart, General, 55
Stomach surgery, L's views on, 266
Stone, cutting for, comparison of English
    and French practice, 305
Strak, Dr., 6
Suez, 29
Summa-Sierra, battle, 104
Sureau, death from cold during retreat
    from Moscow, 196
Suture needle designed by L., 4
Sylly, General, wounded at Alexandria, 50
Syphilis, in Cairo, 46

Thackeray, Joseph, 286
Thackeray, William, 286
Thomson, John, 297
Thorax wounds, L's views, 253
Throat wounds, L's views, 252
Tibial condyles, amputation through, 126
Tilsit, Peace of, 83
Tolecsehyn, 184
Toulon, cholera outbreak, 319
Trafalgar, battle, 59
Trench foot, 199
Trephining, L's views, 245
Triaire, 55
Typhus, 19
    after battle of Austerlitz, 65

Ulm, capture of, 59
Urine, retention, comparison of English and
    French practice, 304

Val-de-Grâce hospital, 22
Valli, inoculation against plague, 38
Valladolid, 106
Valutina, battle, 157
Valmy, battle, 5
Vandamme, defeated at Külm, 213
Vauchamps, battle, 222
Venice, 18
Verdun, capture of, 5
Vesalius, portrait, 289
Vial, General, 25
    death at Dresden, 215
Victoire, 18
Victor, General, 13
Victory, L. visits at Portsmouth, 274
Vienna
    capture of, 60
    surrender of, 110
Vigilante, 1
Villemanzy, 6, 17, 22

Virgili, Pedro, 253
Vittoria, 101
Vrigni, wounded at Heilsberg, 81

Wagram, battle, 116
Walewska, Marie, 71
Waterloo, battle of, 238
Walther, 68
Warsaw, 71
Weissembourg, 7
Wiasma, 179
Wibel, 147
Wilna, 188
  capture of, 150
Witebsk, battle, 153

Wittemberg, 68
  battle, 71
Wittman, William, 48
Wounds, comparison of English and French
    practice, 301
  self-inflicted, 209
Wrede, General, defection, 217

Yonck, 55
York, 297
Yvan, Dr., 114

Zayonchek, General, wounded at Borrisow,
  187